D1128372

WILLIAM K. DURR • **JOHN PESCOSOLIDO** • **WILLIE MAE POETTER**

CONSULTANTS • **PAUL McKEE** • **MARCELLA T. JOHNSON**

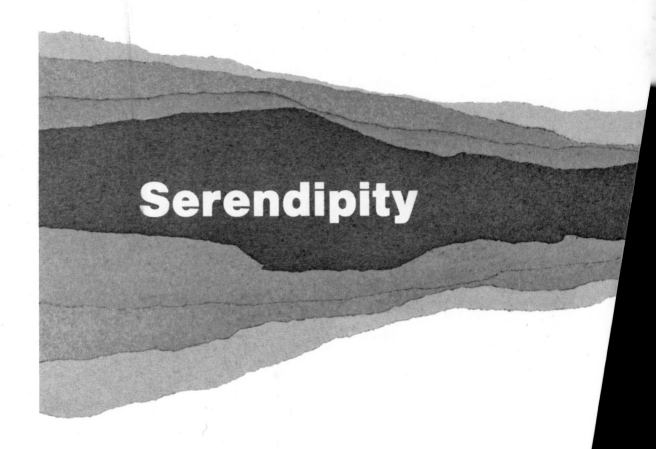

Serendipity

HOUGHTON MIFFLIN COMPANY • BOSTON

ATLANTA • DALLAS • GENEVA, ILLINOIS • HOPEWELL, NEW JERSEY • PALO ALTO

ACKNOWLEDGMENTS

For each of the selections below, grateful acknowledgment is made for permission to adapt and/or reprint original or copyrighted material, as follows:

"Africa," from *Selected Poems,* by Langston Hughes. Copyright © 1959 by Langston Hughes. Reprinted by permission of Alfred A. Knopf, Inc.

"Beat the Queen," adapted from *Porko Von Popbutton,* by William Pène du Bois. Copyright © 1969 by William Pène du Bois. Reprinted by permission of Harper & Row, Publishers, Inc., and A. Watkins, Inc.

"Bitter Is the Hawk's Path," from *Bitter Is the Hawk's Path,* by Jean McCord. Copyright © 1962, 1964, 1965, 1971 by Jean McCord. Used by permission of Atheneum Publishers.

"Blueprint for Survival," from *Animal Instincts,* by Russell Freedman and James E. Morriss. Copyright © 1970 by Russell Freedman and James E. Morriss. Used by permission of Holiday House, Inc.

"Carlos Charles," slightly adapted from *Carlos Charles,* by Patrick J. Murphy and Shirley Rousseau Murphy. Copyright © 1971 by Patrick J. Murphy and Shirley Rousseau Murphy. Reprinted by permission of The Viking Press, Inc.

"Cat and the Underworld," adapted from "Cat and the Underworld," from *It's Like This, Cat,* by Emily Neville. Copyright © 1963 by Emily Neville. Reprinted by permission of Harper & Row, Publishers, Inc., and Angus & Robertson (U.K.) Ltd.

"Cave of Danger," adapted from *Cave of Danger,* by Bryce Walton. Copyright © 1967 by Bryce Walton. Used with permission of the publisher, Thomas Y. Crowell Company, Inc., and Theron Raines.

"Christmas on Wolf Creek," from *Pistol,* by Adrienne Richard. Copyright © 1965, 1969 by Adrienne Richard. Used by permission of Atlantic-Little, Brown and Company.

"A Day for Antonio," from *Antonio's World,* by John Figueroa. Copyright © 1970 by Educational Challenges, Inc. Reprinted by permission of Hill and Wang, a division of Farrar, Straus & Giroux, Inc.

"The Dolphin Girl," from *The Mule of the Parthenon and Other New Stories of Ancient Greece,* by Ethel Parton. Copyright 1932 by Ethel Parton. Reprinted by permission of Doubleday & Company, Inc.

"Equal Rights for Women," from *Pathways to Freedom,* by Edwin D. Hoffman. Copyright © 1964 by Edwin D. Hoffman. Used by permission of Houghton Mifflin Company.

"ESP Impressions," from *Sixth Sense,* by Larry Kettelkamp. Copyright © 1970 by Larry Kettelkamp. Reprinted by permission of William Morrow & Company, Inc.

"Five-Yard Fuller," from *Five-Yard Fuller,* by Bob Wells. Copyright © 1964 by Robert Wells. Reprinted by permission of G. P. Putnam's Sons.

"Giants of the Earth," by Clifford B. Hicks. Copyright 1967 by the National Wildlife Federation. Reprinted from the February/March issue of *National Wildlife* magazine.

"The Goalie Who Scored a Goal," reprinted from *Strange but True Hockey Stories,* by Stan Fischler. Copyright © 1970 by Stan Fischler, Cowles Book Company, a subsidiary of Henry Regnery Company, Chicago.

"Good Sportsmanship," from *Nights with Armour,* by Richard Armour. Copyright © 1958 by Richard Armour. Used with permission of McGraw-Hill Book Company.

"The Great Hoax," from *Scientists and Scoundrels, a Book of Hoaxes,* by Robert Silverberg. Copyright © 1965 by Robert Silverberg. Used with permission of the publisher, Thomas Y. Crowell Company, Inc.

"The Great Storm," from *Abbie Burgess: Lighthouse Heroine,* by Dorothy Holder Jones and Ruth Sexton Sargent. Copyright © 1969 by Dorothy Holder Jones and Ruth Sexton Sargent. Used by permission of Funk & Wagnalls.

Copyright © 1974 by Houghton Mifflin Company

All rights reserved. No part of this work may be reproduced or transmitted in any form or by any means, electronic or mechanical, including photocopying and recording, or by any information storage or retrieval system, without permission in writing from the publisher.

PRINTED IN THE U.S.A.

ISBN: 0-395-16178-9

"The Iceberg Cometh," from *Newsweek.* Copyright Newsweek, Inc., 1972, reprinted by permission.

"John Pappas Tries Out for the Mets," from *Assignment: Sports,* by Robert Lipsyte. Copyright © 1963, 1964, 1965, 1966, 1967, 1968 by The New York Times Company. Reprinted by permission. Copyright © 1970 by Robert M. Lipsyte. Reprinted by permission of Harper & Row, Publishers, Inc. All rights reserved. Use granted by the author and his agent, Theron Raines.

"The Lesson of the Lemmings," by Ola and Emily d'Aulaire. Reprinted with permission from the August 1970 *Reader's Digest.* Copyright 1970 by The Reader's Digest Assn., Inc. Condensed from *Viikkosanomat.*

"Life on Other Worlds," from *The World of Space,* by Robert Silverberg. Copyright © 1969 by Robert Silverberg. Reprinted by permission of Hawthorn Books, Inc., 70 Fifth Avenue, New York 10011. Reprinted by permission of the author and his agents, Scott Meredith Literary Agency, Inc., 580 Fifth Avenue, New York, New York 10036.

"The Little Fishes," from *The Little Fishes,* by Erik Christian Haugaard. Copyright © 1967 by Erik Christian Haugaard. Used by permission of Houghton Mifflin Company and Victor Gollancz Ltd., London.

"The Long Iron Trail," an adaptation from the book *Passage to the Golden Gate: A History of the Chinese in America to 1910,* by Daniel Chu and Samuel Chu. Copyright © 1967 by Doubleday & Company, Inc. Reprinted by permission of Doubleday & Company, Inc.

"Meet the Armored Spoof," by Mary Sayre Haverstock. Copyright 1972 by the National Wildlife Federation. Reprinted from the December/January issue of *National Wildlife* magazine.

"The Messenger to Maftam," from *The Cow-Tail Switch and Other West African Stories,* by Harold Courlander and George Herzog. Copyright, 1947 by Holt, Rinehart and Winston, Inc. Reprinted by permission of Holt, Rinehart and Winston, Inc.

"Mr. Strang Finds the Answers," by William Brittain. Copyright © 1967 by Davis Publications, Inc. Reprinted by permission of the author and the author's agents, Scott Meredith Literary Agency, Inc., 580 Fifth Avenue, New York, New York 10036.

"Music," from *The Complete Poetical Works of Amy Lowell,* by Amy Lowell. Used by permission of Houghton Mifflin Company.

"My People," by Bernice George, from *Here I Am!,* edited by Virginia Olsen Baron. Text copyright © 1967 by Virginia Olsen Baron. Published by E. P. Dutton & Co., Inc. Used by permission of the author.

"My Side of the Mountain," from the book *My Side of the Mountain,* by Jean George. Copyright © 1959 by Jean George. Published by E. P. Dutton & Co., Inc., and used with their permission and the permission of The Bodley Head, London.

"The Mysterious Jinx of the Hope Diamond," by James Stewart-Gordon. Reprinted with permission from the August 1971 *Reader's Digest.* Copyright 1971 by The Reader's Digest Assn., Inc. Condensed from *Status.*

"Navaho Rain," from *Sing Down the Moon,* by Scott O'Dell. Copyright © 1970 by Scott O'Dell. Used by permission of Houghton Mifflin Company and Hamish Hamilton Children's Books Ltd., London.

"Pigeons," by Richard Kell. Extensive research failed to locate the author and/or the copyright owner of "Pigeons."

"A Proper Burial," from the book *Where the Lilies Bloom,* by Vera and Bill Cleaver. Copyright, ©, 1969 by Vera and Bill Cleaver. Reprinted by permission of J. B. Lippincott Company.

"Quilt," from *The Carpentered Hen and Other Tame Creatures,* by John Updike. Copyright © 1957 by John Updike. Originally appeared in *The New Yorker,* and reprinted by permission of Harper & Row, Publishers, Inc., and Victor Gollancz Ltd., London.

"Roland and Oliver," from *French Legends, Tales, and Fairy Stories,* by Barbara Leonie Picard. Used by permission of Henry Z. Walck, Inc., publishers, and Oxford University Press, publishers, London.

"The Secret of the Wall," by Elizabeth Borton de Treviño. Copyright © 1966 by Elizabeth Borton de Treviño. Reprinted from the September 1966 issue of *Boy's Life,* published by The Boy Scouts of America. Reprinted by permission of Virginia Rice.

"Security Check," a slight abridgment by Arthur C. Clarke, copyright 1957, by Fantasy House, Inc. Reprinted from *The Other Side of the Sky,* by Arthur C. Clarke, by permission of Harcourt Brace Jovanovich, Inc. Reprinted by permission of the author and the author's agents, Scott Meredith Literary Agency, 580 Fifth Avenue, New York, New York 10036.

"Sequoyah," from *Word People,* by Nancy Caldwell Sorel. Text copyright © 1970 by Nancy Caldwell Sorel. Used with permission of American Heritage Press, a division of McGraw-Hill Book Company.

"The Shark," by John Ciardi. Copyright © 1967 by John Ciardi. Reprinted by permission of the author and J. B. Lippincott Company.

"The Skating Rink," from *The Skating Rink,* by Mildred Lee. Copyright © 1969 by Mildred Lee. Used by permission of The Seabury Press, Inc.

"Ski Touring," from "The Magic of Ski Touring," by Jean George. Reprinted with permission from *Travel & Leisure* (Feb.–Mar. '72). Copyright 1972 by The Reader's Digest Assn., Inc.

"The Slave Who Bought His Freedom, Equiano's Story," from the book *The Slave Who Bought His Freedom, Equiano's Story,* adapted by Karen Kennerly. Copyright © 1971 by Karen Kennerly. Published by E. P. Dutton & Co., Inc., and used with their permission. A Richard W. Baron book.

"The Sniffle," from *Verses from 1929 On,* by Ogden Nash. Copyright, 1941, by The Curtis Publishing Company. Used by permission of Little, Brown and Company and J. M. Dent & Sons Ltd.

"The Street Kids," adapted from *The Street Kids,* by Herbert Danska. Copyright © 1970 by Herbert Danska. Reprinted by permission of Alfred A. Knopf, Inc., and McIntosh and Otis, Inc.

"Street Scene," by Peter Suffolk. Copyright © *Punch,* London. Used by permission of The Ben Roth Agency, Inc.

"Superstition: The Remnants of Magic," adapted from *Black Magic, White Magic,* by Gary Jennings. Copyright © 1965 by Gary Jennings. Reprinted by permission of the publisher, The Dial Press. Reprinted by permission of Curtis Brown, Ltd.

"Talking Leaves," by Johnny Cash. Copyright © 1964 by Southwind Music, Inc. Used by permission.

"Tsunami," from *More Words of Science,* by Isaac Asimov. Copyright © 1972 by Isaac Asimov. Used by permission of Houghton Mifflin Company.

"Turner and Nature," from *Meaning and Magic of Art,* by Fred Gettings. Copyright © 1963 by Golden Pleasure Books, Ltd. Reproduced by permission of The Hamlyn Publishing Group Limited.

"Two Years in the Woods," from *The Peaceable Revolution,* by Betty Schechter. Copyright © 1963 by Betty Schechter. Used by permission of Houghton Mifflin Company.

"The Ugly Duckling," by A. A. Milne. Used by permission of Curtis Brown Ltd., London.

"An Unpredictable Japanese Lady," from *Nisei Daughter,* by Monica Sone. Copyright © 1953 by Monica Sone. Reprinted by permission of Atlantic-Little, Brown and Co., and Brandt & Brandt.

"Water Picture," by May Swenson, copyright © 1956, first published in The New Yorker, is reprinted from *To Mix with Time* by permission of Charles Scribner's Sons.

"Winter's Tale," from *Story Hour,* by Sara Henderson Hay. Copyright © 1963 by Sara Henderson Hay. Reprinted by permission of Doubleday & Company, Inc.

"Winter Trees," by Conrad Diekmann. Reprinted by permission from *Sports Illustrated,* January 5, 1959. Copyright © 1959 Time, Inc.

"A World to Come," from *Johnny Tremain,* by Esther Forbes. Copyright 1945 by Houghton Mifflin Company. Copyright 1943 by Esther Forbes Haskins. Used by permission of Houghton Mifflin Company and Longman Young Books Limited.

iv

CONTENTS

Variations

Harmonies

Applause

Distinction

Variations

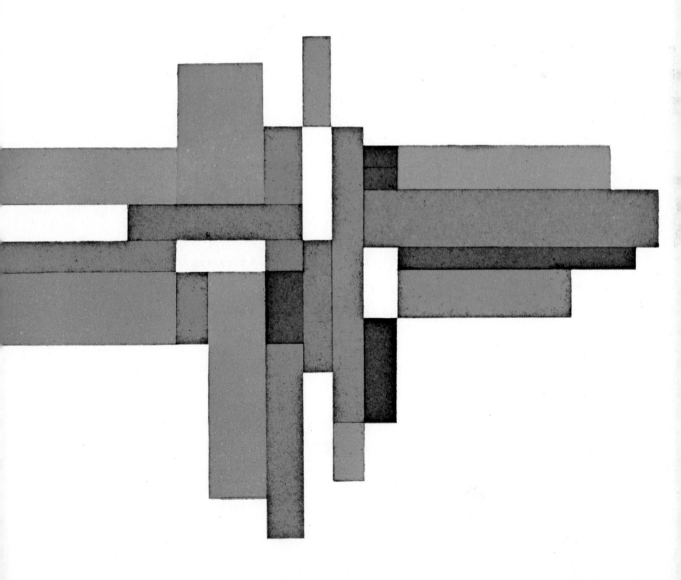

Contents

Variations

Carlos Charles, a twelve-year-old Panamanian street boy, tells the story of a plane crash in the middle of a muddy jungle. The pilot has been killed in the crash, and Carlos's friend Vicente, a Mexican geologist from the United States, is disabled with a broken leg. Johnson, another passenger, attempted to go for help but was drowned in the mire a few feet from the plane.

CARLOS CHARLES

Patrick J. Murphy
and
Shirley Rousseau Murphy

I woke some time before dawn to hear rain pounding on the metal skin of the plane, and I thought I was in the boat shop with rain beating on the roof. Then I felt a terrible thirst and I remembered where I was. I jumped up shouting, "*Ajo,*[1] it is raining!"

I heard Vicente groan. I had not meant to wake him; I stood quietly until he snored again. I felt around carefully in the dark until I located the canteen lying near him. I did not want to stumble against his leg.

I leaned out the door, cupped my hands to drink, then held the canteen out under the rain. It was raining hard but the small-necked canteen filled slowly. I found a piece of plastic from the seats, collected water in it, and poured that into the canteen, spilling half of it on my feet. When the canteen was full, I gathered all the plastic I could find in the dark and pulled wire from the overhead. I filled those pieces of plastic with the rain; then I wired the necks shut. It took me until dawn to make and fill nine containers, but I was very pleased with myself. I knew that a man could go a long time without food but not very long without water. The rain began to come heavier, to blow against the plane. The door was bent and would not close. I took off my wet clothes and lay down under the pile of seat stuffing to keep warm.

---

[1] Ajo (ä'hō): Oh.

When next I woke, it was daylight, still raining hard; and the wind was blowing through the cabin, making a moaning sound, driving sheets of water across the cabin door and against the trees outside, rippling the surface of the black mud.

I was plenty glad for this rain and for the full water bags; but when I was dressed again, I remembered suddenly that one cannot light a signal fire in the rain. It was a very small hole that we had torn among the trees. I thought a plane could fly quite close to it and never see us. For the first time I began truly to wonder if perhaps Vicente and I would not get out of this place.

I knew if I were alone, I would feel very frightened. But Vicente was with me. We would think of something.

By noon the rain had stopped. Vicente looked drawn with the pain of his leg, and I thought he had a fever. I gave him water, then took some of the clothes from Johnson's pack, and went to wipe dry a place on the wing, so I could place the material for the fire. I would cover it with plastic from one of the cockpit seats to keep rain off.

I carried the stuffing, the charts, even the candy wrappers to the wing and arranged them with the crumpled charts on the bottom to act as kindling. I wished I had some gas. I was staring into the swamp, trying to locate the lost wing, when I heard a plane. For a moment I did not move. Then I raced across the wing toward the door yelling, "Matches, matches, Vicente, I hear a plane coming," and next thing I knew, I had slipped on the wing and was waist-deep in the mud. I grabbed the metal threshold of the door and slowly pulled myself out of the sucking stuff. The plane was louder. I grabbed the matches from Vicente's hand, raced back along the wing — sliding with the mud on my feet — lit the charts, and tried to fan the blaze. The plane seemed very low. The charts flamed up. Then shortly they were finished; the stuffing only smoldered. I fanned with both hands and blew on it. The plane was going away.

The fire was out. The plane was gone. I waited for a long time, but the plane did not come back. I left the wing and went to sit beside Vicente.

He was still feverish. The plane was gone; the fire was a failure. Maybe it could be lit again. But with what? The charts were burned. There were two matches. I was feeling very bad.

At least there was water. We had a long drink and sat looking at each other dully. Then I said, "I am going to go for help. The coast is not far. If I am careful and do not panic like Johnson, I can make it. We will never be found otherwise."

He thought about this for a long time. I thought he would say no, but he did not. "The coast must be some half a mile from here. What will you do when you get there?"

"Flag a fishing boat."

"Are there any?"

"They fish along this coast, down from Panama and El Charco. How close do you think we are to El Charco? Maybe I could walk up the coast to it."

"Maybe thirty miles." He studied me. "How will you go? How will you keep from doing what Johnson did?"

"I will stay close to the roots and hang on to them."

"And what if you must cross places where there are no roots?"

"I could take the seat cushion that is out there." I got up and went to look for it, but it was nearly submerged. I returned to tell Vicente, "It has nearly sunk."

"Pull down the rest of the electrical wire from the overhead. Maybe it can get you through. Pull all of it off in one piece."

When I had it loose from the little metal tabs that held it to the ceiling, I thought there must be forty feet of it.

"You must double it for strength. Each time, before you move forward into open mud, you must loop the doubled wire around a solid branch, hold both ends tightly, and back into the clearing. If you go under, you can pull yourself out and try another route. When you are across, you can pull the wire to you. Do not try to cross any place wider than this wire will span. *¿Comprende?*"[2]

I nodded and began to double the wire, then to coil it.

"Carlos?"

"*¿Si?*"[3]

"If you fall in this mud, you must lie still. The more you move, the deeper you go in. Lie still; do not panic. Lie down on it and float. Then slowly, slowly, work your way to safety."

"*Si,* Vicente, I will remember." I thought of Johnson and wondered if I would panic in spite of myself.

"That red shirt. Use it for a signal, a flag. If you reach the shore, tie that shirt to the top of a tree where a rescue party can see it. You could see that shirt for ten miles over water."

"*Si,* it is very red, this shirt." I grinned at him. "It won't takè me long, and they will come to get you."

"Take your time. Don't try to hurry. That could kill you, kill us both."

Before I left, I cut a forked branch and tied one of the pieces of plastic to it so that Vicente could push it out the door to collect water if it should rain again. I refused the canteen, left him the matches and some cloth we thought would burn, took two of the chocolate bars and a plastic bag of water, which I tied to my belt, refused the canteen again, and took his knife. I did not say good-by to Vicente. I went through the door and looked back at him once. He winked at me.

I let myself down off the wing and stepped onto the first mass of tangled roots, then eased myself down into the

---

[2] *¿Comprende?* (kŏm-prĕnd´ĕ): Understand?

[3] *¿Si?* (sē): Yes?

mud. There were good handholds in these roots. I followed a line of roots, going knee-deep, thigh-deep in the slimy black mud. These roots were tall; masses of them rose, tangling higher than my head before they gathered into single tree trunks. In places the tangle spread so far in every direction that I had to squeeze between the roots like a cat. Land crabs skittered away from me; and when they touched each other, they made a clacking noise. They were as big as the palm of my hand and looked not like living creatures but like blue-and-red mechanical toys. I knew if I were to die here, they would eat me.

I was covered to my armpits with the clinging mud, and pulling my body through it became increasingly difficult.

At the first place where I had to back across open mud, I slung the wire around a heavy branch, clutched the wire tightly, and set out, looking over my shoulder as best I could. It was a frightening feeling, walking backward in that swamp. I went down to my armpits once, felt fear, and pulled myself out. I moved to a different spot, and there I was able to cross to another mass of roots. I rested, then pulled the wire after me.

The wire worked very well for the clearings. I pulled myself out twice more, but both times when I sank into the mud, I felt a surge of panic.

After a long time, with no sign of the shore, I began to wonder if I was going in the right direction. Perhaps it was just that the going was hard and slow; perhaps I had not traveled as far as I thought. Vicente said half a mile. Maybe he was wrong and it was farther than that.

Now the widest span yet was ahead of me; I passed the wire over a limb and moved cautiously into it. The mud was to my waist. Then, without warning, I was chin-deep, and the wire was slipping. I grabbed at it. One end of it snapped out of my hands and was gone. I floundered, fell backward, and felt solid ground under my foot. I turned, grasped a root, and pulled the wire in to me. Then I leaned against that root, shaking with fear and fatigue.

At the next clearing I wrapped that wire tightly around my hands. The mud was alive with crabs here. Most skittered away as I approached, but some stopped and seemed to watch me. The shadows were different now. I had been away from the wreck a long time. I would hate to be caught in this place after dark, to spend the night with those crabs.

I worked around a maze of roots, looking for a good branch from which to sling my wire, and climbed the roots to reach one. When I was well above the mud, I slipped, lost my balance, and fell. I had dropped the wire. I began sinking fast. The mud was up to my mouth. I tried to hold still, but I felt terror and my arms flailed in spite of me; then my head was under. I was drowning in the black mud, terrified. Then my hand hit something hard; I grabbed it blindly, pulled myself toward it and up it, and lay over the root, spitting mud and gasping for air. Now I knew how Johnson felt, for sure.

The salty mud stung my eyes, so I could not see. I reached for the plastic bag of water, tried to wipe off the lip of it and to rinse my hands, then cupped a little water into my eyes.

Finally the burning stopped. I had used more than half my water, and the wire had disappeared. It must have sunk in my floundering.

There were three more rootless clearings to cross. I could see where the trees ended, and I knew that the sea must begin there. None of those clearings seemed as wide as the last, but, with the wire gone, I was frightened and unable to make up my mind to go on. I told myself it would be no easier to go back. I promised myself that I would not panic and repeated it several times. Then I began to cut branches. It took a very long time to cut enough of them, so I could weave a rough mat to support me.

I crossed the first clearing with the mud only to my waist. I went slowly and tried to keep myself calm. The second one was not as deep, and I thought perhaps the whole swamp was shallower near the sea.

At the third clearing I sank to my chest and felt the cold fear take me. I lay out on the mud as if I were swimming, pushed the mat ahead of me, and worked my legs like a frog. The mud clung and sucked at my clothes, but I moved slowly toward the last clump of trees.

At last I could stand in the shallow mud. I was at the shore.

But the ocean was not there. In front of me there was no water, only a vast tidal flat of mud stretching away nearly as far as I could see. 'Way in the distance was the thin white line of the surf.

I stood gazing at that far, pale line of surf. There was no boat within sight, no break to the horizon. To my right the mud flat stretched away unbroken; to my left the tangled mangrove growth arched out into a point.

Where the open mud flat met the mangrove swamp, there was a wavering line of driftwood and debris; and on the roots of the trees, higher than my shoulder, was the mark of high water. The tide would come again, if I cared to wait for it. And then what? If it did not come soon, it would be too dark to see or be seen.

Why did I think that once I reached the shore my problems would be over, that there would be someone to help me? Well, I had to do something. I removed my mud-covered shirt and rinsed it as well as I could with the remains of my water, so it looked red again. The candy bars were soft. I opened the wrappers and licked out the chocolate.

I picked out a tree that stood a little higher than the others and tied my wet shirt around my waist. The mud on my feet made the climbing difficult.

Those branches were thin; I tested them carefully. When I was able to stand with my head well above the top limbs, the branch swayed under me. The sun was getting low. I thought there would be perhaps one more hour of light. Except for the point the unbroken shore swept away in both directions as far as I could see. Behind me the roof of the jungle made a solid green carpet to the horizon. There was no sign at all of where the plane had gone down.

This jutting point, if I got out of here, would be my landmark. I laid my shirt on top of the branches and tied it by four corners, so it was facing the sea somewhat, yet could be seen from the sky. I hoped it was as good a signal as Vicente said. It seemed very small there.

I stayed in this tree a long time, watching the horizon. I thought once I saw a small speck that could be a boat, but no, it was nothing. The low clouds were moving toward me; the day had lost its brightness; still the horizon was empty. To my left, beside the point, there was a thin flow of water on top of the mud as if perhaps a small river emptied itself shallowly there. This trickle of water widened as it flowed away toward the distant surf.

When I looked again at the horizon, I could see a speck moving across it toward the place opposite where I was. I watched this for many minutes. It became a little clearer as it drew closer, and I was sure it was a boat. I was wild to signal it. I had no fire, and would such a boat pay any attention to a fire on the shore? I thought not. And anyway, it could not come over the mud to investigate. My urge was to flounder through the mud to the far surf and swim to the boat, but that would be more than foolish.

Now the speck had slowed and seemed no longer to be moving. I wondered wildly if it had anchored for the night. This would be rare good luck. It stayed a long time directly opposite me, and I knew I must go to it; I knew what I must do. I must find a piece of wood among the debris along the shore that would help me over the mud and carry me across the water.

I climbed down and began to work along the edge of the tree line, searching the debris. There were many pieces that were too small and some huge round logs that would be difficult to handle.

Finally, wedged high in the root of a mangrove tree, I found a whitened plank a little wider than my shoulders and maybe five feet long. I knew without question it would carry me. It was stuck tight. I climbed on top of it and rocked on one end to dislodge it. When it broke loose, it hit the mud with a splat. I crawled onto it. It held me well on the mud. I found a small piece of driftwood for a paddle; but I could not move the plank by paddling over the thick mud, nor could I move it by slipping back and kicking my feet. But I could stand in the mud and push the board ahead of me, and it would keep me from sinking. I began moving slowly toward the surf line. Perhaps if I could get into that trickle of water beside the point, I might slide a little on the mud. I headed for it. The day was fading now.

I came at last to a swell in the mud, pushed my way to the top, and looked down the slippery bank to the thin dark sheet of water. One push and I was sliding down onto it. Now I could paddle. The last trees of the point stood silent and black against a darkening sky. I could see the white line of the surf far ahead, and in the last light I could see that this sheet of water, as it fanned itself out, was growing shallower.

Soon I could no longer paddle. Now I had to push once again, rest and push. The breeze off the water was cold, my body ached, but I must not stop.

When I reached the surf, I flopped the plank into it and tasted the salt water that foamed around me. It was too dark to see a boat. I could see no light, but I must pray a boat was there. I paddled out as strongly as I could through the low breakers. I was so tired I wondered if I would make it.

Finally, the last swells were behind me. I leaned up, searched the horizon, but could see no light. Perhaps I was too low in the water to see it. I eased myself up, so I could kneel on the plank; but still I could see nothing,

and the plank began to tip. I lay down fast and scraped my side painfully against the wood.

I paddled as hard as I could now, tried to keep in what I thought was a straight line, and prayed to see a light.

When I rose once more, I saw a tiny light. I yelled. I dipped into a shallow trough and the light disappeared; then once more I saw it and yelled again. It was dead ahead of me but very small. It could be a small running light close to me or a large light far away. I stopped shouting and paddled with all my strength.

Then suddenly I was nearly thrown off the plank. I had hit something so hard that the nose of the plank shot out of the water. There was a splash ahead of me, and a dark shape swam by my face. I turned cold with fear, lay still as still, and did not paddle.

There was no more movement in the water. I began to paddle again. Then I heard a loud splash on my right, and a black swimming shape rose next to the plank. I raised my paddle and brought it down point first, hard, onto a shark. It sank under me, then rose and struck at the plank from the other side. I looked up, and there was the light close to me, outlining the hull of a boat. I tried to yell and could not get the sound out, only a weak whisper. I bit my lip, shook my head, and tried to get hold of myself. Now my throat worked again; I was shouting; more lights came on; men called out; a beam began to search the water. A shark bumped me again; a boat was lowered over the side.

The light shone on me and on the shapes that moved around me. They were huge. Then I was being hauled into the boat, safe. "*Caramba*,[4] where you come from, boy? How you get out here?"

I could not talk.

The small boat was secured, and someone lifted me up to the deck, put a blanket around me, and pushed me down on a bench. One of the crewmen brought me scalding coffee, and I cupped my hands around the mug and felt the steam of it on my face.

They were patient. When I could tell them, finally, how I got there, I wondered if they would believe me. I told them only of the wreck, nothing else. The captain of the shrimper, for that was what she was, a shrimper anchored for the night, nodded gravely at my story, but he refused to move his boat until dawn. "I will take you to the *guardia*[5] at El Charco at first light. We are some twenty miles south of it. He can telephone for help for your friend, but I will not move my boat in the night and get us all drowned in this large sea of sharks, *muchacho*."[6]

I tried to be reasonable about this. This captain, Chiriquí (chē-rē-kē′), knew the waters and knew what care he needed to take with his boat.

---

[4] **Caramba** (kä-räm′bä): Ha.

[5] **guardia** (gwär′dēä), guard.

[6] **muchacho** (mōō-chä′chō), boy.

"Your friend is fairly comfortable and safe. If it is only a broken leg, he will survive the night well; there is nothing to bother him. Does he have water?"

"Sí, mucha agua (mōō′chä äg′wä)."

They gave me hot soup — it was very good — and showed me a bunk.

I did not remember anything beyond this until I woke fighting my blanket and heard the throb of engines. It was a bright day. I had slept a long time. We were coming close to the coast; the tide was in. I could see the mouth of a river and a small village. I knew this must be El Charco. Again I was fed, and Chiriquí came to sit with me. "You were one very tired *hombre,*[7] *muchacho.* Hungry too."

I grinned at him.

We tied up at a rickety dock. This village was made up of wooden shacks with thatched roofs and the *guardia* shack, which had a tin roof, and, inside, an old table and two chairs and a black telephone mounted high on the wall. The *guardia* had not shaved this morning, and his uniform was faded and patched; but to me he looked very fine. I was plenty glad to see that *guardia.*

Chiriquí spread out a wrinkled chart on the table and showed the *guardia* where they picked me up, and I showed them the point where I tied my shirt and the spot where I thought

---

[7] hombre (ŏm′brä), man.

the plane was. I told the *guardia* everything, about the dead pilot and Johnson, about Vicente's leg. Soon the *guardia* was dialing the old phone, calling the *guardia* in Panama City, and shouting into the mouthpiece.

There is no sound like the sound of a helicopter slapping its blades against the air, and for me it was a new sound. It seemed to shake the whole village. This one came straight down upon us to sit like a huge insect in the clearing of the village and to blow the thatch of the houses. It was a United States Army copter, a big one. There were four men aboard her; two were called paramedics. They had medicine kits, a stretcher, and a cable worked by machine to lower them from the hovering copter.

We rose straight up and skimmed along just above the top of the jungle with the nose tipped down so that I, standing behind the pilot, could see the jungle move almost under my feet.

We followed the coast; and when we came to the point where I had left my red shirt tied to the tree, we turned inland. That red shirt could be seen very well from the sky.

Now, two of the soldiers in the back of the copter had the big door open and were leaning against the heavy strap and looking out. When I spotted a slash of silver through the trees, they saw it too; and the pilot swung over the wreck. We hovered in one place and descended to within a few feet of the treetops. I could see my muddy

footprints on top of the plane. There was no sign of anyone alive here. Would not Vicente wave his stick through the door if he were able? I felt a cold chill in me. I wanted to go down with the paramedics, but I was told to stay in the copter. One man worked the cable; two went down it. I stood leaning over the leather strap. I was praying.

When they came out with the stretcher, Vicente's eyes were closed; he was pale and still. They had put a blanket over him. They began to hoist him up to the copter. Halfway up he opened his eyes and grinned at me and said something that I could not hear because of the noise of the copter blades beating at the air.

Vicente was alive. He was very white; his beard was a stubble. His leg was swollen and red around the bandage, but Vicente was grinning. "About time you got back. I just ran out of chocolate bars."

DISCUSSION

1. Why was it up to Carlos to get help? How did Carlos first plan to get through the swamp? Why was that plan no good? What plan did Vicente suggest to Carlos?
2. How did Carlos get to the shrimp boat? What danger did he encounter before he reached the boat?
3. What was used as a signal flag? How was it useful?
4. What did Vicente tell Carlos to do if he should fall into the mud? Why?
5. Why do you think Carlos did not say good-by to Vicente?
6. From reading about Carlos's feelings as he crossed the swamp, what do you think was the greatest danger he faced? Why?
7. Have you ever been lost or in danger and had to think of ways to get help? If so, what did you do?
8. Do you think you would have slept as soundly as Carlos did in an unfamiliar bunk on a boat with strangers? Why or why not?
9. What might have happened if there had not been a helicopter to rescue Vicente? How else could he have been reached?

AUTHORS

Patrick J. and Shirley Rousseau Murphy make their home in Portland, Oregon, where he is a United States probation officer.

The idea for *Carlos Charles,* the first book the Murphys have written together, grew out of their experiences in the Canal Zone in 1963 when Mr. Murphy was selected to establish the first probation office there. It was there, too, while working in the Canal Zone Library-Museum, that Mrs. Murphy got the idea for her book *Elmo Dolan and the Search for the Golden Mouse.*

Mr. Murphy, an ex-Marine, holds a degree in public administration from the University of Southern California.

Mrs. Murphy, who attended the San Francisco Art Institute, has won seven awards for sculpture and five for paintings at several Californian museums and galleries. Although she has had an interesting career as an artist, Mrs. Murphy now prefers to write.

THE SHARK

My sweet, let me tell you about the Shark.
Though his eyes are bright, his thought is dark.
He's quiet — that speaks well of him.
So does the fact that he can swim.
But though he swims without a sound,
Wherever he swims he looks around
With those two bright eyes and that one dark thought.
He has only one but he thinks it a lot.
And the thought he thinks but can never complete
Is his long dark thought of something to eat.
Most anything does. And I have to add
That when he eats, his manners are bad.
He's a gulper, a ripper, a snatcher, a grabber.
Yes, his manners are drab. But his thought is drabber.
That one dark thought he can never complete
Of something — anything — somehow to eat.

Be careful where you swim, my sweet.

John Ciardi

THE GREAT
STORM

Dorothy Holder Jones
and
Ruth Sexton Sargent

In 1853, Samuel Burgess was appointed keeper of the lighthouse on Matinicus Rock, off the coast of Rockland, Maine, and the family went to live on this barren and lonely station. During the stormy winter of 1856, the supply boat was unable to deliver provisions. When there was a lull in the bad weather, Mr. Burgess set sail for Rockland to replenish their lean stock of supplies. As his wife was not well, he depended upon his oldest daughter, fourteen-year-old Abbie, to keep the oil lamps of the lighthouse burning to save ships from disaster on the rockbound coast.

The girls stamped about in their snowshoes for over an hour, pelting one another with snowballs and playing with the hens. It was good to hear them laughing again, Abbie thought, as she finished her morning chores.

While they were eating dinner, the kitchen became so dark that Abbie got up to light the lamp. As she did so, a gust of wind whined down the chimney, followed by a blast that set the shutters slamming furiously against the house.

She ran to the window. The clear sky had deepened to an ominous dark gray. Gulls screamed wildly as if bewitched by the wind. From the way the flag on the pole was blowing, she knew the wind had veered to the northeast.

Esther and Mahala began to cry, and Mrs. Burgess called out from the parlor, "Abigail, your father's caught in this storm!"

"Now, Mother, he's halfway to the mainland by now. And it may be just a gale that'll blow right out to sea."

Esther and Mahala rushed in to them. "What'll we do, Abbie?" Esther asked worriedly.

"We'll do exactly what Father would if he were here. We'll batten things down." She directed Lydia and Esther to latch all the shutters, and Mahala was sent to bring in the flag.

Abbie closed up the sheds and moved the hen coop to a more protected spot. After all was done, her sisters sat around the fire, complaining about being alone on the Rock without their father.

"Now Father can't bring back the supplies until the storm's over," Lydia whined. "And that might be several days!"

"We won't dwell on that," Abbie told her. "We'll take each day as it comes. I'd best light the lamps early today. It's so dark."

With each hour the wind grew more frenzied, until it was battering the Rock unmercifully. Huge breakers flung themselves at the ledges.

Abbie lost count of the hours she spent minding the lamps. In between her vigils she kept her loved ones warm and fed and calmed their fears. She watered down her mother's tonic as much as she dared, wishing she could spoon courage into her as easily as she did the tonic. Yet, she marveled at her mother's composure in view of their serious situation.

At night Mahala slept with Mrs. Burgess, and Lydia and Esther spread pallets by the fireside. Abbie, exhausted from her labors, was glad to have the comfort of the couch.

For a week there was no relief from the hurricanelike winds. It was as though the elements had gone mad and were venting all their fury upon the Rock. On the eighth morning Abbie was awakened by a loud boom. She sat up, every nerve taut. A breaker had slammed against the house!

She hurried up to the tower and was relieved to find the lamps still glowing. The sky was so dark, she let the lamps burn on, though the oil was scarce. In the light the towers cast, she could see gray

billows heaving offshore. Each one rose higher than the one before it and splashed farther upon the Rock.

When Abbie returned to the kitchen, she found Lydia struggling to help Esther make a batch of griddle cakes. Mahala was using towels to mop up water from a leak under the kitchen door. They all turned to Abbie with frightened faces.

"It's worse," Lydia said, her lips quivering.

Mahala shouted, "Are we going to be washed away?"

"Not likely." Abbie tried to smile. "After we eat, things won't seem so gloomy."

The morning passed swiftly and without incident; but just as they began to eat dinner, a breaker crashed on the roof with the boom of a cannon. They clung to each other in terror, as if waiting for the end. Time passed, and there was only a terrible, deafening roar.

When the furor quieted some, Abbie sprang to her feet. "Mother, the coop is bound to be flooded. I must get my hens before they drown ——"

Her mother grabbed her dress. "Abigail, you daren't go outside! You'll be swept right out to sea!"

"But I can't bear to part with my hens. If I go before another breaker comes — there's a chance."

She grabbed a basket; and when the sea fell back a little, she ran down the steps. The water came up to her knees, but she pushed on until she came to the coop. She opened the door and the hens tumbled out. She scooped two into the basket, and the others flapped about frantically. Two white feathery forms were sinking into the water, but she pulled them out and dropped them into the basket. She couldn't find the fifth hen. There was no time left to search, for another breaker was rumbling toward her.

Mahala opened the back door, and Abbie dashed inside. "Oh, look!" Mahala exclaimed. "Look there! The worst sea is coming!"

A gigantic billow, about thirty feet in height, was lunging toward the Rock.

"*Close the door!*" Abbie yelled.

Mahala screamed and shut the door. Abbie flung the basket down, the hens scattering, and hurried to the sideboard near the door.

"Help me bar the door!" she cried, pushing against the weight of it. Her sisters came and pitted their strength with hers, and the chest slid in front of the door just as the breaker struck. The house trembled from the impact. They leaned limply against the sideboard, certain this was the final blow.

After a moment, when it appeared the house had survived, Mrs. Burgess burst into sobs. The younger girls ran to her, while Lydia took pity on the squawking hens and gathered them into her lap. Suddenly, she shrieked, "Where's Patience? Abbie — what happened to Patience?"

Abbie shook her head sadly. "I — I couldn't find her. The water was so deep." She was as heartsick over the loss as the girls; but she decided to let them cry, for it would relieve the strain. Right now she had to check to see what damage had been done. Entering the tower, she stepped into a pool of water. She held her breath and quickly opened the door leading to the wooden chamber.

"Sakes' alive!" she gasped. The space where the room had been was an abyss of swirling water. Only the stone foundation stood. She shut the door and leaned against it as horror filled her mind.

She took stock of the situation. The ocean had already washed away the wooden section of the house; and if the storm got any worse, the house itself might not stand. The towers, she decided, were their only chance.

In the kitchen she removed her wet boots, put on dry shoes, and hung all her wet clothing near the fire to dry. She bided her time in telling the others about the plans that were forming in her mind.

As they were finishing their evening meal, she said, "Mother, we'd best move into the tower until the storm's over. The lamp room would be right comfortable."

"The tower!" Lydia interrupted. "It smells horrid in there!"

"We'd freeze," Esther put in.

Mrs. Burgess shook her head. "Abigail, I won't let anyone sleep up there."

"The lamps give a lot of heat," Abbie pointed out.

"But there's no sense going up there, Abigail."

Abbie sighed. "Then I'm obliged to tell you," she said, struggling to keep her voice steady. "The — the wooden chamber was washed away this morning. The timbers are probably strewn about Penob-

billows heaving offshore. Each one rose higher than the one before it and splashed farther upon the Rock.

When Abbie returned to the kitchen, she found Lydia struggling to help Esther make a batch of griddle cakes. Mahala was using towels to mop up water from a leak under the kitchen door. They all turned to Abbie with frightened faces.

"It's worse," Lydia said, her lips quivering.

Mahala shouted, "Are we going to be washed away?"

"Not likely." Abbie tried to smile. "After we eat, things won't seem so gloomy."

The morning passed swiftly and without incident; but just as they began to eat dinner, a breaker crashed on the roof with the boom of a cannon. They clung to each other in terror, as if waiting for the end. Time passed, and there was only a terrible, deafening roar.

When the furor quieted some, Abbie sprang to her feet. "Mother, the coop is bound to be flooded. I must get my hens before they drown ——"

Her mother grabbed her dress. "Abigail, you daren't go outside! You'll be swept right out to sea!"

"But I can't bear to part with my hens. If I go before another breaker comes – there's a chance."

She grabbed a basket; and when the sea fell back a little, she ran down the steps. The water came up to her knees, but she pushed on until she came to the coop. She opened the door and the hens tumbled out. She scooped two into the basket, and the others flapped about frantically. Two white feathery forms were sinking into the water, but she pulled them out and dropped them into the basket. She couldn't find the fifth hen. There was no time left to search, for another breaker was rumbling toward her.

Mahala opened the back door, and Abbie dashed inside. "Oh, look!" Mahala exclaimed. "Look there! The worst sea is coming!"

A gigantic billow, about thirty feet in height, was lunging toward the Rock.

"Close the door!" Abbie yelled.

Mahala screamed and shut the door. Abbie flung the basket down, the hens scattering, and hurried to the sideboard near the door.

"Help me bar the door!" she cried, pushing against the weight of it. Her sisters came and pitted their strength with hers, and the chest slid in front of the door just as the breaker struck. The house trembled from the impact. They leaned limply against the sideboard, certain this was the final blow.

After a moment, when it appeared the house had survived, Mrs. Burgess burst into sobs. The younger girls ran to her, while Lydia took pity on the squawking hens and gathered them into her lap. Suddenly, she shrieked, "Where's Patience? Abbie — what happened to Patience?"

Abbie shook her head sadly. "I — I couldn't find her. The water was so deep." She was as heartsick over the loss as the girls; but she decided to let them cry, for it would relieve the strain. Right now she had to check to see what damage had been done. Entering the tower, she stepped into a pool of water. She held her breath and quickly opened the door leading to the wooden chamber.

"Sakes' alive!" she gasped. The space where the room had been was an abyss of swirling water. Only the stone foundation stood. She shut the door and leaned against it as horror filled her mind.

She took stock of the situation. The ocean had already washed away the wooden section of the house; and if the storm got any worse, the house itself might not stand. The towers, she decided, were their only chance.

In the kitchen she removed her wet boots, put on dry shoes, and hung all her wet clothing near the fire to dry. She bided her time in telling the others about the plans that were forming in her mind.

As they were finishing their evening meal, she said, "Mother, we'd best move into the tower until the storm's over. The lamp room would be right comfortable."

"The tower!" Lydia interrupted. "It smells horrid in there!"

"We'd freeze," Esther put in.

Mrs. Burgess shook her head. "Abigail, I won't let anyone sleep up there."

"The lamps give a lot of heat," Abbie pointed out.

"But there's no sense going up there, Abigail."

Abbie sighed. "Then I'm obliged to tell you," she said, struggling to keep her voice steady. "The — the wooden chamber was washed away this morning. The timbers are probably strewn about Penobscot Bay right now. I figure the towers are stronger than the house. We'll be safer there."

Lydia continued to protest, and Abbie's mother insisted she couldn't endure the climb up the tower stairs. Abbie argued with them until she was hoarse.

She put soapstones on top of the stove to heat, to help keep their feet warm. She collected the bedding and a basket of food; and when all was ready, she led the two younger girls up to the tower off the kitchen. When she had them settled comfortably in the lamp room, she went back down and asked her mother once more.

"No, Abigail," she replied, "I'll stay here and keep the fire going. Lydia can stay with me."

Abbie went back to the tower, knowing that if things worsened, they'd come up to the lamp room.

Sometime after Esther and Mahala were finally asleep, Abbie went to the shelf where the lamps were burning and opened the logbook. It was just after midnight. She dipped a pen into the inkwell and made this entry: "January 27, 1856. A nor'easter blowing in. We're prepared for the worst."

She donned the oilskins and boots she'd brought up to the tower. After another breaker passed overhead, she quickly went out on the catwalk to scrape the windows before the next breaker struck.

She stepped into a pit of blackness that was terrifying. The wind screamed and buffeted her against the tower, and needles of ice pricked her cheeks. The ocean lapped viciously below the tower, as though it were a monster eager to swallow the house and towers.

With the below-zero temperatures the ocean spray froze instantly on the glass panes, yet there was only a thin layer of ice on each window. The heat from the lamps inside, she decided, kept the windows slightly warm. The warning grumble of another breaker sent her back inside.

On the next try she finished scraping all the windows. She rested a spell, then began the journey to the other tower. It seemed peculiar not to hear her own footsteps, for in good weather her feet fairly boomed in the granite tower. But tonight it was as though she walked on velvet.

She went on through the house, passing her mother, who was

the precious oil. The ocean's fury was still blasting the Rock, but it was easier to bear in daylight, Abbie discovered.

She managed to build a fire in the stove and put on a pot of corn-meal mush. In between the breakers she swept salt water out the kitchen door. Then she built a fire in the fireplace. When the room was fairly warm, she brought the others down.

Once their stomachs were filled, everyone cheered up a little — even dozed a while. But the day was a mixture of gratitude and discomfort. The house had withstood the onslaught, but its furnishings were soaked. Their food supply was dangerously low, and there was no relief in sight.

Abbie flew the flag at half-mast, with the hope that some ship, plowing through the rough waters, might think it a signal of distress and send some supplies to them. But they saw no ship.

In the days that followed, Mrs. Burgess kept to her bed; so Abbie was in full charge of the household and the lamps. Though Lydia was willing to cook, Abbie was afraid she'd waste their food; and she wouldn't allow the younger girls to help her in the towers for fear they'd spill the valuable oil. She gave Lydia the task of attending to their mother's needs, and Esther and Mahala were to keep the kitchen clean and warm.

Abbie encouraged them to carry on with their handiwork, and she tutored them in their studies. The busier she kept them, the less they complained about their hunger, for she now had to cut down on everyone's rations in order to stretch the food.

Throughout the days she thought of her father. He'll come today, for sure, she'd tell herself each morning. He *must* come today. I'm so tired, and there's so little to eat.

The storm continued to rage for two weeks. The ocean never broke over the Rock again, but angry breakers pounded steadily, spraying the windows of the house. Abbie lost sleep and rest, but she kept on.

In mid-February the ocean receded. Abbie opened the shutters; and for the first time in weeks, daylight flooded in.

A few evenings later, when she was up in the tower checking the lamps, Abbie noticed a tiny light offshore. She wasted no time getting down to the landing site. Her sisters soon caught up with her, and they all waited on the ledge.

A deep voice called out, "Ahoy there!"

"It's *Father!*" Abbie cried joyously.

"Father! Father!" the girls shouted as they scampered down the steps. Abbie caught the end of the rope he tossed and hauled the boat up on the ways. As soon as he touched shore, they rushed to him, chattering all at once.

He turned to Abbie and his voice choked. "I knew I'd find you all well and safe. Everyone in Rockland feared for your lives, but I told them this house would endure. And I knew you'd keep the lights burning, Daughter. They certainly welcomed me."

"Oh, Father, it's so good to have you home!" was all she could say.

DISCUSSION

1. To what did the author compare the vicious ocean during the storm?
2. Why did Abbie not let her younger sisters help with the lamps and the cooking?
3. Why did Abbie feel that it was necessary to keep everyone busy during the storm?
4. Abbie's father "knew" that he would find his family well and safe. Why did he think that?
5. Why do you think Abbie watered down her mother's tonic?
6. Abbie kept entries in the logbook. Why was that a good idea?
7. Why was it necessary for Abbie to scrape the windows of the tower?
8. If the storm had lasted another week and Father had not returned, do you think the family would have been able to survive? Why or why not?
9. Why did Abbie think it would be good for the girls to cry over the lost hen? Do you think that crying ever serves a worthwhile purpose? Why or why not? Has it ever helped you? How?

10. Do you think that Abbie showed wisdom in the way she took care of the family and the towers during the storm? Why or why not? Have you ever had to cope with a difficult situation when you were taking care of younger children or sick persons? What happened?

11. Do you think it was wise to have a fire in the fireplace? Why or why not?

AUTHORS

"The Great Storm," from *Abbie Burgess: Lighthouse Heroine,* was written by Dorothy Holder Jones and Ruth Sexton Sargent.

Mrs. Jones attended schools in Texas, Kansas, and Georgia and is the author of four other novels for young people: *An Understanding Heart, Dress Parade, Those Gresham Girls,* and *The Oldest Ones.* As a contributor of short stories and articles to more than forty magazines, she has won several literary awards. She is the mother of two children and lives with her family in Virginia.

Mrs. Sargent has lived in Maine for thirteen years. Her research on Abbie Burgess, the first woman lighthouse keeper, included interviewing the great-granddaughter of Abbie Burgess as well as other authorities on Maine history.

Old Mr. Serendipity is the watchman at a partially completed skyscraper being erected on New York's West 21st Street. Here he has only his pet goat, Agamemnon (ăg'ə-mĕm'nŏn'), to converse with, for the workmen are on strike and the construction site is deserted. Being an enthusiastic gardener, Mr. Serendipity whiles away the hours by planting flowers, fruits, and vegetables on every available spot surrounding his construction-shed home. His solitary life is pleasant and peaceful until the arrival of the street kids.

THE STREET KIDS

by Herbert Danska

Perhaps Mr. Serendipity was becoming hard of hearing; but as he worked in his garden, he did not seem to catch the shrill sounds that began coming from behind the fence. More than likely though, the old man was ignoring them. Delighted with the way the seedlings were taking hold, he prepared another section of ground for vegetables. "The land's going to waste, wouldn't you say, Ag?"

Agamemnon heard the giggles and sniggers coming from behind the fence and said nothing.

"Some cukes or beans and tomatoes would do fine, maybe even squash," the old man said, caught up in his thoughts.

Suit yourself; I prefer fresh alfalfa myself.

Mr. Serendipity said that he didn't think that would grow here and was about to suggest clover when the first can came. Lofting up over the wooden fence, it flashed, spinning in the sunlight, then crashed onto the metal shed roof.

Ag bolted for cover. Rolling to the ground, the can came to a stop at the old man's feet.

"Weirdo!"

Along with this shriek a fusillade of empty cans came raining onto the roof and all round the shocked watchman. He stumbled about, shielding his head with his bent arms. A soda bottle spun and shattered against the bulldozer.

"Weird — weird — WEIRDO!"

Shrill laughter filled the spring air.

His tormentors stood planted out on the boardwalk in a cluster, slouched and swaying lightly and waiting.

The oldest, about thirteen, had ball-point tattoos on both forearms and an unblinking smile. Mugging and darting eye signals at one another the youths held their snickers at-ready. The two girls among them were on the verge of giggles.

Old Serendipity stepped through the gateway and peered at the brash faces before him. This nervy crew was all new to him. Bold dark eyes in faces ranging from tawny olive to deep brown, similar to those he had once been acquainted with, but this was 21st Street, a different turf — theirs. He was finding out that moving just one block in the city could be like crossing a foreign border.

Willie was unable to hold back any longer. "Some loony creep things you up to, man!" he sneered. "We seen ya!" The boy bobbed out from the rear of the group, a tiny Santa Cruz (săn'tä kro͞oz') medallion swinging over his sweaty, bare chest.

Hoots and giggles broke loose, the kids jostling one another in delight.

A maroon-brown girl with stringy legs skipped forward. "Seen you, Mister Weirdo, yeah!" Alma screeched, getting caught on a trailing sneaker lace.

"Gotta be loony, man — what else?" called Lucky, the youth with the ball-point tattoos. He grimaced at the watchman from under a tangle of jet hair.

Mr. Serendipity sniffed. "Beg your pardon?" he said, unwittingly adding fuel to their fun.

"Not for real, mister," Otis shouted into his ear. This brought howls of glee, someone shouting, "Creepy loon!"

Willie's cousin Pequita (pĕ-kē'tä) screwed her pretty face into a scornful smile. "Sneaking around in there doing nutty things."

"Hey, man — you a crazy?"

"Crazy creepy?"

"Yeah-yeah-yeah," the girls sang.

Chino tugged the bicycle chain around his neck, whirling a finger in circles alongside his temple. "Talking to goats, man. Bug-bug, man!"

"Oh wow, man," Otis added, "like if you don't know whut you doing — then somebody have to wisen you up. Right?"

"Yeah," Chino's twin, Chico, jeered. "Us."

A gawky boy with his arm in a grime-stained plaster cast threw his chest out. "Somebody got to keep this neighborhood shaped up," boomed Louie-Louie. "Dig? Like, high-class, re-spec-ta-ble."

"Dig it." Willie pointed about at his friends. "We got enough freaks around without you."

Alma's shriek rose up above the hilarity that followed. She stood motioning at Agamemnon, who had made a sudden appearance, the goat coming up alongside Mr. Serendipity. Everyone fell back, holding their noses and stumbling about, gasping exaggeratedly for air. Chico collapsed against the fence as though mortally wounded.

Casting catcalls and taunts back over their shoulders, the street kids drifted off, groping through their pockets to find enough change for sodas. The watchman murmured something to himself, then shut the gate from the inside. "Only words, old friend, pay them no mind."

Except for a Coke bottle, which came crashing onto the shed roof, the next week was uneventful. The foreman phoned, directing Mr. Serendipity to paint *No Posting* signs along the fence and informing him that the strike was "still in negotiations" with no end in sight yet.

With nothing but time on his hands old Serendipity seeded a patch of clover for Ag and got the squash vines curling their way up a grid of framing at the foot of the steelwork.

Under the steady care he gave them, the garden plots thrived. The weather was ideal now for growing things. And, by the first day of June the strawberry plants had doubled in size on their wooden supports and they soon flowered.

When June days grew steamy, even the best of street games could become a drag. This was when everybody thought of water. For

35

decades the Hudson had been too polluted to swim in. There were always the hydrants if the cops felt lenient and if the older guys didn't have a stickball game going in the road.

One day the kids tried the public pool way downtown. It was mobbed as ever. By the time they paid their quarter admission, the chlorinated water was lukewarm. Still it was better than nothing. They felt refreshed afterwards — until the airless subway ride home. By the time they arrived on the block again, damp towels rolled under their arms, they were feeling hot and clammy once more.

Louie-Louie squinted up at a toro that skipped through the haze overhead. "Man," he panted, "wish I was tied to a kite string. Fly, man, fly."

"Yeah. Right on," Otis agreed. "Then just cut the string, man, and take off, *shoomdeedo.*"

"To where, Otis man?" Alma said, teasing. She tugged at her little sister's hand as Doreen tried to keep step.

Otis looked outward. "I don't know, just anywheres but here."

Several heads bobbed in agreement. "I wish I was superman," Hands murmured.

"Me — I'll take P.R., man," Willie said dreamily. "My uncle says the water's all blue and green down Puerto Rico."

"With palm trees and banana trees all over, mm," Pequita sighed.

Louie-Louie spotted the old creep first. Waggling his plaster encased forearm, he pointed ahead toward the construction fence. The kids began a wail of whinnies and brays, mimicking what they thought to be a barnyard. Pequita came to a stop a pace from the old man, who stood over a bucket of blue paint, a wet brush in his hand.

She curtsied. "Hel . . . lo, Mister Creepsie," Pequita hissed in a honey-sweet voice. Her wide grin brought forth a chorus of hoots.

"Hello, miss," the watchman replied, dipping his brush. He painted a foot-high letter N on the fence.

Willie eyed it and loosed a guffaw. "Oh, wow! Like N for Nuts!"

"Right, right!" Malcolm called.

The watchman remained quiet, now completing a letter O.

"O for . . . for . . ." Alma paused to pin down her thought.

"*Outasight,* baby!" Otis crowed. "Like this kook here."

"Outa his skull!" Willie jeered, the others giggling.

Alma and Pequita began to dance around Mr. Serendipity, the boys beating out a rhythm with their handclaps and chanting, "Loony-loony-*uh!* Loony-loony-*uh!* . . ."

Without glancing to either side of him, old Serendipity drew the first letter of a second word, P.

Louie-Louie leaned in and examined it. "Beautiful. Dig it — P for Putrid, man! The way that goat and him stink!"

The old man shook his head and seemed to smile to himself. He put the brush down atop the bucket. "Some of you are right good with words," he said calmly. "Now, this young fellow, for example — sorry lad, I don't know your name." He stood looking to Louie-Louie for a response; there was none.

The boys fell silent, suspicious that he was baiting a trap of some kind.

"Louie-Louie," piped a small voice from the rear.

Alma spun round at her sister Doreen. "Shush up, brat!"

"Yeah, Doreen," Willie said melodramatically in a hushed voice. "Gotta watch these old creeps. Anybody see that movie on TV once where there was this weird old guy? . . ."

"Interesting name — Louie-Louie," said Mr. Serendipity. "Two names, is it?"

"Nah — they only call me that," Louie-Louie said before he knew it.

Doreen stepped forward and stood looking down at the can of blue paint. "I don't know spelling words yet," she mumbled. "But I'm good making pictures."

Alma swooped, poking her to be still, others cawing at the four-year-old traitor to their cause.

"Would you care to try painting one?" The old man handed her the brush. He pointed to the fence. "Lots of space."

Before Alma could get a hold on her wrist, Doreen had slipped out of reach and begun a heavy blue scrawl on the fence with the brush.

Mr. Serendipity smiled, asking, "Anyone else? It's a long fence."

A fast huddle between three of the boys took place. After some buzzing among them, Willie came over, a blank look masking his intentions. "Got another one, man?" he asked.

Old Serendipity was startled for a second, then he beamed. "Yes, yes . . ." he called, rushing off through the open gate. "Back in a minute."

Stirring out of a nap under the shed porch, Ag saw the man go to a locker, rummage about within, come up with a paintbrush, and then run out to the boardwalk again.

"Here we are!" he announced. He blinked seeing Willie sputter and break into a howl of laughter. Their fingers pointing at the fence behind him, the kids broke into gleeful jeers. The watchman turned stiffly and saw the ten-foot-long slogan now emblazoned across the wooden panels:

THE WORLD'S BIGGEST WEIRDO
LIVES HERE!!!

Mr. Serendipity looked on unperturbed, or so it seemed. He felt a nip at his shirt sleeve and saw Doreen waving a blue-smeared hand up at him.

"Like," she began, pointing at her drawing, "is that the — the way a goat looks?"

The others drowned out her last words with whoops and hollers. Squinting at the boldly painted picture, the watchman put on his glasses.

"Hmm . . . Agamemnon might not agree," he said. "But I would say it does . . ."

"Doreen," the little girl filled in.

"Brat!" Alma snapped, turning her sister toward the curb and marching her off.

Another hail of cans came over the 21st Street fence, followed by taunts and the sounds of escaping feet.

Later that afternoon the watchman noticed Willie, Pequita, and Lucky huddled together outside the gate. Pretending not to see, he edged closer to them, working a hoe among the vegetables as he went.

Willie watched him through the opening in the gate. "Can't grow stuff in that junk," he scoffed.

Lucky let a top fly onto the boardwalk.

"Looks like," Pequita said, "he's doing pretty okay."

"And what d'you know about it, anyhow?" Lucky muttered.

Willie shrugged. "From our uncle in . . ."

"What's he know, man?" the older boy shot back. "These ain't bananas; besides he's from San Juan (sän' hwän'), not the country part." Lucky squatted down and slipped his flattened palm under the top, bringing it, still spinning, up with him as he straightened.

Willie bristled. "Knows more'n you, dude," he said hoarsely.

Lucky grinned, then jutted his chin towards the lot. "Some boss machines in there, huh?"

The trio pressed up to the fence, peering through gaps in it at the spread of abandoned machines; the bulldozer, derricks, and trucks were frozen in positions in which they had been left weeks before. Willie stiffened abruptly and elbowed Lucky. The big gate had opened, and the old guy stood there.

"Quite right," he said to Lucky. "Bananas would never grow here at all — but strawberries can. Wasn't sure when I put them in, but only this morning I saw the first little green ones."

Bananas? Little green ones? He's really freaked out, the boys thought as they stared back coldly.

"Strawberries?" Pequita asked Mr. Serendipity.

Mr. Serendipity nodded cheerily, suggesting they come inside and have a look for themselves. Otis came trotting from across the street, a cracked broomstick in his hands.

"Send that billy goat to the meat factory?" he hooted. "Like, I don't smell him around, man." Otis snickered, the others joining him, except for Pequita, who had walked ahead and now stood a pace inside the lot looking about.

"Guess the wind's blowing the wrong way," the old man said. "Actually, you can find Ag over behind that bulldozer somewhere; he's not always cheerful, but he is gentle." Mr. Serendipity ambled back through the gateway.

The boys exchanged amused looks and whispered something to one another. Willie left them, saying with a smirk he had better things to do.

Moving stiffly, her eyes swiveling warily as if she had entered a cemetery at night, Pequita trailed after the watchman between the garden plots. "They sort of spruce up the place, don't you think?" he said. Pequita made no reply; they went on. The watchman pointed out a line of cement troughs. "All under those plastic sheets are new seedlings, flowers."

"Now, here," he said, and grinned proudly, "these are the strawberry plants."

He led the girl over to the patch of bushy plants, which stood before the fence. She gazed at them for a moment, then bent over and fingered some berries; tiny and still yellowish-green, they were the size of peas.

"These," she breathed, "really going to be . . ."

"If everything goes well, they should be ripe for picking inside of ten days, I think."

A murmur of surprise came from the girl; her eyes ran from plant to plant. "You put in, I mean like seeds, and got these?"

Mr. Serendipity shook his head. "Takes too long to start them from seed; these came from runners." Then, seeing her puzzlement, he knelt down and pointed to one of the green tendrils, which grew outward from the base of the nearest vine. "Runners," he said, "are cut from the best of mature plants, then rooted in a special way to make growing stock for new plants."

"Hey!" They looked up at the call that had come from the steelwork. "Hey mister! What's he eat?" Otis and Lucky were seen standing alongside Ag in the distance.

"Most anything, when he's hungry enough!" the watchman called back.

Pequita knelt down beside him. "What'd you mean before when you said 'if everything goes well'?"

His fingers reached for and picked a mealybug off a leaf, where it had been feeding. "Oh," he said, "soil and weather conditions, you know, and keeping blights and bugs like this one from doing damage."

The old man nodded to himself. "Plants are living things. . . ." He spoke on for several minutes, telling about root systems and how they develop and describing the ways

40

in which plants make use of sunlight, water, and foods from the soil. So delighted was he to find a curious listener, especially a young person, the information just rolled from him; so much was stored inside him, which had gone unshared during his solitary years. With barely a pause he rattled on, facts tumbling from him at a rather bewildering rate. Pequita's black eyes fluttered, squinted, and at times opened wide as she tried to follow his words. Finally, laughing at himself for running on so, Mr. Serendipity asked the girl to wait and hurried into the shed.

He returned with a thick volume in his hand, his best botany text. Pequita turned the pages and scanned the numerous diagrams and detailed illustrations.

Otis and Lucky had since discovered that a bulldozer could become a spaceship. Now, noisily manning the array of frozen controls up in the cockpit, the boys were defending themselves against an attack from some awesome enemy — Martians, from the sound of things.

It doesn't take long for word to spread to the kids of West 21st. By five the rest of the machines were filled with youngsters, several squeezed into each of the cab seats. Willie scoffed that they were suckers for going, and he went down to the river to scale stones at the pier when Hands and Louie-Louie left for the lot.

The twins drifted over and joined the watchman as he and Pequita toured the garden plots. Mr. Serendipity was still talking away, pointing out everything he thought might be of interest.

All the while the sound effects of battle filled the air, the derricks now attacking the bulldozer and trucks. It was a wonder that anyone heard the supper calls when they came from windows across the way.

"I think," piped Doreen, "Mom's calling."

"Um ..." murmured Alma, ducking the rockets, which whizzed by their cab window up in the derrick. She felt a poke from her sister. "Yeah, okay ... go on, Dorie," she said in her nicest big-sister voice. "Tell Mom I'll be five minutes."

Doreen waggled her head. "Uh uh."

"Now, c'mon, Dorie hon', go on."

The little one's pout tightened, her spindly arms folded across the stripes of her T-shirt.

Alma's eyes flashed. "You go on, brat — or you don't get to come here tomorrow!"

That did it. Scrambling to the ground, pout and all, the four-year-old ran off like a shot.

From that day on any worries old Serendipity might still have had about attacks on his garden could be put to rest.

They would arrive right after school, books under their arms, and on weekends in the late mornings. Mr. Serendipity usually greeted the early comers at the gate, Ag at his side, peering out from behind him.

It's not the gardens they come for, old man.

Old Serendipity got this comment from Agamemnon after the kids' second visit. He laughed; it didn't matter to him why. He had overheard Otis crack that flowers were jive stuff for girls.

It was only Pequita at first, and at times Chico and Chino, who lent the watchman a hand, helping to water and fertilize the planting areas. For the others what were flowers compared with a bulldozer, which could be turned into a submarine one moment and a spaceship the next with the remarkable flexibility of diving fifty fathoms into the sea, then blasting off into the cosmos? "Power, man, pour it on!" Otis was heard commanding.

Street kids, after all, were born and raised in a world of tired brick and asphalt, knowing much more from TV about the moon than about growing things. To them greenery meant a park, if you could get to one. Flowers — these were things you glimpsed in shop windows or the waxy plastic kind your old lady got at the five-and-dime and kept on top of the TV set.

It was the strawberries becoming full and ripe that brought about the change, a big one.

"Oh, oh, gee, wow!" Louie-Louie

breathed when he picked a huge berry off and held it before his eyes.

"Big as a Torpedo," Lucky said, holding a top alongside the luscious-looking strawberry, a small exaggeration that everyone agreed with.

"You made, I mean, grew these just from the ground like?" Louie-Louie asked.

"From runners," replied Pequita, looking to Mr. Serendipity for confirmation.

"That's right. Here." He handed the youth a plastic bucket and motioned toward the strawberry patch. "Why don't we have some?"

There was no need to make the suggestion again. Chico found a small empty carton, and among them the kids picked enough of the fruit for a feast. They washed the berries under a standpipe tap that was outside the shed. Then, sitting cross-legged or lying sprawled in the shade of the steelwork, they gorged themselves. Mr. Serendipity had his strawberries with milk in a bowl, offering the same to anyone who would try them this way.

Otis wagged his head, a trickle of sweet juice curling down the side of his chin. "I like 'em better straight."

"Yeah," Hands admitted after popping his twentieth into his mouth. "Something else. You pretty cool, mister. That's for sure!"

Mr. Serendipity stretched his legs, settling back against a pillar and loosening his belt a notch. He wasn't entirely sure what the boy had meant but knew it was all right.

DISCUSSION

1. What was Mr. Serendipity supposed to be painting on the fence? How did the street kids interpret what he was painting? What did they paint on the fence?
2. What did Mr. Serendipity mean when he said, "If everything goes well, they [the strawberries] should be ripe for picking inside of ten days, I think"?
3. What changed all the kids' attitudes toward the strawberry plants?
4. Why could moving the distance of one block in a city be like crossing a foreign border?
5. Why do you think the kids ridiculed Mr. Serendipity?

6. What did the watchman mean when he said, "Only words, old friend, pay them no mind"?

7. Do you think Mr. Serendipity really was unperturbed about the slogan on the fence? Why do you think that?

8. Do you think the kids should have made insulting remarks to an old man? Why do you think that?

9. If you had been Mr. Serendipity, how would you have responded to the bad treatment of the kids? Why?

10. Why do you think the author named the watchman Mr. Serendipity? Try to think of an example of serendipity that you have encountered.

11. Mr. Serendipity wasn't entirely sure what Hands meant when he said, "Something else. You pretty cool, mister. That's for sure." How could you express approval so that Mr. Serendipity would clearly understand?

AUTHOR

The Street Kids, from which the selection you have just read was taken, is the first novel that Herbert Danska has both written and illustrated. A native New Yorker, Mr. Danska has had a highly successful career as a graphic artist, illustrator, and film maker. In addition to awards for his watercolor paintings he has won thirty-one citations from the Society of Illustrators, the Art Directors Club, and the American Institute of Graphic Arts as well as eight film awards from the Vancouver, Edinburgh, Venice, and American film festivals. He has made two feature films, numerous documentaries, and written the screenplay for an adaptation of *The Street Kids.*

The father of two teen-agers, Mr. Danska, who has traveled extensively in Europe and Mexico, now resides on Manhattan's upper West Side. He is currently working on another book for young people and two adult books, one chronicling his experiences as a film maker.

by Isaac Asimov

TSUNAMI

When an earthquake takes place on one of the continents, it can do a great deal of damage. It might seem that a quake far out at sea, however, could be ignored. The water would shake a bit, but surely no one would be hurt. And yet an earthquake at sea can be more dreadful than one on land.

The seaquake will set up a wave that is not very high in mid ocean but stretches across the surface for an enormous distance and therefore involves a large volume of water. Such a wave spreads outward in all directions from the point at which the quake took place. As it approaches land and as the ocean gets shallower, the stretch of water in the wave is compressed front and rear and piles up higher, then much higher. If the wave moves into a narrowing harbor, its volume is forced still higher, sometimes fifty to one hundred feet high.

That tower of water, coming suddenly and without warning, can break over a city, drowning thousands. Before the wave comes in, the preceding trough arrives. The water sucks far out, like an enormous low tide, and then the wave comes in like a colossal high tide. Because of this out-and-in effect the huge wave has been called a *tidal wave*. This is a poor name, though, for it has nothing to do with the tides.

In recent decades the name *tsunami* (tsoo-nä-mē) has been used more and more frequently. This is a Japanese word meaning "harbor wave," which is an accurate description. The Japanese, living on an island near the edge of our largest ocean, have suffered a great deal from tsunamis.

The largest in recent years was in 1883, when the volcanic island Krakatoa (krăk'ə-tō'ə) in the East Indies exploded and sent hundred-foot tsunamis crashing into nearby shores. About 1400 B.C., an Aegean island exploded and a tsunami destroyed the civilization on the nearby island of Crete. Still a third famous tsunami destroyed the city of Lisbon in 1755.

PIGEONS

They paddle with staccato feet
In powder-pools of sunlight,
Small blue busybodies
Strutting like fat gentlemen
With hands clasped
Under their swallowtail coats;
And, as they stump about,
Their heads like tiny hammers
Tap at imaginary nails
In nonexistent walls.
Elusive ghosts of sunshine
Slither down the green gloss
Of their necks an instant, and are gone.

Summer hangs drugged from sky to earth
In limpid fathoms of silence:
Only warm dark dimples of sound
Slide like slow bubbles
From the contented throats.

Raise a casual hand —
With one quick gust
They fountain into air.

RICHARD KELL

46

SKILL LESSON 1

USING REFERENCE AIDS

One of the most useful reference aids is an ENCYCLOPEDIA. It may be a single volume, but more often it is a set of volumes that contains articles on a wide range of topics. The topics on which an encyclopedia supplies articles are arranged in alphabetical order, and an index to those topics may be included in each volume or in a separate volume. Each volume in a set has a guide letter or guide letters on the spine that tell you with what letter or letters the topics in the volume begin.

When you need to use an encyclopedia to get information on a question you have in mind, you must do three things. *First,* you need to choose one or more key words, usually from your question, to look for among the topics in the encyclopedia. *Second,* you must select the particular volume that contains an article on the topic your key word names. *Finally,* you must find the topic itself and read the article.

The key word is easy to choose in a question like *What are the major uses of wax?* You are looking for information about WAX and that would be your key word. What is the key word in each of these questions?

1. *Who was elected President in 1936?*
2. *What is the capital of Sweden?*

Sometimes there are two key words in a question, and to get all the information you need, you should look for both words among the topics in an encyclopedia. In the question *How is steel used in making automobiles?* you would need to use both STEEL and AUTO-MOBILES. What key words are in each of these questions?

1. Why is olive oil such an important product in Italy?

2. What were some of the contributions made by Albert Einstein to the study of physics?

One of the key words in the first question is really two words, OLIVE OIL. Most two-word entries in an encyclopedia are alphabetized by the first word. In the second question the name of a person, ALBERT EINSTEIN, is one of the key words. When a person's name is listed among the topics in an encyclopedia, his last name comes first, as in EINSTEIN, ALBERT.

Look at the picture of an encyclopedia below. In which volume would you look for information about each topic listed below?

1. PHOTOGRAPHY
2. SOLAR SYSTEM
3. WRESTLING
4. MOON

5. GOLD RUSH
6. ANDREW JACKSON
7. CRAB
8. FERDINAND MAGELLAN

After you have selected the volume that contains the topic you are looking for, you then locate the topic in that volume by using the guide words that appear at the tops of many of the pages. The guide word on the left-hand page names the first topic on that page. The guide word on the right-hand page names the last topic on the right-hand page. Any other topics on those two pages come alphabetically between the two guide words.

Look at the portion of the pages of an encyclopedia reproduced on pages 50–51. Find the guide words. What is the first topic on the two

A	B	C-Ch	Ci-Cz	D	E	F	G	H	I	J-K	L	M-Mic	Mid-My	N-O	P	Q-R	S-Sn	So-Sz	T	U-V	W-X Y-Z
1	2	3	4	5	6	7	8	9	10	11	12	13	14	15	16	17	18	19	20	21	22

TWEED

TWEED is a rough, heavy, hairy, woolen cloth that may contain synthetic fibers. Tweed is usually woven of fibers in two or more colors. Some tweed has a plain weave. Other tweed has a *twill* weave, with raised diagonal lines. A third way of weaving tweed is with the diagonal raised lines of yarn meeting each other to form "V's." This is called *herringbone twill*. In Scotland, where tweed was first woven, *twill* is often pronounced *tweel*, and *tweed* may have developed from this. Some people believe the cloth was named for the River Tweed. Genuine Harris tweeds are made by hand. They are woven on the islands of the outer Hebrides—chiefly on Lewis with Harris Island.

The yarns are dyed the colors of the heather in the New Hebrides. The dyes are made from plants called *lichens*, which grow on the rocks of the islands. The lichen has an odor, called *cretal smell*, which never leaves the cloth. Rainy weather brings out this smell in a Harris tweed suit. After the yarn is dyed, special songs are sung while the longwise, or *warp*, threads are put on the looms. When the cloth is woven, the weavers have a ceremony called *waulking*, which means *shrinking*. The cloth is soaked in soapy water. Young girls and women stand around a table and pass the cloth around while each one pounds it and rubs it. As they do this, they sing *waulking songs*. The cloth is then washed and dried and is ready to be made into clothing.

TWELFTH AMENDMENT. See UNITED STATES CONSTITUTION (Amendment 12).

TWELFTH NIGHT is the traditional English name given to the holy day celebrated on January 6, the twelfth night after Christmas. It is also called Epiphany. It used to be the last day of the holiday season that began with Christmas. In the Catholic calendar, Epiphany is an entirely distinct feast from Christmas, and lasts eight days, from January 6 to 13. This is the ancient church custom even for England, where the civil holidays ended on January 6. During the time of Queen Elizabeth I, Twelfth Night was observed in England with wild celebration. This custom died out, but special church services are still held on the date. *Twelfth Night* is a play by Shakespeare. See also EPIPHANY; SHAKESPEARE, WILLIAM (Synopses).   FULTON J. SHEEN

TWELVE LABORS OF HERCULES. See HERCULES.

TWELVE TABLES, LAWS OF THE, were the first written laws of the Romans. The laws were inscribed on 12 tables, or tablets, that were fastened to the speaker's stand in the Roman Forum. They were the basis of private rights of Roman citizens. They dealt with legal procedures, property ownership, building codes, punishments for crime, and marriage customs.

The laws were drawn up in 451 and 450 B.C. by *decemvirs* (members of a council of ten men). The decemvirs based the laws on earlier Roman civil, criminal, and religious customs. The laws applied equally to all Roman citizens, and were written out so the common

pages? What is the last topic? Which of the following topics would appear on one of these pages: TWILIGHT, GEORGE THOMAS, TYCOON, NATHAN F. TWINING, TYPE?

Notice the topic TWELFTH AMENDMENT on the encyclopedia pages. It is followed by the words *See* UNITED STATES CONSTITUTION (Amendment 12). Such a direction is called a cross-reference and means that all the information the encyclopedia gives about the TWELFTH AMENDMENT can be found under the topic UNITED STATES CONSTITUTION. At the end of the article about the topic TWINE, you find the direction *See also* ABACÁ; BINDER TWINE; SISAL. This, too, is a cross-reference and means that further information about twine can be found under the three topics ABACÁ, BINDER TWINE, and SISAL.

In addition to the set of volumes in an encyclopedia, yearbooks are published to keep the set up-to-date. Such topics as political events, sports, science, medicine, and other newsworthy happenings are included. Usually more details can be given because only the events for a particular year are included in a yearbook.

From The World Book Encyclopedia. ® *1973 Field Enterprises Educational Corporation.*

TWILL is the name of a weave which is used in making many kinds of cloth. In twill, the lengthwise threads, known as *warp*, meet the crosswise threads, called *weft*, in such a way as to form diagonal, raised lines on the finished cloth. The lines may be made either by the warp or the weft yarn. They may be raised only a little or a great deal. Twill weaves can be varied in many ways to produce broken, entwining, figured, or reversing lines. *Cashmere cloth* is a twill made with the weft threads. *Drilling* is a twill made with the warp yarns. The materials *serge*, *gabardine*, and *cheviot* are twill-weave fabrics.   Kenneth R. Fox

TWIN CITIES. See Minneapolis; Saint Paul.

TWIN FALLS, Ida. (pop. 21,914; alt. 3,745 ft.), is the trading center for a rich farming and food-processing region. It lies in the Snake River Valley (see Idaho [political map]). Twin Falls has meat- and fish-packing and food-processing plants, farm-equipment factories, and dairies. The city, founded in 1904, was named for two nearby waterfalls. Twin Falls has a council-manager government.   William S. Greever and Janet Groff Greever

TWINE is tough cord made from the twisted strands of hard leaf fibers, usually those from the sisal or henequen plants. The strands are mixed with abacá to make manila hemp. Twine is manufactured by drawing the raw fibers into slivers, which are combed and spun into twine. String is a type of twine, thinner than a cord and thicker than a thread. See also Abacá; Binder Twine; Sisal.   Elizabeth Chesley Baity

Identical Twins are of the same sex. Such twins are born from a single egg cell which separated into two parts early in its development. Each of the parts became one of the twins. They are usually much more difficult to tell apart than fraternal twins. But some identical twins have almost exactly the same characteristics in reverse. The hair of one twin may part on the right, for example, while the other's hair parts naturally on the left. These twins come from a common egg cell which did not separate until it began to develop right- and left-sided characteristics.

Identical twins are sometimes born joined together, usually at the hip, chest, or abdomen. Such twins are called *Siamese*, after Eng and Chang (1811-1874), Chinese twins who were born in Siam. Siamese twins may look different from each other. Sometimes they can be separated by surgery. But if they share a vital organ, surgery is rarely attempted.

Craniopagus Siamese twins are joined at the head. In 1952, a series of operations leading to the separation of 15-month-old twins of this type was performed at the University of Illinois Research and Educational Hospital in Chicago. One of the twins died a month later. But the other twin lived until May, 1963—more than ten years.   George W. Beadle

See also Multiple Birth.

TWINS, THE. See Castor and Pollux; Gemini.

An ALMANAC is a yearly publication that contains a wide variety of facts, often in the form of lists, tables, and charts. It is an excellent source of information about such things as annual awards, sports records, important dates, population statistics, and government leaders. It contains a complete index that helps you find quickly the page or pages that give the facts you need.

Suppose you wanted to find out who won the National League batting championship in 1969. You would first look for the entry, or main topic, BASEBALL in the index. Under that entry you would find a number of subtopics, among them Batting champions, which would refer you to the page that has a list of the National League batting champions.

The information on page 52 about the busiest airports in the United States for the year 1970 is typical of the kind of information that you will find in an almanac. To find this information, you would first look in the index for the main topic AVIATION and then for the subtopic Traffic. There you would be referred to the page that has

this list on it. What was the busiest airport in 1970? The tenth busiest airport? Which state has the most airports on the list? Which airport was busier, San Francisco or Miami International?

BUSIEST AIRPORTS IN THE UNITED STATES
Source: Federal Aviation Administration
Airports are listed in order of total operations (takeoffs and landings).

AIRPORT OPERATIONS, 1970

O'Hare International, Chicago, Ill.	641,390	Miami International, Fla.	370,327
Van Nuys, Calif.	575,784	Oakland, Calif.	366,455
Los Angeles International, Calif.	544,025	Denver, Colo.	357,849
Long Beach, Calif.	529,221	Boeing, Seattle, Wash.	354,997
Fort Lauderdale, Fla.	518,556	Phoenix, Ariz.	349,224
Tamiami, Miami, Fla.	504,032	Bowman, Louisville, Ky.	344,163
Hollywood, Fla.	483,852	La Guardia, N.Y.	336,449
Santa Ana, Calif.	472,907	Columbus International, Ohio	330,678
Opa Locka, Miami, Fla.	450,066	Meacham, Fort Worth, Tex.	325,421
Atlanta Municipal, Ga.	428,392	Santa Monica, Calif.	323,589
Torrance Municipal, Calif.	412,365	Logan International, Boston, Mass.	323,425
Love Field, Dallas, Tex.	410,154	Flying Cloud, Minneapolis, Minn.	321,052
San José Municipal, Calif.	408,360	St. Louis, Mo.	319,522
John F. Kennedy International, N.Y.	395,938	Washington National, D.C.	319,449
San Francisco, Calif.	386,674	Hayward, Calif.	318,434

An ATLAS is another reference book that you will find useful, especially when you are looking for information about geographical locations. An atlas is a collection of maps.

On page 53 you will find a map of Rhode Island and a map index to help you locate specific towns and cities. The letter and numeral following each place name in the index are called reference points. For Woonsocket the reference points are A4. On the left edge of the map you will see the letters A, B, C, and so on. At the top edge of the map you will see the numerals 1, 2, 3, and so on. To find Woonsocket (A4), place a finger of your left hand on the letter A on the left edge of the map. Move it toward the right edge until it is directly under the 4 at the top edge. You will find Woonsocket in the general area where your finger has stopped. Can you find Newport? Westerly? Bristol?

Notice the distance scale below the map. It will help you find the mileage distances between points on the map. Use a ruler to find the straight-line distance between Westerly and Wakefield. The distance measures about 1⅝ inches, which on the scale measures approximately 18 miles. What is the distance between Westerly and West Warwick? Between Point Judith and Cranston?

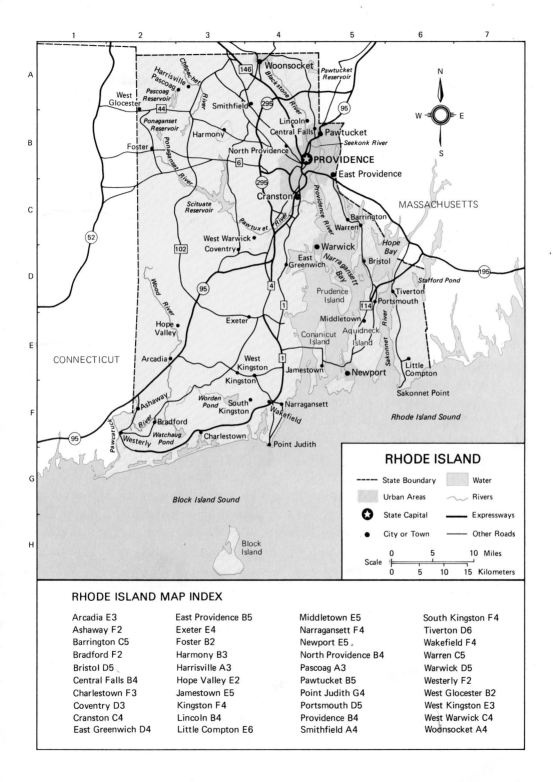

RHODE ISLAND

- - - -	State Boundary		Water
	Urban Areas	~~~	Rivers
⭐	State Capital	▬▬▬	Expressways
●	City or Town	——	Other Roads

Scale

0	5	10 Miles
0	5	10 15 Kilometers

RHODE ISLAND MAP INDEX

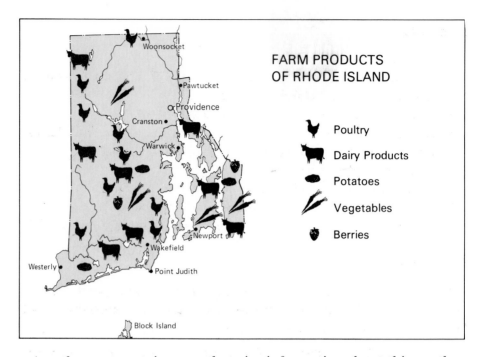

FARM PRODUCTS
OF RHODE ISLAND

Poultry
Dairy Products
Potatoes
Vegetables
Berries

An atlas may contain maps that give information about things other than the location of places and distances between places. Some maps give information about such things as climate, manufactured products, mineral deposits, and land elevations. Usually, special symbols or different colors are used on such maps to represent different products or the measurement of something. Look at the map of Rhode Island above. How is it different from the map on page 53? The second map gives information about the farm products of Rhode Island. It uses symbols to indicate the sections of the state where the products come from. The key beside the state tells what each symbol stands for. For which product does the map have the most symbols? The fewest symbols? Why do you think there are no symbols near the areas of Pawtucket, Providence, and Warwick? Which products do you find in both the northern and southern parts of the state? Which product do you find in the southern part but not in the northern part?

Encyclopedias, almanacs, and atlases are all important sources of information. Knowing how and when to use them can be helpful to you, whether you are using them for school assignments or for a personal reason.

Discussion

Help your class answer these questions:
1. What three steps must you follow when using an encyclopedia?
2. How are key words and topics related?
3. What are guide words? What do they tell you?
4. In which volume of the encyclopedia would you locate information about each of the eight topics listed on page 49?
5. What is a cross-reference?
6. In what ways is an almanac different from an encyclopedia?
7. How can specific places be found quickly on a map?
8. What answers did you find for the map questions on page 52?

On your own

In which reference aid — an encyclopedia, an almanac, or an atlas — would you most likely find an answer to each of the questions below? Write and number your answers on a sheet of paper.

1. How much corn did the United States produce in each of the years from 1970 to 1973?
2. How do pearls form in oysters?
3. What is the approximate distance between Hartford, Connecticut, and Albany, New York?
4. For what accomplishment is Jane Addams best known?
5. Which of the two major leagues in baseball has won more all-star games in the last twenty years?

Make up three questions of your own, the first to be answered by using an encyclopedia, the second by using an almanac, and the third by using an atlas. Then write how you would use the reference aid in finding the answer to each question.

Checking your work

Read aloud your answers to the questions in the first part of On your own if you are asked to do so. Find reasons for any mistakes you made. For the second part of On your own be ready to read your questions and your procedures for finding the answers. Be sure you understand the correct procedure for using each reference aid.

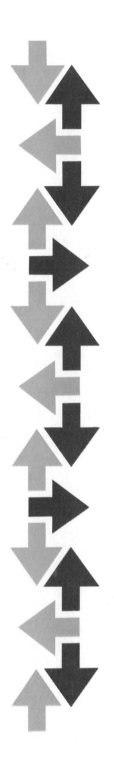

SUPERSTITION:

The Remnants of Magic

by Gary Jennings

Most magic beliefs are extinct in our civilization but by no means all of them. One reason is that we don't always recognize the remnants of magic even when we encounter them in daily life.

The word *superstition* means "standing over" from the past; and when you perform such a simple act as shaking hands with a friend, you are carrying on a magical tradition that is ages old.

The handshake itself was originally a gesture to show that one was concealing no weapon. But it was and is always done with the right hand, which since time immemorial has been considered the lucky hand (no doubt because with most people it's the stronger). An honored guest is always seated at the host's right hand. We speak of a valued friend or assistant as a right-hand man. The weaker left hand, or anything situated or occurring on a person's left, has always been slightly suspect.

Innumerable other modern-day superstitions can be traced to the magical beliefs of medieval times, distant antiquity, and even prehistory. Stone Age man's earliest and most unbearable fear was that of the night, and his dread of darkness gave rise to superstitions that are still with us. He never could understand why some animals *didn't* fear the night and came out to prowl only after dark. From that time to this, man has instinctively connected mystery and malice with these creatures — the cat, the owl, the bat — whose only sin was in preferring the darkness to daylight.

To be rendered temporarily sightless each night was so terrifying that man came to fear blindness above all other afflictions and came to regard his eyes as his most essential faculty. Through history he has honored the precious power of sight by using pictures of eyes as mystic symbols indicating discovery, enlightenment, wisdom, or "all-seeingness." Today,

the all-seeing eye endures. For instance, even in the Great Seal of the United States of America it is seen on the back of a dollar bill.

Some people went a step further in their regard for the power of eyesight and began to believe that the act of looking could be used for black magic. This was known as having the evil eye, the power to command others' obedience or affection with a glance or, by a different sort of look, to blight crops, cripple cattle, and paralyze or kill human beings.

The belief was always stronger in Italy than elsewhere, and the Italians invented a gesture that supposedly would ward off the evil eye. The hand was clenched with the index and little fingers extended in the direction of the evil. The sign was called the *cornu.*[1]

Just a hundred years ago the Italians became convinced, for some strange reason, that Pope Pius IX had somehow been endowed with an evil eye. Nothing could have been less likely, even if there *were* such a power, but the rumor persisted to the day of the pontiff's death. Whenever he led a procession through Rome, the streets emptied before him. Any superstitious person who couldn't put a safe distance between himself and the Pope would kneel in the proper position of homage — but when he crossed himself, as Pius passed, his hand was clenched in the *cornu.*

Incredible as it seems, the evil eye

---

[1] **cornu** (kôr′nyo͞o), horns.

still has many believers. In the 1930's, according to sports writers, one New York man earned his living by renting his evil-eye powers to prizefight managers. They would hire him to sit at the ringside at boxing matches and stare balefully at the fighter they wanted defeated. Some of the boxers were sufficiently ignorant and superstitious that the evil eye *did* paralyze them long enough to set them up for a knockout punch.

The charm bracelet, a favorite piece of feminine jewelry, was also inspired by magical beliefs of the long ago. Many early societies worshipped nature spirits in the form of carved idols. A man might have a large image in his front yard (a totem pole is one example) and a table model inside his hut. Then he took to carving smaller images, which he could wear or carry so that the spirits would be with him wherever he went.

In time these portable images of the different spirits came to be worn for differing purposes. One of them might be considered an amulet, a carrying-piece to protect a man from accident, illness, or other people's malice. Another might now be a talisman to bring him good fortune in whatever ventures he might undertake. Still another might be a charm, giving him the power to inflict harm on others or influence them to obey him.

There are plenty of echoes of this belief in the present day. Some people won't go anywhere without their rabbit's foot or four-leaf clover or some similar good-luck talisman. Charms have pretty much gone out of fashion as actively working magic. The schoolgirl who wears a charm bracelet today, purely for ornament, is probably unaware that her distant ancestors wore them for more subtle and sometimes sinister purposes.

The rabbit's foot became a valued amulet because the wild rabbit drums an alarm with its hind foot when danger threatens, and superstitious men apparently hoped that the foot would do something of the same sort for them. So if you want to indulge this fancy, make sure you get a rabbit's *hind* foot. The ones sold in novelty shops nowadays, attached to key chains and sometimes dyed a pretty color, are *front* paws (because they make a neater item).

The only thing that originally made a four-leaf clover seem lucky to superstitious people was that it was rare, and anything scarce or novel has always been presumed magical. (Some people used to believe that a man or woman with dimples had magical powers just because so few people *have* dimples.) If a man suddenly spotted a clover with four leaves, he could hope that maybe he would stumble on something else rare, like a hidden treasure. But four-leaf clovers have never been *that* scarce; you can find one without too much searching in almost any clover patch. Anyhow, the novelty manufacturers have now bred a strain of clover that

is *all* four-leaved to supply the sealed-in-plastic charm industry.

Among the many nature spirits that have been worshipped by men, the tree was always one of the most popular all over the world, especially the evergreens and the sturdy oak. This reverence for trees, and the belief that they held some kind of protective magic, is still reflected in our frequent gesture of knocking on wood when we make a wish or utter a hopeful remark — and it even persists in the use of a tree or pole as the "home-safe" base of a game of hide-and-seek. Our decoration of the Christmas tree is another reminder of the tree worship of former times.

No one knows Christ's actual birth date, so Christmas Day was officially established as December 25th to make this highest Christian holy day coincide with pagan midwinter celebrations that "hailed the returning sun" when the short days began to get longer again. The exchange of Christmas gifts is an idea borrowed from the Romans, whose festival honoring the god of agriculture was celebrated at that time of year. Kissing under the mistletoe recalls the high regard in which mistletoe was held, as both magic and medicine, by the Druids of ancient Britain.

One of today's most common superstitions stems from the primitive belief that ordinary salt had magical properties. In early times salt was too scarce to be used just as a seasoning. Then, it was valued as a preservative to keep meats and other perishables from spoiling. From being the foe of decay, salt gradually came to be symbolic of never-dying life, so witches, sorcerers, and the devil were all supposed to fear it. To spill salt was to leave oneself unprotected by its magic, so one hastily tossed a pinch of it over one's shoulder to fend off any pursuing demons. Multitudes of us still do it.

And those old-time demons are still pursuing us, in a sense, even though we no longer believe in them. At our New Year's Eve parties we toot horns and twirl noisemakers — just for the fun of it now, but once it was done to frighten the demons of the old year and keep them from following into the new one. Today it is considered polite to cover one's mouth when yawning; in former days people did it to keep demons from taking that opportunity to sneak inside their bodies.

Another tradition still observed is that on the day of marriage the groom must not see his bride until the moment the ceremony begins. This comes to us from an old belief that a bride is the target for all sorts of demons who delight in hurting anybody who is about to embark on a "new life." Years ago the bride was secluded from seeing *anybody*. The veil she wears to her wedding was originally meant to disguise her from those same prowling demons. And today's horn blaring in the automobile procession when the newlyweds drive away from the church is an echo of the wild clamor of shouts and bell ringing that was originally meant to keep the demons scared away.

Although early man's world teemed with demons and evil spirits, he wanted to *stay* in that world nevertheless; so one thing he feared even more than demons was death. He could take some precautions to avoid dying by violence or accident, but death by magic was something else again. Our modern-day dread of breaking a mirror is no more than early man's fear that something would "get him" by harming an image of him. He wouldn't even dare stir the pond water in which he was reflected.

The act of sneezing might not seem to have much connection with man's dread of death, but it does. Down to quite recent times many people held to the primitive belief that the soul escapes from the body at death by way of the mouth or nostrils. Therefore, when one sneezed, one was in danger of blowing the soul out before it was destined to go; one might die in the very middle of a kerchoo!

So it became the custom for the sneezer, or anyone standing handy, to say something very quickly to comfort and soothe the soul, so it would stay where it belonged. The ancient Roman would say to a sneezer, "Jupiter preserve you!" We still say, "God bless you!" and practically everyone else in the world does likewise.

The Malay says quite bluntly, "Soul, come back here!" The Zulu follows his sneeze with, "I am now blessed!" The Moslem says, "Praise to Allah!" The Samoan says, when someone else sneezes, "Life to you!" The German says, "Good health!" The Jew says, "Good life!" The Hindu says, "Live!"

According to the diary of Hernando de Soto, an early explorer of the North American continent, he once sneezed in the presence of some Florida Indians and received this long-drawn blessing: "The sun guard thee, be with thee, enlighten thee, magnify thee, protect thee, favor thee, defend thee, prosper thee, save thee!" De Soto turned to a lieutenant and murmured in wonderment, "Do you not see that all the world is one?"

Many old and respected superstitions are hard to explain. They have no apparent connection with any known aspect of magic, nor do they have any slightest basis in truth; nobody with common sense would expect them to work. Their only reason for existing seems to be that they've been around for so long that people just hate to give them up. Here are a few of these unexplainable superstitions that are still widely believed:

If you get out of the wrong side of the bed in the morning, your whole day will go wrong. (But which *is* the wrong side? According to another superstition it's the side opposite from the one you got in.)

If you accidentally put on an article of clothing inside out, you'd do well to wear it that way all day. It means good luck.

If you sing before breakfast, you'll cry before night.

If you put on your hat backwards, you'll have bad luck.

If you step on an ant, you'll cause a rainstorm.

If you open an umbrella inside the house, you're inviting bad luck.

If you have to patch a tear in your clothing while wearing it, be sure to hold a pin in your mouth during the sewing or risk bad luck.

A person born with webbed toes will have good luck all his life.

To ward off rheumatism, carry a small potato in your pocket at all times.

To cure asthma, swallow a wad of crumpled-up spider web.

If a person steps over a baby crawling on the floor, the child will stop growing.

There are thousands, probably tens of thousands, of other superstitions. Many of them are common to a great part of the world, and many are so firmly fixed in everyday life that we never notice them. Other superstitions have been confined to one particular time or locality, like the English belief that if one has empty pockets on New Year's Eve, one must look forward to a whole year of poverty.

Still other beliefs are peculiar to one special sphere of interest. There are superstitions about the weather, farming, sports, foods and eating, love and marriage, birth and death, traveling, money, and nearly every human

activity. As any actor can tell you, the superstitions infesting the theater alone would fill an entire book.

But of all the subjects in which man has imagined he saw magic, mystery, and mysticism, numbers have given rise to the greatest variety of good and bad superstitions.

It would be impossible to list all of them here because, although almost all societies have attached special significance to the various numerical digits and combinations of digits, they have seldom agreed on which are the "good" numbers and which are the "bad." For example, the Chinese have long considered thirteen a lucky number. They used to measure time by a lunar calendar; and because the moon goes through thirteen cycles a year, the Chinese year consisted of thirteen months.

Whether considered good or bad, seven has always been one of the important numbers. The Orientals honored the Seven Precious Things (gold, silver, rubies, emeralds, crystal, amber, and agate). In the Western world the ancients liked to lump all sorts of things together in groups of seven — the Seven Wonders of the World, the Seven Sages of the Greeks, the Seven Liberal Arts, and so on.

The early religious leaders lamented mankind's Seven Deadly Sins and looked forward to a Seventh Heaven (its highest level). Early astronomers refused to believe there could be more than Seven Heavenly Bodies (the sun, the moon, Mercury, Venus, Mars, Jupiter, and Saturn). Early mariners charted the Seven Seas.

Seven was also a meaningful figure to the medieval sorcerers and alchemists. They thought it a "strong" number because it was made up, they said, of the four elements of the human body (flesh, bone, blood, and spirit) and the three of the human soul (passion, desire, and reason). But the number's importance is more likely based on the story of Creation, in which God rested on the seventh day and called it blessed.

Shakespeare divided the human life span into the Seven Ages of Man. The number seven even set limits to some laws; to this day certain crimes cannot be prosecuted and certain debts are not collectable if action is not taken on them within seven years. And the number persists in such superstitions as the broken mirror's seven years of bad luck, the lucky seven of dice games, and the luck that's supposed to follow a man who is the seventh son of a seventh son.

The number nine signified "truth" to the ancient Hebrews because they believed that truth is always triumphant over falsehood and because the number nine, however it is multiplied, always reasserts itself. For example, $3 \times 9 = 27$, and $2 + 7 = 9$. Or try $1,234,567 \times 9$, and you get $11,111,103$ with the digits adding up to nine. Or in the case of 999×9 you get $8,991$, which adds up to 27, which in turn adds up to nine.

The number forty appears again and again in the Bible. Noah's rainstorm lasted forty days and forty nights. The Israelites who fled from Egypt wandered in the wilderness for forty years. Moses spent forty days and nights on Mt. Sinai, copying down the Lord's ten commandments. The number's seeming significance so impressed the medieval Europeans that they assigned it a rather odd job.

In those days plagues and other epidemics had become so frequent that in the 1600's the port cities of Europe made all incoming ships anchor outside the harbor and wait there until it was certain that they weren't bringing a new disease in with them. Nobody knew how long a ship should have to wait, so they arbitrarily applied the Biblical number of forty; if none of the people aboard ship showed signs of sickness after forty days, the ship was allowed to dock and the passengers to go ashore.

The practice was first instituted in Italy; and the Italian word for forty is *quaranta* (kwä-rän′tä), so the isolation period became known as "quarantine." The practice is still observed, not only for travelers, but for individual cases of infectious diseases. The isolation no longer lasts a tedious forty days; it varies according to local laws.

But of all the numbers poor thirteen must carry the heaviest weight of superstition. You know the taboos — don't take chances on the thirteenth day of the month, especially if it's a Friday; never seat thirteen at a table, and so on. And you know how many hotels, apartment houses, and even office buildings have no thirteenth floor.

Most Christians believe that the number's disfavor dates from the Last Supper, when Christ dined with the twelve apostles just before the final betrayal. Jews associate the number with a legend that after the thirteen chiefs of the tribes of Israel enjoyed the first Feast of Passover, the tribe of the youngest chief (Benjamin) was wiped out in battle.

Actually, the number's unpopularity is far older than either of these traditions. It began when the first men learned to count. They did this with the only computer they had: their ten fingers and two feet (they didn't count toes). These added up to twelve. Beyond twelve was the incalculable Unknown, which man didn't like to think about. He still doesn't.

1. How did the handshake originate?
2. What natural event caused man to regard his eyes as his most essential faculty?
3. How did the charm bracelet originate?
4. How was sneezing connected with man's fear of death?
5. What made the number thirteen unpopular? What are some of the ways people still avoid using the number thirteen?
6. What did the author mean by "There are plenty of echoes of this belief [in charms] in the present day"?
7. Do you practice and believe in any of the superstitions mentioned in this article? If so, which ones? What other superstitions do you believe in? Why do you believe in them?

AUTHOR

In his own words Gary Jennings, author of the selection you have just read from *Black Magic, White Magic,* is "a Virginian by birth, a New Yorker by choice, and a constant traveler by necessity."

Mr. Jennings was an army correspondent during the Korean conflict, was awarded the Bronze Star, and was given a citation by the Korean Ministry of Information. A one-time newspaper reporter, an advertising copywriter, and an account executive, Mr. Jennings now devotes full time to free-lance writing. In addition to many articles and stories for adult magazines, he has written and illustrated several books for young people, particularly on subjects that interested him as a teen-ager. If you enjoyed *Superstitions: The Remnants of Magic,* you may wish to read Mr. Jennings's latest book, *The Teenager's Realistic Guide to Astrology.*

THE SLAVE WHO
BOUGHT HIS FREEDOM

Equiano's Story   Adapted by Karen Kennerly

Olaudah Equiano was born in Africa in 1745. After being kidnapped from his village at the age of ten, he was sold and resold as a slave, serving a variety of masters, good and bad, in Africa, America, and England. In England, Equiano learned to read and write; he became a Christian and thereafter considered himself, according to British law, immune to being resold. However, he was resold once again to a Mr. King, a Caribbean trader who allowed Equiano a good deal of freedom as a hand on one of his trading sloops.

In this excerpt from his autobiography Equiano tells about the part of his life that leads to his becoming a free man.

A sloop owned by Mr. King, my master, was sailing up to the island of St. Eustatia (sānt′ yōo-stā′shē-ə), and he had sent me along to help load the cargo. I carried some fowls and pigs with me because I knew they sold well on that island. When we landed, a white man came aboard and bought them from me. But the next day he returned, explosive with rage, and demanded his money back. I refused to give it. He began forcing the lock of my chest when an English sailor — not yet rotted by the West Indian climate — saw him and threw him off the boat. That was my first trade.

The sloop was commanded by a Captain Thomas Farmer, who made good money for my master by trading wisely in the other islands. He took a liking to me and had me sail with him whenever Mr. King allowed it. I worked hard, while the white sailors often got so drunk that they cracked the bows of the ships on rocks while trying to slide out of a narrow harbor. Captain Farmer depended on me more and more until finally he refused to sail without me. Mr. King was not happy about this because he had been training me to serve as clerk in his stores. I was called in before them and was told to make a choice. Much as I cared for Mr. King, I remembered the success of my first trade. Only by sailing and trading could I earn the forty pounds sterling that my freedom would cost.

In St. Eustatia I bought a blue tumbler, or drinking glass, with the three pennies I had. St. Eustatia is a Dutch island, and the tumbler had come across the ocean from the city of Amsterdam. I sold it on Montserrat for six pennies. The next time in St. Eustatia I bought two tumblers made of a white glass you could almost see through, like thin clouds. On Montserrat I sold them for twelve cents, or one shilling sterling. On the third trip I bought two ruby-colored glasses and a jug of a liquor, which the Dutch made from crushed grain and juniper berries. They called it gin. All this earned me a dollar on Montserrat!

My friend the fisherman — this was before he was sold — and I bought citrus fruit. We put it into sacks to sell in Santa Cruz (the place I sailed to next). I had two sacks, one filled with limes and the other with oranges. My friend brought one sack of mixed fruits. As soon as we landed, we set out on a chalky road that led to the markets. A fortress ran along the sea side of the road. Its squared rocks were a hardened and cool version of the stuff the soft road was made of. It was very hot, and we slipped into the shadow of the wall as we walked. We went a good mile without saying much. The fruits rolled like jugglers' balls against my back, and I watched my shoes grow white with the dust.

When I looked up, I noticed two figures bobbing like sunspots down the road. Two white men, I saw, as they came closer, and obviously talking about the bundles we were hunched under. They sidestepped to the wall.

"Heavy, aren't they?" one asked, and poked his friend. "Suppose *you* could lift one of those bags?"

The other laughed low in his stomach.

The first grabbed one sack from my back, and I skipped off balance. He passed it to his friend. "How about two?" And taking the second, he tossed it at the feet of the other one, who had his arms wrapped around the first sack as if it were a baby. "Never mind," he continued, "*I'll* try two," and swung the sack out of the fisherman's hands. The white man clowned at trying to balance the two sacks at once, and we laughed at the joke. We laughed a polite bit more, then reached down to take back our bundles. The two men swung them beyond our reach.

"Uh uh ... you gave us these sweet fruits ... now don't try ..." And with our bags they ducked through an opening in the fort wall and into a house on the other side. We followed, begging for our fruits. They threatened to beat us if we didn't lay off. I continued. We were only just in from Montserrat, I told them, come in on that ship — I pointed. And these limes and oranges were all we owned.

But our being strangers as well as blacks angered them still more. They grabbed for sticks and we ran. I was still English enough to demand my rights and went to the commanding officer of the fort with my complaint. All we got were more shouts and threats of a horse-whipping. My temper was up. Returning their curses in my head, I went back to the house and asked again and again for what belonged to us. It must at last have been as annoying as the drone of a fly, for finally they agreed to return two of the sacks if we'd stop pestering them. As the two were mine, I gave a third of what was in each of them to my friend. We continued into town and sold them for a fine profit.

I bought and sold and soon had several pounds. Only once did I spend some "freedom money" for a luxury, and that was a Bible. They were hard to come by in the islands. When I finally saw one on St. Kitts, I asked my captain to lend me a few pence — I had brought very little money with me. This he did. He was generally very good to me — defending me when merchants tried to cheat me — and he even gave me lessons in navigation. Some white men got very upset when they heard this. They insisted I would only mutiny when I had learned enough, and navigation was the most dangerous thing you could teach a slave. Captain Farmer listened to them and got jumpy and was gruff with me for a while. But I wouldn't take it and threatened not to sail with him unless he continued the lessons. I was taking a chance in speaking to him like that. But I knew he would be taking an even greater chance in losing me — I was the only reliable man he had.

To have a Bible again! My belief in God had kept me going all these months. Trusting in His goodness and justice allowed me a blind belief that one day I would be free. I hadn't forgotten the religious lessons taught to me in England. I was able to read better now, and there were so many passages I hadn't understood before. But one question continued to trouble me: why did God tolerate such treatment of black men? White men left England as men and after a few years in the islands turned into monsters. Why? But I still carried from Africa my belief that what happens to all of us in our lifetime is decided before we are born. Some black men have become free. But — this made me anxious — how free were we even after it was "legal"?

The story of a man from Montserrat rooted in my mind like a nightmare. He was a free, young mulatto, married to a freed black woman. Everyone in the islands knew about him and knew he'd been free since childhood — even the natives of Bermuda knew. But one day the captain of a Bermudian sloop walked up to him and said he had orders from his master to take him to Bermuda. The man showed him his certificate of birth, which proved he was free. The captain paid no attention and dragged him closer to shore. The man asked at least for an interview with the legal

secretary or magistrates of the island. "Yes," the captain said, "but tonight you stay on my ship." And in the middle of the night the ship set sail. No one heard of the man again.

We pulled into Guadeloupe (gwŏd′l-ōōp′) one day and found the harbor fluttering with a fleet of merchant ships getting ready to return to France. They were desperately short of men, we learned when we went ashore. Fifteen to twenty pounds would be paid to anyone who would sail with them. The mate on our sloop and all the white sailors were so excited that they abandoned my captain and joined the French fleet. They wanted me to go with them, and I was tempted. If ever there was a chance to escape, this was it. Freedom and Europe in two months! But up until now I'd been honest with white men. And hadn't my captain shown trust in me by teaching me navigation? If I ran away now, he would never again trust a black man. So I didn't go.

In the late spring of that year my master traded in the old sloop for one large enough to make trips to America. The new ship was called the *Providence*. As well as cargo we would be carrying new slaves because America was growing fast, and the white servants sent there from Europe were not enough to work the expanding plantations. At first we touched only the sea edge of the city of Charles Town in the colony of South Carolina, and my impression of America remained confused. Tight, fast-moving cities squinched on the edge of an endless, silent land. That didn't seem to make much sense. I wanted to get to Philadelphia. Somehow I felt *that* city would explain it all to me. We returned to Montserrat and learned that our next trip *was* to be to Philadelphia. I was excited! Carefully, I planned what to take that would sell well there. I questioned everyone for descriptions of the city. In the midst of all this business I was called into my master's house. He was there with the captain.

"I understand," my master said, "that when the *Providence* anchors at Philadelphia, you plan to run away."

I was stunned.

"And, therefore," he went on, "I must sell you again. You cost me a great deal of money — forty pounds sterling — and it will not do to lose so much. You are very valuable now. Captain Doran's brother-in-law would pay a hundred pounds to make you his overseer."

"Much more than a hundred," Captain Farmer blurted out, "could I get for him in Carolina. I know a man right now who wants him to command one of his rice vessels."

Not being able to tolerate this any longer, I interrupted. Had the captain ever seen the slightest sign of my attempting to escape, I asked. And if I had intended to do so, why wouldn't I have gone with the French fleet that time back in Guadeloupe?

At this point the captain was very silent. After a minute or so he admitted that what I said was true. Besides, he had given me a great deal of freedom in Charles Town, just so he could watch for signs of rebellion. Surprisingly enough, he'd found none at all.

My master nodded, convinced by the captain's realization of his own mistake. Thank God! I now dared to ask who had told them such lies. It was the first mate, whom I had caught stealing sugarcane from the ship's cargo a few months back. I remembered now that he had muttered through his teeth, "I'll pay you back for this — you're still a slave." I shuddered to think how careless I'd been to ignore his threat. He had almost won.

My master more than made up for his moment of distrust. He gave me some sugar and rum to sell in Philadelphia and told me the profit on them would be mine to keep. As we parted, he advised me to deal with the Quakers, and then we sailed off. Mr. King was himself a Quaker, I'd heard that, and I knew him to be the kindest master on the island. That Quakers were a type of Christian, I also knew — perhaps they were Christians who were particularly honest. I was more and more curious about Philadelphia.

Delaware Bay narrowed to a river, and the city of Philadelphia began its orderly run along the west bank. The shore was toothed by jutting docks, where ships waited before their owners' houses like giant but obedient servants. At empty docks the dark water jostled the reflection of bricks and windows. Behind the shore a seawall of houses was unbroken except by sudden shifts in color — from red brick to green shingles to smooth white with black shutters. The roofs were low and rose steeply. But just where the two sides should have met at a sharp angle, the roof was sawed off. A flat, narrow walk bounded by white railings rested on top between two great chimneys. There the owner of the house would walk impatiently, lifting his spyglass to his eye every few minutes to stare down the river for a first glimpse of his ship returning home.

If he tilted his head, or swung the spyglass around too far, he might see a patchwork of gray-green leaves and a cow's rump. For right across the river from Philadelphia were neatly fenced farms, each tree rounded and separate. Growing things never seem to grow out of order in northern countries. Then letting his spyglass drop to his side, he would relax again and watch whatever ship was sailing into port — past Philadelphia's floating windmill, spinning and sputtering at the mouth of the harbor, past his own house. I, in turn, was watching such a man as we sailed in; and when he picked up his glasses a few minutes later, I felt uncomfortable. Would he find a small hole in my pants or the sweat spots that faintly shadowed my arms? I turned my back and helped a sailor roll down the sails.

The center of the city was marked by the courthouse dome and Christ Church's high steeple. Two wide streets, High Street and Market Street, ran on either side of the courthouse like canals. The length of Market Street was crossed by covered sheds, under which the trading took place. My captain told me how I could recognize the Quakers, and the following morning I went there first thing to sell my sugar and rum. I did find them to be perfectly honest — it was the first time I traded without tensing, watching, preparing for an ugly argument. After making a very good profit, I walked through the city. I was forever entering mazes of narrow cobblestone streets with slate sidewalks, which eventually emptied into sunlit squares. There were two or three places in town — in front of the statehouse and on the corner of the Merchant's Exchange — where people gathered all day and evening. They talked mainly of politics: colonial laws, taxes, King George of England. These Philadelphians seemed earnest and intellectual people. In Georgia all I heard was talk of crops and stories about slaves.

One thing I overheard that was not about politics was talk of a wise woman who was known for her power to predict things. A man in front of the Exchange was telling such an extraordinary story about her that the crowded listeners kept interrupting him with noises of amazement. I couldn't hear the story but went back to some shopkeepers I'd met that morning to ask about her. She did exist, they said, and told me where she lived. That night I dreamed of her. It was an ordinary dream, the kind you forget

when you wake and remember later in the day, only if something reminds you. So, as I made plans to see her that evening — a jingled-jeweled gypsy in bright colors — I remembered with a shock what I'd dreamed. In my dream she was not a gypsy at all but a small woman dressed in the quiet gray of the Quakers. Only her eyes, unblinking as a bird's, were strange.

After work I quickly went to her house and was speechless when I saw her. She was exactly the same. The very same buttons on her high-throated blouse, the fringe on her shawl was the same cocoa-brown. But *she* was not surprised by my startled face and spoke first: "You dreamed of me last night. Come in." We had tea like two ordinary visitors, while she related all the things that had happened to me since leaving England. She then told me that I would not be a slave much longer and that within the next eighteen months I would be in great danger two times. But if I escaped both times, everything would go well for me from then on. She blessed me and I left.

Captain Farmer wanted to sail the following afternoon. I hadn't counted my savings yet but knew I had close to the forty pounds sterling that could buy my freedom. That morning I bought a superfine suit of clothes to wear at my freedom dance.

Back in Montserrat I sold my goods and counted up forty-seven pounds. Forty pounds sterling and seven to spare! The captain told me to approach my master on a certain morning when the two men would be having breakfast together. I came. My stomach tight and knotted to keep me from shaking, I spoke my request. While I was speaking, I listened to my voice as if it were quite separate from myself — a play I was watching in which the main character was someone I wanted to be. I finished. The imaginary play vanished as disappointment and even anger showed in my master's face. My stomach went soft, and I indeed began to shake.

"What?" said my master. "Give you your freedom? Where did you get the money? *Have* you got the forty pounds?"

"Yes, sir," I answered.

"How did you get it?"

"Very honestly, sir," I said.

Captain Farmer quickly backed me up by describing my dealings in various cities, and my master was silent for a moment. Then he said: "You make money much faster than I do! If I had known that, I wouldn't have given such a rash promise."

The captain jumped up and playfully slapped my master on the back. "Come, Robert, you must let him have his freedom. You laid out your money well and have received

good interest for it all this time. Now that it is being paid back, you must accept it. He will still earn you money — he'll continue to work for you. You know that."

My master caught some of the captain's high spirit, in spite of himself, and said, yes, he'd be as good as his word, and off I must go to the Register Office. I ran as easily as a small child, for at last I regained the freedom I'd possessed only as a child. I loved everything I'd known and not loved before: the hot wind against my eyes, the puff of shoe prints in the dust, the thud of the surf, which now was a congratulating drum.

By evening I was a free man. I danced that night in my Philadelphia superfine blue clothes, and the women noticed. Handsome black girls who used to snub me now stood before me. What splendid proposals I could have made. But my heart was set on returning to London. The next morning I went aboard my former master's ship. But this time it was as a paid worker, earning thirty-six shillings a month. I was twenty-one years old.

Equiano, who was renamed Gustavus Vassa, spent many quiet years in England. In 1789, his autobiography, The Interesting Narrative of the Life of Olaudah Equiano, or Gustavus Vassa, the African, *was published and became a best seller in England and America. Equiano spent much time speaking against slavery in England. He also made several attempts to return to Africa, even offering to go as a missionary, but he never saw his native land again. In 1792, three years after his book was published, Equiano married. History does not relate if he had any children or the exact date of his death, but it is thought that he died sometime between 1797 and 1811.*

DISCUSSION

1. How did Equiano increase his savings from three pennies to forty-seven pounds? What did he buy the first time he spent some of his freedom money? Why did he do this?
2. What exciting offer tempted Equiano to run away to obtain his freedom? Why did he decide against the temptation? Why did this decision prove to be a wise one?
3. Why was Equiano surprised when he met the Quaker woman who could predict things? What did she tell him?
4. How did Mr. King feel at first about Equiano's becoming a free man? How did Captain Farmer help Equiano get his freedom from Mr. King?
5. Why do you think Equiano and his friend laughed politely when the two white men took their bags of fruit?
6. What do you know about Quakers? Why do you think Equiano guessed that they might be "particularly honest"?
7. What did Equiano mean by saying that "growing things never seem to grow out of order in northern countries"?
8. Why do you think Equiano had his heart set on returning to London?
9. What do you think Equiano meant when he said that he was still English enough to demand his rights?
10. Why do you think Equiano felt that Philadelphia would explain America to him?
11. How did Equiano feel when he spoke to Mr. King about buying his freedom? Was there ever a time when you felt this way? If so, what happened?
12. Do you believe there are people who can predict things accurately? Why do you think that?

THE ICEBERG COMETH

Roughly two-thirds of the earth's supply of fresh water is imprisoned in ice — Antarctic ice. Because this source is so inaccessible,
it rarely figures in estimates of the world's readily available water
resources. But now two researchers, John Hult and Neill Ostrander,
have devised a plan for delivering some of this vast fresh-water supply to such a dry area of the earth as southern California.

The keys to the scheme are the icebergs that continually break off
the vast ice shelf extending into the Antarctic Ocean from the land
mass of Antarctica. These huge icebergs, ranging from half a mile to
10 miles in length and up to 900 feet in depth, annually carry as
much fresh water into the ocean as do rainfall deposits on the whole
of the continental United States. Unfortunately, because of the
circular ocean currents in southerly latitudes, the icebergs tend to
float around in the Antarctic Ocean rather than drift northward. But

    Copyright Newsweek, Inc., 1972, reprinted by permission.

Hult and Ostrander propose to send atomic-powered tugboats into southerly waters to corral the icebergs and tow them to deep-water ports in dry regions.

Surprisingly, this idea is far from new. Antarctic icebergs were transported by steamships as far north as arid Callao (kä-yä'ō), Peru — just twelve degrees south of the equator — at the turn of the century. But the work of Hult and Ostrander, which is being financed by a grant of $50,000 from the National Science Foundation, represents the first attempt to develop a practical plan for capturing icebergs and towing them to dry areas.

A major factor in making the scheme possible is the shape of the icebergs. Unlike the craggy Arctic growlers that sank the Titanic sixty years ago, Antarctic icebergs are relatively smooth in shape and float on the water like tabletops. Hence, say the researchers, lassoing

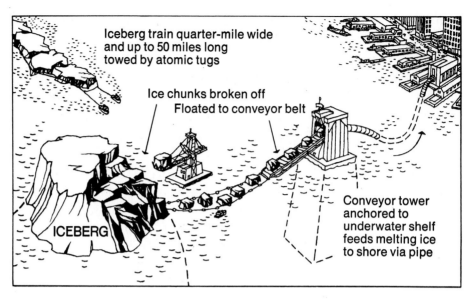

Iceberg train quarter-mile wide and up to 50 miles long towed by atomic tugs

Ice chunks broken off Floated to conveyor belt

ICEBERG

Conveyor tower anchored to underwater shelf feeds melting ice to shore via pipe

them with cables and arranging them into trains up to fifty miles long should be a simple process.

Because of the drag the icebergs would exert in the ocean, however, towing the trains to port across tens of thousands of miles of open sea is a much more difficult undertaking. Analysis of this problem convinced Hult and Ostrander that the most economical towing speed would be just one knot — about 2,000 yards an hour. To avoid refueling problems, the eight- to ten-month journey would require atomic-powered tugboats, accompanied by an assortment of auxiliary launches, helicopters, and other equipment. And to reduce the problem of melting en route, Hult and Ostrander are planning to cover the icebergs with special plastic "quilts," which they believe should restrict the loss of water to ten per cent of the icebergs' weight.

Once the icebergs are near port, Hult and Ostrander believe they could be anchored off the continental shelf and cut into ten-foot chunks by a floating scoop. After being fed onto a conveyor belt, the chunks would end up in a flexible underwater pipe that would carry them — melting along the way — to a storage plant on land. As simple as it seems, this process would call for industrial technology of a high order. "If you take the largest coal-mining machine that we know of," says Ostrander, "it would take literally thousands of them to harvest the ice from just one of these large icebergs. It's a tremendous undertaking when you think you'd have to harvest three million tons a day."

The advantages of the scheme, however, are obvious. For one, the iceberg water would be appreciably purer than the aqueduct water that now supplies smog-blighted southern California. What's more, the analysis by the two researchers indicates that water could be delivered by iceberg at about twenty-five dollars an acre-foot, as compared with sixty-five dollars for aqueduct water. And, while cautioning that the first iceberg is unlikely to arrive off the California coast for some years, Hult reports that he is already awaiting results of a study to determine whether likely-looking icebergs can be pinpointed by a new orbiting satellite.

DISCUSSION

1. How much of the earth's supply of fresh water is imprisoned in Antarctic ice? How do John Hult and Neill Ostrander propose to make use of this huge store of fresh water?
2. When and how was the idea of using icebergs for water tried before?
3. What is the shape of the Antarctic icebergs? How will this shape be helpful in making Hult and Ostrander's plan work?
4. What are some of the problems involved in the researchers' scheme? How may these problems be solved?
5. What are the obvious advantages of the researchers' scheme?
6. Besides atomic-powered tugboats, what new scientific invention may be helpful in making Hult and Ostrander's plan a success?
7. Why is this large part of the earth's supply of fresh water so inaccessible?
8. Try to think of ways, other than the way given in this article, in which atomic power can be useful to mankind. What are they?
9. Do you think Hult and Ostrander's plan is a good one? A necessary plan? Why do you think that?

Five-Yard Fuller

by Bob Wells

"Mister, excuse me for bustin' in, but you look like you're the boss of this football team. I'm looking for a job."

Coach Murray Ding and his assistant, Mike Corning, had been watching the Knights run through a ragged practice scrimmage. They turned around impatiently.

A tall, sunburned youth with a great shock of straw-colored hair stood looking down at them. Working with a football squad, they were accustomed to associating with large masses of muscle, but the stranger was something special. His shoulders were several feet wide. His arms, which were longer than they should have been, hung down to his knees. He slumped forward a little, as though apologizing for his height. Coach Ding, who was a six-footer himself, had to look up to meet the guileless, blue eyes partially concealed by the mop of hair.

The youth was wearing faded overalls that were several sizes too small for him. His ankles hung out at the bottoms. Even the ankles, the coach noted, looked muscular.

"I come here lookin' for a job," the stranger said, when no one spoke. "I heard you was hiring people."

"Who told you that?" Ding demanded.

"Some fellow down at the feedstore. 'The Knights could sure use a good man,' he says. I figured that meant you might be in the market for a hired hand."

"What kind of a job do you have in mind?" Corning asked. His first impulse had been to laugh; but considering the young man's size, he decided not to. "We got a fellow who mows the stadium grass, and we don't do much plowing around here."

"I wasn't planning to hire out for plowing," the youth explained, patiently. "I got plenty of that to do at home. I heard you needed somebody to play football."

"He heard we needed somebody to play football, Murray," Mike said, winking.

But the coach didn't laugh. He was looking up at the large young man, studying him speculatively.

"What college did you play for, kid?"

"I didn't go to no college."

"You played in high school then?"

"No, I can't rightly say I did."

The faint hope that had appeared in the coach's eyes was rapidly flickering out. He took off his hat and rubbed his hand over his bald head, then put the hat back on.

"You couldn't even make the team in high school, but you want to play with the professionals?"

"Rock Creek Consolidated, where I went, didn't have no football team. Some of the guys used to choose up sides after school. Some of the time they wouldn't let me play, though. They said it wasn't fair."

"How come? Because you were so much bigger than the rest?"

"Oh, we've got some pretty big boys around Rock Creek. It's just that when they tackled me, I wouldn't quit runnin'. They said it wasn't fair not to go down after they'd went to all the trouble to tackle me."

Coach Ding decided he was wasting his time. He turned away. For just a moment, after he had seen those muscular shoulders and legs, he had allowed himself the luxury of hoping that his luck had finally changed. But of course it hadn't.

He walked off along the sidelines, turning his attention to the field, where Moose Walpurgis (väl-poōr′gĭs) had just missed an easy tackle by a good three feet. Mike Corning took the youth's arm. It was up to him to get rid of the boy; he could see that.

"Look, kid," he said, "you might not believe it from last year's standings, but the Knights are a pro team. I admit you're built like a football player. Go get yourself a college background and the kind of training a good college coach could give you, and we might be interested. But we don't have time to train somebody who's never played before. Sorry."

"But I walked all the way here from Rock Creek, on account of I figured you might have a job for me. I could sure use the work, mister."

"You walked here? How far is Rock Creek anyway? I never heard of it."

"About ninety miles, the way I reckon it. It's farther by road, but I came 'cross lots part of the way."

Mike Corning had been around football teams for eighteen years and had met his share of oddballs, but this was something new. How could he explain to this massive young man that you don't just walk off across the countryside and apply for a job with a professional football team, even a last-place team like the Knights? What you do is get yourself a reputation in high school, so the college recruiters notice you; then you play your heart out in college, so you get on somebody's draft list. And then, if you're lucky, you make the big time.

"What makes you think you can play football?" Mike demanded.

"A guy never knows till he tries."

"You ever watch a pro game?"

"On the TV once, last fall. They had this set goin' down at the hardware store, and I watched it for a while. The Knights was losing 48 to 0."

"Sounds like one of our better days," Mike said. "So what did you think of football, the way the pros play it?"

"Seemed like a pretty simple sort of game to me."

"Oh, it did, did it!" Coach Ding had strolled back just in time to hear the last remark. "Nothing to it, you thought?"

"Sure. Seemed like all you had to do was take the ball and carry it across that line near the two posts. It looked easier than the way I was making my living on the farm. I made up my mind to take a crack at it, once the hay was cut and the other work around the place slacked off a bit."

"Now, Murray," Mike said. He could see the back of the coach's neck getting red. He knew from experience what that meant. "Take it easy, Murray."

"What's your name, kid?" Coach Ding asked. His voice was deceptively mild.

"Fuller. Clarence Fuller."

"How old are you, Clarence?"

"Twenty, last July."

Suddenly, Ding dropped his gentle manner. He thrust out his jaw and glared up at Fuller, who looked down at him in mild surprise.

"Who put you up to this, kid?" the coach demanded. "You don't look smart enough to figure out a gag like this. What practical joker paid you to come walking in here in those undersized overalls and add to my troubles? Isn't it bad enough I've got to put up with a bunch of clowns like the Knights? Do I have to put up with things like this too?"

Fuller looked genuinely puzzled.

"Why, no one paid me, mister," he said. "Just like I told you, I was watching the Knights on the TV down at the hardware; and I decided it looked like an easy way to make a living. So when this fellow said the Knights sure could use a good man, I just —"

"Quiet!" Ding yelled. "I don't have to stand here and listen to things like this. Say the team is no good, I'll agree with you. Say it ought to be playing shuffleboard or drop the lace handkerchief, I'll go along. But don't stand there in those size fourteen shoes and tell me playing football's easy."

"Don't get excited, mister," Fuller said, looking embarrassed. "If you ain't hiring today, I'll walk on back home and no hard feelings. Only I still say all you have to do is take that little ball in your hand and move it down to where them two posts are standing. And I don't see nothin' so hard about that."

The red had spread from Ding's neck across his bare scalp and down to his face. He opened and closed his mouth a few times, but no sound came out. Then he jammed a whistle into his mouth and blew it. Scrimmage stopped. The players came ambling over to see what was up. Corning grabbed the coach's arm. "Don't do something you'll regret, Murray," he said. "He's just a dumb kid. He doesn't mean anything by it. Let me give him bus money and send him home."

But the coach was still seething. He was going to educate this boy, he said. He was going to prove something to him. As Fuller watched, puzzled but unworried, the coach had the first-string defensive team line up on the fifty-yard line. Facing it was the offensive unit, except for Les

Mickle, the fullback, who was kept on the sidelines. Ding reached in his pocket, walked around behind the defensive unit, and put a wadded-up ten-dollar bill on the forty-yard line. Then he half ran to where Fuller was standing and dragged him out to a point just behind the quarterback, Marty O'Brien.

"Boys," he told the players, "here's a member of the great American football public. He sees you play on television, and he figures the only reason you keep getting beat so bad is that you don't understand the game. He understands the game, though. He understands all you've got to do is take the ball and move it down across the goal line."

Several players laughed. Ding glared at them. What he was proposing, he said, was to let Fuller fill in for Mickle at fullback. O'Brien would hand him the ball when it was snapped from center, and the offensive team would block for him. All he had to do was move the ball to the forty-yard line in four plays, and the ten dollars was his.

"But if he does," Ding shouted, "I'm going to trade the entire defensive unit for the Ladies Auxiliary of the Midtown Badminton Club. You guys know what I want you to do?"

"You want us to clobber him, Murray?" Moose Walpurgis growled.

"Don't break any bones. Just educate him a little, that's all." He turned to Fuller. "You willing to do this, kid? You can still back out."

"I'm willing."

"You got any questions?"

"You want me to stop where you put the ten bucks, or should I go all the way to the posts?"

The coach ripped off his hat, threw it on the ground, and jumped on it. It seemed to make him feel a little better. He picked it up, jammed it on his bald head, and walked over to the sidelines. He blew his whistle. The opposing teams took their positions. O'Brien called a signal. The center snapped the ball. The quarterback pivoted and handed it to Fuller. It slipped from his fingers. He stood looking down at it in mild surprise while everybody else dived for it. O'Brien was on the bottom of the heap and the fumble was his.

"That's one play," Ding said grimly. "You've got three more."

"Look, Murray," Mike Corning said, "I know you're sore, but I don't think you ought to —"

Ding ignored him. He blew his whistle again. Once more the ball was snapped; again it was thrust toward Fuller. This time he held onto it, lifting it high above his head in one of his hamlike hands. He plunged forward into a solid wall of onrushing tacklers. There was a flurry of motion, a momentary struggle; then suddenly Fuller was past the scrimmage line and churning forward. Moose Walpurgis was hanging grimly to his back, another lineman had him around the legs, but he ignored them. He dragged them for a few feet. Then he shook his massive shoulders, wriggled free of the tacklers, and was all by himself running down the field. Half a dozen men gave chase. Fuller didn't seem to be running hard, but the long legs ate up so much ground that his pursuers fell steadily behind. When he got to the goalposts, he stopped and looked back to where Coach Ding was standing open mouthed.

"This far enough, mister?" he called. "Or you want I should keep going?"

Ding made a mighty effort and got control of himself. He stalked down the sidelines, glaring right and left at the sheepish defensive players. It had been an accident, he said. It had been a fluke. It could never happen again. Still, it went to show what he'd said all along. With a team like this anything could happen, anything bad, that is. He looked up at Fuller.

"You win the ten bucks, kid. Go on back and pick it up."

Fuller was still holding the football in his right hand. He thrust out his left hand, palm up. It contained the ten-dollar bill.

"I already got it, mister. I grabbed it off the ground on the way. Ten dollars is a lot of money. I didn't want to see it get trampled."

DISCUSSION

1. What gave the coaches of the Knights football team the impression that Five-Yard Fuller was a plowboy?
2. What experience had Five-Yard had in playing football? What kind of background and experience did Coach Corning feel he should have before attempting to play professionally?
3. Why did Coach Ding think someone had put Five-Yard up to asking for a job?
4. What do you think Coach Ding meant when he told Moose Walpurgis to "Just educate him a little, that's all"?
5. Why do you think it was an effort for Coach Ding to get control of himself after Five-Yard crossed the line in two plays?
6. What made Five-Yard seem an unlikely prospect for playing professional football? What made him seem a likely one? If you had been a member of the Knights team, how would you have reacted to someone who looked like Five-Yard?
7. How did Five-Yard's use of language differ from that of Coach Ding's? Do you think this affected their ability to communicate? Why do you think that?
8. Did you ever have to change a hasty judgment that you had made about someone on the basis of the clothes he wore or his use of the English language? Why? Why are hasty judgments best avoided?

AUTHOR

After having written more than a dozen short stories that were published in national magazines, Bob Wells wrote his first book for young people, *Five-Yard Fuller*. Since its publication he has written several other books featuring Five-Yard as the main character. Three of them are *Five-Yard Fuller and the Unlikely Knights, Five-Yard Fuller of the New York Gnats,* and *Five-Yard Fuller's Model T.*

Mr. Wells grew up in Orwell, Ohio, graduated from Ohio State University, and served in the Navy during World War II. He is on the staff of a newspaper in Milwaukee, Wisconsin.

CAT
and the
UNDERWORLD

by Emily Neville

Cat makes himself at home in my room pretty easily. Mostly he likes to be up on top of something, so I put an old sweater on the bureau beside my bed, and he sleeps up there. When he wants me to wake up in the morning, he jumps and lands in the middle of my stomach. Believe me, cats don't always land lightly — only when they want to. Anything a cat does, he does only when he wants to. I like that.

When I'm combing my hair in the morning, sometimes he sits up there and looks down his nose at my reflection in the mirror. He appears to be taking inventory: "Hmm, buck-teeth; sandy hair, smooth in front, cowlick in back; brown eyes, can't see in the dark worth a nickel; pimples on the chin. Too bad."

He catches sight of himself in the mirror, and his tail twitches mo-mentarily. He seems to know it's not really another cat, but his claws come out; and he taps the mirror softly, just to make sure.

When I'm lying on the bed reading, sometimes he will curl up between my knees and the book. But after a few days I can see he's getting more and more restless. It gets so I can't listen to a record for the noise of him scratching on the rug. I can't let him loose in the apartment, at least until we make sure Mom doesn't get asthma, so I figure I better reintroduce him to the great outdoors in the city. One nice Sunday morning in April we go down and sit on the stoop.

Cat sits down, very tall and neat and pear-shaped, and closes his eyes about halfway. He glances at the street as if it isn't good enough for him. After a while, condescending,

he eases down the steps and lies on a sunny, dusty spot in the middle of the sidewalk. People walking have to step around him, and he squints at them.

Then he gets up, quick, looks over his shoulder at nothing, and shoots down the stairs to the cellar. I take a look to see where he's going, and he is pacing slowly toward the backyard, head down, a tiger on the prowl. I figure I'll sit in the sun and finish my science-fiction magazine before I go after him.

When I do, he's not in sight, and Butch, the janitor, tells me he jumped up on the wall and probably down into one of the other yards. I look around a while and call, but he's not in sight, and I go up to lunch. Along toward evening Cat scratches at the door and comes in, as if he'd done it all his life.

This gets to be a routine. Sometimes he doesn't even come home at night, and he's sitting on the doormat when I get the milk in the morning, looking offended.

"Is it my fault you stayed out all night?" I ask him.

He sticks his tail straight up and marches down the hall to the kitchen, where he waits for me to open the milk and dish out the cat food. Then he goes to bed.

One morning he's not there when I open the door, and he still hasn't showed up when I get back from school. I get worried and go down to talk to Butch.

"Wa-a-l," says Butch, "sometimes that cat sit and talk to me a little, but most times he go on over to Twenty-first Street, where he sit and talk to his lady friend. Turned cold last night, lot of buildings put on heat and closed up their basements. Maybe he got locked in somewheres."

"Which building's his friend live in?" I ask.

"Forty-six, the big one. His friend's a little black-and-white cat, sort of belongs to the night man over there. He feeds her."

I go around to Twenty-first Street and case Forty-six, which is a pretty fair-looking building with a striped awning and a doorman who saunters out front and looks around every few minutes.

While I'm watching, a grocery boy comes along pushing his cart and goes down some stairs into the basement with his carton of groceries. This gives me an idea. I'll give the boy time to get started up in the elevator, and then I'll go down in the basement and hunt for Cat. If someone comes along and gets sore, I can always play dumb.

I go down, and the coast is clear. The elevator's gone up, and I walk softly past and through a big room where the tenants leave their baby carriages and bicycles. After this the cellar stretches off into several corridors, lit by twenty-watt bulbs dangling from the ceiling. You can hardly see anything. The corridors go between wire storage cages, where the tenants keep stuff like trunks and old cribs and parakeet cages. They're all locked.

"Me-ow, meow, me-ow!" Unmistakably Cat, and angry.

The sound comes from the end of one corridor, and I fumble along, peering into each cage to try to see a tiger cat in a shadowy hole. Fortunately his eyes glow, and he opens his mouth for another meow, and I see him locked inside one of the cages before I come to the end of the corridor. I don't know how he got in or how I'm going to get him out.

While I'm thinking, Cat's eyes flick away from me to the right, then back to me. Cat's not making any noise, and neither am I, but something is. It's just a tiny rustle, or a breath, but I have a creepy feeling someone is standing near us. Way down at the end of the cellar a shadow moves a little, and I can see it has a white splotch — a face. It's a man and he comes toward me.

I don't know why any of the building men would be way back there, but that's who I figure it is, so I start explaining. "I was just hunting for my cat. . . . I mean, he's got locked in one of these cages. I just want to get him out."

The guy lets his breath out, slow, as if he's been holding it quite a while. I realize he doesn't belong in that cellar either, and he's been scared of me.

He moves forward saying, "Sh-h-h-h," very quietly. He's taller than I am, and I can't see what he really looks like; but I'm sure he's sort of a kid, maybe eighteen or so.

He looks at the padlock on the cage and says, "Huh, cheap!" He takes a paper clip out of his pocket and opens it out, and I think maybe he has a penknife too, and next thing I know the padlock is open.

"Gee, how'd you do that?"

"Sh-h-h. A guy showed me how. You better get your cat and scram."

Golly, I wonder, maybe the guy is a burglar, and that gives me another creepy feeling. But would a burglar be taking time out to get a kid's cat free?

"Well, thanks for the cat. See you around," I say.

"Sh-h-h. I don't live around here. Hurry up before we both get caught."

Maybe he's a real burglar with a gun, even, I think; and by the time I dodge past the elevators and get out in the cold April wind, the sweat down my back is freezing. I give Cat a long lecture on staying out of basements. After all, I can't count on having a burglar handy to get him out every time.

Back home we put some nice jailhouse blues on the record player, and we both stretch out on the bed to think. The guy didn't really *look* like a burglar. And he didn't talk "dese and dose." Maybe real burglars don't all talk that way — only the ones on TV. Still, he sure picked that lock fast, and he was sure down in that cellar for some reason of his own.

Maybe I ought to let someone know. I figure I'll test Pop out, just casual like. "Some queer-looking types hanging around this neighborhood," I say at dinner. "I saw a tough-looking guy hanging around Number Forty-six this afternoon. Might have been a burglar, even."

I figure Pop'll at least ask me what he was doing, and maybe I'll tell him the whole thing — about Cat and the cage. But Pop says, "In case you didn't know it, burglars do not all look like Humphrey Bogart, and they don't wear signs."

"Thanks for the news," I say, and go on eating my dinner. Even if Pop does make me sore, I'm not going to pass up steak and onions, which we don't have very often.

However, the next day I'm walking along Twenty-first Street, and I see the super of Forty-six standing by the back entrance, so I figure I'll try again. I say to him, "Us kids were playing ball here yesterday, and we saw a strange-looking guy sneak into your cellar. It wasn't a delivery boy."

"Yeah? You sure it wasn't you or one of your juvenile pals trying to swipe a bike? How come you have to play ball right here?"

"I don't swipe bikes. I got one of my own. New. A Raleigh. Better than any junk you got in there."

"What d'you know about what I got in there, wise guy?"

"Aw, forget it." I realize he's just getting suspicious of me. That's what comes of trying to be a big public-spirited citizen. I decide my burglar, whoever he is, is a lot nicer than the super, and I hope he got a fat haul.

The next day it looks like maybe he did just that. The local paper, *Town and Village,* has a headline: "Gramercy Park Cellar Robbed." I read down the article:

"The superintendent, Fred Snood, checked the cellar storage cages after a passing youth hinted to him that there had been a robbery. He found one cage open and a suitcase missing. Police theorize that the youth may have been the burglar or an accomplice with a guilty conscience or a grudge, and they are hunting him for questioning. Mr. Snood described him as about sixteen years of age, medium height, with long hair, and wearing a heavy black sweater. They are also checking second-hand stores for the stolen suitcase."

The burglar stole a suitcase with valuable papers and some silver and jewelry in it. But the guy they were hunting for — I read the paragraph over and feel green. That's me. I get up and look in the mirror. In other circumstances I'd like being taken for sixteen instead of fourteen, which I am. I smooth my hair and squint at it.

Slowly I peel off my black sweater, which I wear practically all the time, and stuff it in my bottom drawer under my bathing suit. But if I want to walk around the street without worrying about every cop, I'll have to do more than that. I put on a shirt and necktie and suit jacket and stick a cap on my head. I head uptown on the subway. At Sixty-eighth Street I get off and look around for a barbershop.

"Cut it," I tell the guy.

"That's right. I'll trim you nice and neat. Get rid of all this stuff."

And while he chatters on like an idiot, I have to watch three months' work go snip, snip on the floor. Then I have to pay for it. At home I get the same routine. Pop looks at my disguise and says, "Why, you may look positively human some day!"

Two days later I find out I could've kept my hair. *Town and Village* has a new story: "Nab Cellar Thief Returning Loot. 'Just A Bet,' He Says."

The story is pretty interesting. The guy I met in the cellar is named Tom Ransom, and he is nineteen and just sort of floating around in the city. He doesn't seem to have any family. The police kept a detective watching Number Forty-six, and pretty soon they see Tom walking along with the stolen suitcase. He drops it inside the delivery entrance and walks on, but the cop collars him. I suppose if it hadn't been for me

shooting my big mouth off to the super, the police wouldn't have been watching the neighborhood. I feel sort of responsible.

The story in the paper goes on to say that this guy was broke and hunting for a job, and some other guy dares him to snatch something out of a cellar and finally bets him ten dollars, so he does it. He gets out and finds the suitcase has a lot of stocks and legal papers and table silver in it, and he's scared stiff. So he figures to drop it back where it came from. The paper says he's held over to appear before some magistrate in court.

I wonder, would they send a guy to jail for that? Or if they turn him loose, what does he do? It must be lousy to be in this city without any family or friends.

At that point I get the idea I'll write him a letter. After all, Cat and I sort of got him into the soup. So I look up the name of the magistrate and spend about half an hour poring through the phone book under "New York, City of," to get an address. I wonder whether to address him as "Tom" or "Mr. Ransom." Finally I write:

Dear Tom Ransom,

I am the kid you met in the cellar at Number Forty-six Gramercy, and I certainly thank you for unlocking that cage and getting my cat out. Cat is fine. I am sorry you got in trouble with the police. It sounds to me like you were only trying to return the stuff and do right. My father is a lawyer, if you would like one. I guess he's pretty good. Or if you would like to write me anyway, here is my address: 150 East 22nd St. I read in the paper that your family don't live in New York, which is why I thought you might like someone to write to.

Yours sincerely,
Dave Mitchell

Now that I'm a free citizen again, I dig out my black sweater, look disgustedly at my haircut, and go out to mail my letter.

Later on I get into a stickball game again on Twenty-first Street. Cat comes along and sits up high on a stoop across the street, where he can watch the ball game and the tame dogs being led by on their leashes. That big brain, the super of Forty-six, is standing by the delivery entrance, looking sour as usual.

"Got any burglars in your basement these days?" I yell to him while I'm jogging around the bases.

He looks at me and my short haircut and scratches his own bald egg. "Where'd I see you before?" he asks suspiciously.

"Oh — Cat and I, we get around," I say.

DISCUSSION

1. What made Dave think the person who opened the cage might be a burglar? What made Dave think that maybe he wasn't?
2. How did Dave's bragging about his bike get him into trouble?
3. Why did Dave feel responsible when he learned that the burglar was caught returning the stolen suitcase? How did Dave offer to help?
4. According to the newspaper story, why did Tom Ransom take the suitcase?
5. What did Mr. Mitchell mean when he said burglars "don't wear signs"?
6. Do you think Tom made a habit of stealing? Why do you think that?
7. What did the letter that Dave wrote tell you about him as a person?

8. Do you think Dave should have sneaked into the basement to find Cat? Why do you think that?
9. How do you think Cat got locked in the cage?
10. Why did Mr. Mitchell's comments make Dave sore?
11. If you had been Dave, what would your reaction have been to Mr. Snood's description of Dave in the newspaper?

AUTHOR

It's Like This, Cat, the book from which "Cat and the Underworld" was taken, was Emily Neville's first book for young people. "Cat," Mrs. Neville claims, was written because of her own reactions to the many sentimental boy-and-dog stories that she read as a child. She believed it was time a book was written about a boy and a cat. *It's Like This, Cat* first appeared as a short story in the *New York Daily Mirror.* Later Mrs. Neville turned this story into a book that won the Newbery Medal for 1964.

Mrs. Neville is the author of another prize-winning book, *Berries Goodman,* and several other books that are popular with young people: *The Seventeenth Street Gang, Traveler from a Small Planet,* and *Fogarty.*

The mother of five children, Mrs. Neville lives in New York State. Among her varied interests are travel, reading, and animals. She plays tennis and golf, is an excellent swimmer, and is one of the country's best woman flycasters.

SKILL LESSON 2

TOPICS AND MAIN IDEAS

Sometimes you need to study carefully an article that is made up of one or more informative paragraphs. To help you in better understanding the information, you often need to decide what the topic and the main idea of each paragraph are.

In an informative paragraph that is well written, all the sentences talk about only one thing. That one thing is called the TOPIC of the paragraph. The most important idea that the sentences give about the topic is called the MAIN IDEA of the paragraph. Can you decide what the topic and the main idea of the following paragraph are?

Man's misuse of his natural resources has resulted in damage to the environment. Over the years so much land has been cleared of trees and then plowed unwisely or overgrazed that floods and dust storms have swept away the important topsoil. Improper disposal of wastes has polluted the water in lakes, rivers, and streams to the point where animals and plant life have died. In major cities the air itself has become polluted by smoke and gases, further visible evidence of man's misuse of his precious natural resources.

You can readily see that all the sentences in the paragraph talk about only one thing, *Man's misuse of his natural resources.* That one thing is the topic of the paragraph.

What is the most important idea that the paragraph gives about the topic? If you think carefully about what each sentence is saying, you will see that it is telling about some kind of harm or damage that man's misuse of his natural resources has done to the environment. By putting together ideas that the different sentences give, you can make the statement *Man's misuse of his natural resources has damaged the environment.* Such a statement tells what the main idea of the paragraph is.

Does the following paragraph talk about only one topic? What do you think the main idea of the paragraph is?

All animals consist mostly of water. Man averages about 65% water in his body. Many animals, including the elephant, the chicken, the jellyfish, and the earthworm, are more than 70% water. All plants, too, are made up primarily of water. An ear of corn is about 70% water; a potato, 80%; and a watermelon, 92%. The cucumber and the tomato average about 95% water.

You can see that the first three sentences in the paragraph you just read talk about *Water in animals.* The rest of the sentences talk about *Water in plants.* Neither of these two topics can be called the topic of the paragraph. To decide what to use as the topic of the paragraph, you will need to think of an expression that includes or combines the two topics that the paragraph talks about. Such an expression could correctly be *Water in animals' and plants* or *Water in living things.*

What is the main idea of the paragraph? By putting together ideas that the different sentences give about the topic, you can make the statement *All animals and plants are made up mostly of water.* Such a statement tells what the main idea of the paragraph is.

The following paragraph has a topic and a main idea that are expressed in the paragraph. What are they? Remember that a topic is expressed as a phrase, or group of words, but that a main idea is always expressed as a statement.

Unlike fish and other sea animals that live in the ocean, the sea anemone generally remains fixed in one spot, attached to a rock, a shell, or other support. In appearance it resembles a flower more than it does the usual sea animal. In fact, its very name derives from its resemblance to the common woodland wild flower, the anemone. Tentacles of brilliant color stretch out from the body of the sea anemone, swaying in the smooth movement of the water. This "flower of the ocean" is, however, a deadly enemy to tiny fish and other small sea animals. The luring tentacles conceal a poison that can paralyze its prey. Once its victim has been made helpless, the tentacles draw the food into the small mouth opening. Beautiful but deadly, the sea anemone has to be acknowledged as one of the most unusual animals of the ocean floor.

In the paragraph that follows, the topic and the main idea are not directly expressed in the paragraph. You will need to decide for yourself what they are. Read the paragraph and think what the topic and the main idea may be.

The most valuable of the precious stones used in expensive jewelry are generally considered to be diamonds, emeralds, rubies, and sapphires. Diamonds, the hardest and most brilliant of gems, have been found in Asia, South America, and, to a small extent, in the United States. However, most diamonds come from southern and central Africa. Most emeralds come from Colombia in South America, but they may also originate in Africa, Russia, and India. Some emeralds have been found in North Carolina, but they are of rather poor quality. The best rubies and sapphires, gems of the same mineral but of different color, come from countries in southeast Asia. Sapphires are also found in Australia, but they are less prized because they look black rather than blue under artificial light. Perhaps the most highly prized sapphires are those that come from India.

Sometimes you need to decide what the topic and the main idea of a group of paragraphs are. What do you think the topic and the main idea of the following group are?

What does the shape of the bill, or beak, of a bird have to do with the bird's choice of the food it eats? Swallows, swifts, and nighthawks are among the birds having small bills, a clue to their role as insect eaters. Behind these bills are large mouths that open wide to scoop up flying insects.

The seed eaters among birds have strong, heavy bills that can easily crack hard seeds and pry apart the scales of pine and spruce cones. The most common of the seed eaters are sparrows, but this group also includes finches, cardinals, and grosbeaks.

Chisel beaks belong to woodpeckers and other related birds, including the common flickers. These birds use their beaks to poke through the bark of trees for insects.

Along river, lake, and ocean shores are found wading birds that eat small fish, shellfish, worms, and frogs. To obtain these delicacies, sandpipers, curlews, herons, and other wading birds are equipped with spear bills, long bills that are just right for digging in sand and mud.

The birds of prey, among them owls, hawks, and eagles, feed on mice, rats, snakes, lizards, and squirrels. Hooked bills, large and powerful, enable these birds to pierce and tear the flesh of their unfortunate victims.

It should have been easy for you to decide that the one thing the group of paragraphs that you just read talks about is *The bills and food of certain birds.* That is the topic of the group of paragraphs. But what main idea do the paragraphs give about the topic? If you put together ideas that the different paragraphs give about the topic, you can make the statement *The shape of the bill of a bird helps to determine the kind of food that the bird eats.* Such a statement gives the main idea of the group of paragraphs.

What one thing do most of the sentences in the following group of paragraphs tell about? What is the main idea that the paragraphs give about that topic?

Batteries, generators, and other man-made devices produce the electricity that brings heat and light to homes. In the world of nature the most familiar form of electricity is lightning, which may produce a flow of electricity measuring millions of volts. Less familiar than lightning are the species of fish that are capable of producing electric current. Although the electricity produced by these fish is most often used for defense purposes, it is sometimes used in stunning and killing smaller fish for food. The electrical discharge of some species is even strong enough to stun a man who happens to step on or otherwise touch one of these fish.

Among those fish that can give electric shocks are torpedoes, also called electric rays. Special glands, located in the head of the torpedo, contain a system of electric storage cells. Any contact with the body of a torpedo brings a discharge of electricity from its storage cells. Since this fish is large, flat, and round and likes to lie on the sandy bottoms of the warm coastal waters of the Atlantic from Cape Cod south, it is not unusual for swimmers to come in contact with torpedoes. It is thought that this strange and dangerous fish may account for some mysterious drowning incidents.

The strongest electrical shock is discharged by the electric eel, a fish that looks like an eel but is really a relative of the catfish. Some interesting experiments with the electric eel have proved that it can produce an amazing amount of electricity. It has been used to light neon lamps, start engines, and even power advertising signs. Discharges of 200 to 300 volts are normal, but in some experiments electric eels have discharged over 600 volts. That amounts to a great deal of electricity, particularly when you realize that an electric eel can produce 1,600 discharges in five seconds.

Discussion

Help your class answer these questions:
1. What is the difference between the topic and the main idea of a paragraph?
2. How do you decide on the topic and the main idea of a paragraph?
3. If the topic and the main idea are not clearly expressed in the paragraph, how do you decide what they are?
4. What are the topic and the main idea of the paragraph at the top of page 103? Of the paragraph at the bottom of page 103?
5. What are the topic and the main idea of the group of paragraphs on page 105?

On your own

The following paragraph has a topic and a main idea that are expressed in the paragraph. Decide what they are.

One of the most common and useful instruments in our everyday lives, the Fahrenheit thermometer, has changed little since it was developed in the early 1700's. Gabriel Daniel Fahrenheit, a skilled thermometer-maker of that time, was the first to switch from alcohol to mercury, which is still used in thermometers today. He developed a scale in which the freezing point was designated as 32°, the boiling point as 212°, and man's normal temperature as 96°. More than two hundred years later those points remain the same except for the normal temperature of man's body, now designated as 98.6°.

Decide on the topic and the main idea of the following group of paragraphs:

As seen from the earth, the moon has dark spots that somewhat resemble a face and account for the expression "the man in the moon." So too does the sun have dark spots, but these spots are made up of gases, just as is all the sun. Scientists who study these sunspots do not know how or why they are formed. It is believed that the violent electrical storms that take place in the sun cause some gases to become cooler and thus to look darker.

Measurements have been made that show sunspots to be thousands of miles wide, some of them covering an area greater than the size of the earth. The area of the greatest activity of sunspots is near the sun's equator, where they seem to occur about every eleven years. Like almost everything else about sunspots, these things have been observed but have not been explained.

What are the topic and the main idea of the following group of paragraphs?

Sound travels in waves that spread out in all directions from the source of the sound at a speed far slower than the speed of light. Sound travels in air at a speed of a little less than 1,100 feet per second while light travels at a speed of more than 186,000 miles per second. If you have ever watched a golfer hit a ball when he or she was a few hundred yards from you, then you know that you see the ball start its flight before you hear the sound caused by the impact of club on ball. The sound that you hear as you watch a jet plane streak across the sky is the sound made by the plane when it was several miles back. Lightning and thunder occur at the same time, but you see the lightning before you hear the thunder.

In certain substances sound travels at quite a higher rate of speed than it does in air. In water sound travels about 4,700 feet per second or about four times faster than in air. In wood sound travels more than ten times faster than in air, and in steel the speed of sound is more than 16,000 feet per second, about fifteen times faster than in air.

Air, however, is not the poorest conductor of sound. Certain kinds of cloth, such as felt and cotton, for example, absorb sound

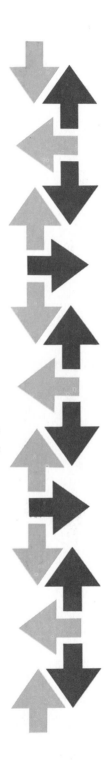

waves. Corkboard, rubber, linoleum, and carpeting are other materials that slow down the speed of sound. That is why these materials and others, such as heavy curtains and various types of tiles, are used in soundproofing rooms in hospitals, offices, libraries, and auditoriums, where all but useful sounds need to be controlled.

Checking your work

If you are asked to do so, tell what you think the topic and the main idea of the single paragraph are. Then do the same for the groups of paragraphs. Listen while others in your class tell what they think the topics and the main ideas are. Make sure you understand why particular topics or main ideas are good choices.

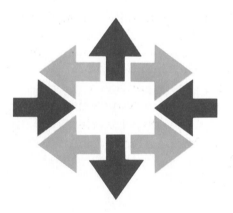

BLUEPRINT FOR SURVIVAL

Russell Freedman and James E. Morriss

Innate patterns of behavior are an essential part of an animal's equipment for survival. If baby turtles were not instinctively drawn to the sea, their species would become extinct. If a migratory bird was not equipped with a built-in flight plan, its journey might end in disaster. The ready-made responses of inborn behavior make it possible for an animal to perform acts it has neither the time, the ability, nor the opportunity to learn.

A barn swallow does not have to explore the earth or consult weather charts before it finds a place where the seasons are right for breeding and where there is plenty of food. A rabbit doesn't have to learn from experience that overcrowding might threaten its survival; the rabbit automatically safeguards its food supply and nesting site by defending a private territory. No one teaches a firefly how to attract a mate, a wasp how to build a nest, or an eyed hawk moth how to defend itself. These acts are all controlled by instinct.

Though the instinct for self-preservation is strong, the instinct to preserve the species is even stronger. Migrating salmon overcome staggering obstacles as they return to their spawning grounds, where they lay their eggs and die. Animals whose young are born helpless often risk their own lives to protect their offspring. With shrieks and dashes a robin takes an almost suicidal stand as she attempts to drive away the prowling cat that threatens her nest.

Yet a bird who instinctively endangers her life for her young will

let one of her nestlings starve if it falls accidentally out of the nest. She has no built-in response to deal with this situation. Instinct tells her to stuff the mouths inside her nest; she is blind to other gaping mouths, even if they belong to her own young and are only a short distance away.

When a cowbird, a cuckoo, or some other parasitic bird is hatched and raised by foster parents, it often pushes its foster brothers and sisters out of the nest. The victims usually fall to the ground, but occasionally, one is left lying on the edge of the nest. With a simple movement of her beak the mother bird could tip the helpless infant back to safety, yet instinct has not equipped her to perform this act. She lets the nestling die of cold and hunger before her eyes — apparently without realizing what is happening.

Instinct is too inflexible to cope with every situation that may arise. In Germany a few years ago a highway was built through a marshland where toads came to spawn each year. Like salmon, toads will lay their eggs only in the place where they themselves were born. But when these particular toads returned to their ancestral spawning grounds, they found a concrete strip instead of a muddy pond. Though other ponds suitable for spawning were not far away, the toads were unable to change the pattern of behavior passed down by their ances-

tors. Crawling desperately about on the highway, they were slaughtered by passing cars.

Many species have become extinct because they were unable to adjust to changes in their environment. On its comfortable island home in the Indian Ocean, the dodo bird had no natural enemies and no need to fear or flee other living creatures. Over countless generations these birds grew fat and sluggish and even lost the ability to fly. Yet their easy life allowed them to flourish until the early 1500's, when men first began to settle on the island. The settlers brought with them dogs and pigs, and the trusting dodo was no match for these human and animal newcomers who fed on its eggs as well as its flesh. Unable to change either its flightless body or its defenseless behavior, the dodo vanished in less than 200 years.

Today, the green sea turtle may be on its way to extinction. These reptiles are valued for their meat and hides, and increased hunting in recent years has taken a heavy toll of the world's green turtle population. Despite legal restrictions the hunting continues, and the turtles are now being killed in remote places where they were not hunted before.

As long as the turtles are at sea, their great size makes them almost immune to danger. But they must come ashore to lay their eggs, exposing themselves and their offspring to the hazards of the land.

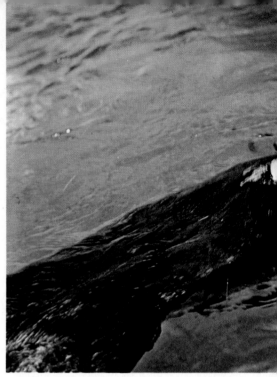

For millions of years, as long as the dangers they faced were natural ones, the turtles were quite successful. From each batch of 100 turtle eggs enough hatchlings survived to maintain the species. Now, however, the species may suffer the same fate as the dodo bird. Since the turtles cannot change their nesting behavior, they face the danger of extinction as instinct leads them back to the same beaches year after year, where armed hunters are waiting for them.

There is nothing very new about extinction, of course. Countless species became extinct long before man ever appeared on earth. Gigantic dinosaurs once dominated the earth; then they vanished, unable to cope with the natural changes that occurred in their environment. In modern times, because of changes caused by man, there has been an alarming increase in the rate of extinction. At this moment about 100 species of birds and 600 species of mammals are in imminent danger of disappearing permanently from the earth.

One species, the sea otter, helped save itself from extinction because of its ability to learn. At one time sea otters were primarily land creatures, inhabiting island beaches at the northern edge of the Pacific Ocean. Though they were expert swimmers who lived intimately with the sea, it was mainly along the shore that they found food, slept, mated, and bore their young. Eskimos, who shared the otters' islands, killed a few of the animals to make clothes of their fur; but there

were hundreds of thousands of sea otters then and not many Eskimos.

Sea otters have the most exquisite fur in the world. Starting about 200 years ago, the beauty of their skins nearly resulted in their extermination. Otter furs became so valuable that hunters converged on the animals' islands from all over the world. As massive expeditions were organized, the otters began to disappear. Year after year the desperate animals were driven from their beaches, pursued in small boats, and slaughtered ruthlessly.

In 1911, when the species was nearly extinct, the governments of the United States, Great Britain, Japan, and Russia agreed to stop all killing of sea otters. By then, however, the few surviving otters were living in the safety of the sea.

They had moved from the beaches where their ancestors had lived, out into the sea, making a new home for themselves in thick beds of floating kelp, or seaweed. To succeed in this environment, the otters had to learn how to find their food away from shore and how to wrap themselves in strands of seaweed while they slept, so waves would not carry them back to the perils of the beaches they had abandoned. They had to learn how to mate and give birth amidst the dense, tangled water plants where they had sought refuge, how to raise their young there, and how to hide.

Today, sea otters are gradually increasing their numbers again. Yet after living on land for so many generations, they are still adapting to their watery environment; and each young otter must learn anew the difficult art of surviving at sea.

Some animals can learn a great deal more than others. An insect is primarily a creature of instinct: For the most part it is locked into innate patterns of behavior, which have developed over millions of years. Mammals, on the other hand, learn constantly from experience.

Of all mammals man is the only one whose behavior depends almost entirely on learning. In fact, man's seemingly limitless ability to learn has made him the most successful living creature on earth.

No animal has been able to mold its life or environment in the way man has done. He has leveled mountains, uprooted forests, and paved the land with cities, factories, and highways. He has learned to travel through the air, live beneath the sea, fly to the moon, and bring the whole world into his living room. Having penetrated the mystery of life's genetic blueprint, man is on the threshold of controlling his heredity and shaping human destiny. And having unlocked the secret of the atom, he holds in his hands the power to transform the earth or destroy it.

Many of the changes brought about by man have enriched his life. Others threaten his very existence. For as man has worked to reshape his environment, he has at the same time fouled the lakes and rivers essential to his survival and has poisoned the very air he breathes.

Today, thoughtful people wonder if man can meet the challenges of the dangerous new world he has created — if he can, in fact, survive. Unlike the dodo man has the capacity to change his old habits of behavior. And this is precisely what the human species must do if it is to prevent its own extinction.

DISCUSSION

1. What is meant by innate patterns of behavior? Why are these patterns of behavior an essential part of an animal's equipment for survival? Give some examples.
2. What instinct is stronger than the instinct of self-preservation? Give an example.
3. The behavior of which animal depends almost entirely on learning? How has this fact affected his life?
4. What do you think the author meant when he spoke of a bird's "built-in flight plan"?

5. Why did the author refer to the cowbird and cuckoo as "parasitic birds"?
6. Do you think man shows as much concern for preserving his species as animals do? Why or why not?
7. If you were asked to suggest ways of preserving some of the scarce species, what would you suggest?
8. Do you think the fur of wild animals should be used for clothing? Why or why not?
9. Do you think the world would be a better or worse place in which to live if man did not have this limitless ability to learn? What makes you think that?
10. What must man do to prevent his own extinction? What are some ways in which you think you could help change the things that are wrong with "the dangerous new world"?

AUTHORS

Russell Freedman and James E. Morriss, co-authors of "Blueprint for Survival" from *Animal Instincts,* both live in New York City.

Mr. Freedman teaches a writing course at the New School for Social Research and spends the rest of his time writing. He is the author of several books for young people, including *2000 Years of Space Travel, Teenagers Who Made History,* and *Jules Verne: Portrait of a Prophet.*

Born in San Francisco, Mr. Freedman graduated from the University of California at Berkeley. He began his writing career as a reporter for the Associated Press in California. Later, he became a TV publicity writer for a New York advertising agency and, after a few years, an editor and a contributor to the *Columbia Encyclopedia* and the *Merit Students Encyclopedia.*

Mr. Morriss, a high-school biology teacher, grew up in Arkansas, graduated from John Brown University there, and did graduate work in biology and psychology at several other colleges. It was at the City College of New York that he took one of the first courses given in this country in ethology, the study of animal behavior. In addition to teaching, Mr. Morriss directed the research for fifteen films on animal behavior that were produced by the National Broadcasting Company.

Mr. Freedman and Mr. Morriss have written two other books together: *How Animals Learn* and *The Brains of Animals and Man.*

MY PEOPLE

I am a Navajo, the Navajos are my people.
They live in the hogans upon the dry desert,
With a little shade house and a sheep corral.
It is nice and peaceful there away
From the city street.
There were the sad, dark years for my people,
But my people didn't disappear.
They started rebuilding, increasing
In population.
I am proud that the desert floor,
The lonely hogans,
Have made me thoughtful and
Respectful of my people.
I am proud to be born in my people's land.
I shall never forget my home and people.

Bernice George

masterworks

NAVAHO RAIN

by Scott O'Dell

In the 1860's, when Bright Morning, a young Navaho girl, lived in Arizona's Canyon de Chelly (kăn'yən də shā'), *it was her duty to tend her family's sheep. Now her people have been rounded up by the soldiers and are camped at Bosque Redondo* (bŏs'kā rā-dŏn'dō), *the plain surrounding Fort Sumner, 180 miles southeast of Santa Fe, New Mexico; but she still believes that some of the sheep are safe somewhere in the canyon. Her husband, Tall Boy, whose arm was wounded the previous year by a Spanish slaver, is now imprisoned in the fort for breaking an Apache's arm in a fight over some firewood. Bright Morning wants to escape with Tall Boy from the Long Knives, the Indians' name for the soldiers, and return to the canyon to live.*

The snows melted and warm winds blew over Bosque Redondo and green grass began to show along the banks of the river. The big gate at Fort Sumner opened every day, the Long Knives marched out, the drums beat, and horns sounded; then the soldiers went back in and the gate closed. I waited every day, but my husband did not come.

With spring settled on the land, the wagons brought more food for us, and I was able to save another gourd of flour. We now had enough food to last us on a journey of six days.

Besides the two good blankets, we had a knife, which was like those the soldiers used on the ends of their rifles. I found it on one of the mornings when I went up to the fort. It was wrapped in a cloth and hidden in the grass. I sharpened it on a stone and put it away in the lean-to. The cloth, which was an arm's length of red velvet, would make a girl's small dress or a jacket for a boy.

It was a warm night with many stars and the sound of the river running far away. We had just eaten our supper when Tall Boy came. He walked in so quietly that my black dog did not hear him. He sat down at the fire and ate everything that was left in the pot, hurriedly as if he had never eaten before. He looked gaunt and fearful.

My father said, "Did the Long Knives open the gate for you?"

"They did not open the gate," Tall Boy replied.

"The gate was not open?"

"No."

"But you are here."

"I am here because of a hole in the wall," Tall Boy said, "which I have known about for many weeks."

"Where is this hole you have known about?"

"It is in the place where they cook the food."

"Is it a round hole or one that is square?"

"Neither one nor the other," said Tall Boy. "It is a hole where they shove all the garbage."

"Yes, I have heard of this hole," my father said. "The garbage goes through and falls on the ground outside the wall, and the people go there and pick it up."

"That is the hole," Tall Boy said.

"Of a size right for crawling."

"When no one looks. When everyone has left the place where they cook the food."

"And the people have come and carried away all the garbage."

"That is the time," Tall Boy said.

"When will the Long Knives know that you have crawled through the hole?"

"In the morning when they come to cook breakfast."

"No sooner nor later?"

"Then," my husband said.

He sat staring into the empty pot. I brought him a bowl of corn mush, which he ate in a hurry; and then he fell silent, sitting on his haunches with one arm dangling and the other on his thigh. I thought that he would get up at any moment, that the two of us would flee the camp; but he sat there beside the fire, looking as if he might fall asleep.

"The Long Knives will come in the morning," I said. "You will wake up behind the walls of the fort again."

He glanced at me, blinking his eyes; and I suddenly knew that he had gone as far as he wished to go. He was back with his family. He had eaten our food. He would sleep beside our fire. What happened to him tomorrow did not matter.

"Are you an old woman?" I asked him.

He stopped blinking.

"An old woman," I went on, my voice rising, "a woman who eats a lot and dozes beside the fire?"

My mother said, "He is worse than an old woman. He is like the old men of the Navahos. All of them."

Tall Boy got to his feet and unhitched his belt, making room for the big supper he had eaten.

My mother looked at him, at his feet. She would have liked to look him in the face, as she did with me when she was angry. But it was against our tribal law for a mother-in-law to look at her son-in-law this way. She looked at his feet for a long time.

"He will soon have to change his name again," she said. "What do you think it should be? Boy-Who-Sits-at-the-Fire? Boy-Who-Sleeps-Standing-Up? Or something else, such as Crawling-Through-a-Hole?"

"I will need to think hard," I said.

"We shall both think hard," my mother said.

Tall Boy looked at my mother's feet and then at me. He walked slowly around the fire and went outside. I heard him take a deep breath. I stood there and felt like crying. I had not cried since the day we left our home. After a while I sat down beside the fire and cried.

I cried for a long time, and nobody tried to stop me. Then Tall Boy came to the doorway and spoke my name and beckoned me to follow him.

When I went outside, the first thing I saw was the old speckled horse that belonged to my father-in-law.

"We go now," Tall Boy said.

He made a saddle of the two blankets and tied down the gourds that were filled with flour. The sharp knife he put in his belt.

We did not say good-bye to our family. They knew that we would take their thoughts with us and leave our thoughts for them. Tall Boy got on the horse, and we set off through the warm darkness. I had to run to keep pace with him; but when we got to the river, he let me climb up behind him.

I untied the two gourds and hung them around my neck to keep them out of the water. My black dog I held in my lap. The river ran swift and cold. As the horse plunged into the water, the current swept us out and then back to shore.

On the third try we kept going toward the far shore. We would have drowned except for the old horse. He must have been across the river many times in his life, for he knew how to float with the current and swim if he needed to. There was no moon, but all the stars were out, shining on the water.

When we reached the shore, I jumped off the horse; and we went along the trail we had used once before. Someday I hoped to have a horse of my own, and then I would ride beside my husband. Perhaps he would not own a horse by this time;

then it would be he who would have to walk. Across the river the evening fires of Bosque Redondo glowed softly.

We left them far behind, moving along the trail until dawn. Then we made a fire and cooked some mush beside a small lake.

My husband said, "This is the time the Long Knives will find that I have gone. We have the night between us, but they will come fast."

"They will not follow us," I said to calm him and myself. "There are thousands of Indians at Bosque Redondo. Will the Long Knives bother to look for one? And if they do, which way will they go? If they do anything, it will be to search the village. Our friends will tell them nothing."

We slept until the sun was high and awakened to the barking of my black dog. There were soldiers on the trail. By putting our ears to the earth, we could hear the steps of their horses. But they came from the west. From our hiding place we watched them pass, driving a small band of Navahos toward Bosque Redondo.

Tall Boy pulled the knife from his belt, and I think that he would have rushed out and attacked the soldiers alone if I had not pleaded with him. As it was, we made so much noise that one of the Long Knives stopped his horse and looked in our direction before he rode on.

We left the small lake and rode to the northwest, but we had not gone far when my husband said, "There are places closer than Canyon de Chelly where we can hide. These places are safer also. The Long Knives do not watch them as closely as they watch the canyon."

"But the canyon is our home," I said. "We have lived there. We know where wood is and water and food. The sheep. What of the sheep?"

I was walking beside him, and he glanced down at me in scorn. "Sheep? They are eaten by the wolves, as I have told you," he said. "If not, if there are some left, what do we do with them? Where can we graze them that they will not be seen by the Long Knives?"

"We will be careful where we graze them," I said. "There are hidden places that I know."

He shrugged his shoulders, which he did when he did not want to talk about something, and fell silent.

We went on for six suns, ate the last of our flour, and then snared rabbits and squirrels. I was certain that my husband had decided to go to Canyon de Chelly after all.

But on the seventh day Tall Boy left the trail, and we went northward over a ridge into wooded, rolling country. He had hunted there once and called it Elk-Running Valley.

A stream ran down from the high mountains and wandered through a meadow until it came to a dam beavers had made from brush and trees. There the stream backed up and formed a small pond with grassy banks. We built a hut beside the pond

and lived in it through the summer. It was here that my son was born.

After that, Tall Boy brought down poles from the high country, dragging them behind the speckled horse. He made the hut larger and strengthened the roof for winter snow. He fashioned a throwing stick and killed two young deer. He was busy all the time, hunting or making something. He still could not use his injured arm, but he had become quick and skillful with the other one. He no longer seemed to think about his injury.

I was busy too. I worked the deer hides with a bone scraper and softened them in my mouth and made a pair of leggings for my son. I also made him a jacket out of the velvet I had saved and a heavy coat from a beaver pelt. Yet not a day went by that summer or when the snows came that I did not think of my sheep.

One morning early in the spring while we were eating breakfast, soldiers appeared on the ridge. Our lean-to was hidden among the pine trees and could not be seen from where they stood. Nor could they see the speckled horse, which was tethered beyond the lean-to. We felt uneasy nonetheless.

The Long Knives came down from the ridge, riding fast. We were ready to flee, but they turned away from us and headed into the south.

"The Long Knives will travel for one day, no longer," Tall Boy said. "I have been in the canyon where they are going, and they cannot get through. They will have to turn back. We can look for them tomorrow."

We finished eating our breakfast. The spring sun was warm. Beaver were working on their dam, cutting brush on the banks and swimming across the pond with it. Tall Boy sat with his son in his lap and watched them for a long time going back and forth.

Then we loaded the old horse with our clothes and some dried deer meat and left Elk-Running Valley before the sun was high. We kept off the trail the soldiers had used.

At the top of the ridge we went north and west. It was in the direction of our canyon, but I was afraid to ask my husband whether we were going there or not. If we were, then it would be better not to ask him. Sometimes, if he was asked too many questions, he would change his mind and do something else.

I was not certain that we were going home until on the evening of the fifth day I saw the high ramparts against the northern sky. They were crimson in the setting sun; even the tall trees along their edges were crimson. I felt like shouting and dancing, like running around in circles, as I always did when I was very happy. But I walked quietly through the spring grass as if I saw nothing there in the sky.

Tall Boy was riding in front of me. He spoke and pointed into the north.

"Yes," I said calmly.

"We go because I am tired of hearing about sheep," he said. "And for no other reason. It is a dangerous place to go. There are no sheep left, but still I go. If there is one left, it will be shaggy like a buffalo and so wild you will have to catch it in a trap. But I go because I am tired of the sheep talk. Oh, Coyote Brothers in the far and near hills, I am tired of sheep."

He nudged the speckled horse and rode on, out of sight.

My son was strapped to a carrying board slung over my back. I stopped and took him out of the harness and held him in my arms. The crimson ramparts had changed to gold, and a gold mist drifted over the sky. I turned his head so that he faced the stone cliffs as they changed to purple, and the first star came out.

The next morning Tall Boy left to go into the canyon. He wanted to find out if any of the Long Knives were camped there or if other tribes, the Apaches or the Utes, had come while we were gone. The old horse had grown slow and lame, so he left it behind and went on foot. In two days he returned, carrying a braided rope, which he had picked up somewhere, and two horseshoes.

"I saw no Indians," he said while we were breaking camp. "No signs of the Long Knives. Nothing has changed."

After a time, not right away, I asked, "Did you see any of my sheep?"

"One," he said, "on the trail to the mesa. It had much more hair than a buffalo. At first I thought it was a buffalo."

"It has not been shorn for a long time," I said.

"Nor will it be shorn soon," my husband answered. "It is wilder than a mountain sheep. You will have to catch it in a trap. But after you catch it, how you will shear it I do not know."

"I have shears," I said. "I hid them in the cave when we left."

"You hid many things," Tall Boy said.

"Yes, we will need many things," I answered.

The river ran full. Blue snow water brimmed over the banks and flowed into the meadow. The cornfield was the same field the Long Knives had left. The peach trees, which they had stripped of bark, stood in black rows. Our hogan was still a ring of gray ashes and tumbled weeds. We stopped there and talked, deciding where we would go.

"The high mesa is safe," my husband said. "But if the Long Knives come, we will be cut off from water like we were before."

"From water and from the sheep," I said.

"What sheep?" Tall Boy asked. "The one that looks like a buffalo?"

"There is a small canyon where the river forks," I said. "I have been there with my sheep. It has grass and a spring comes out of a rock. It is hidden from the big canyon so that you can pass by and not know it is there."

"Let us go then to this place," Tall Boy said.

I started off, leading the way along the river to the big rocks that stood at the entrance to the hidden canyon. The rocks and the gnarled sycamores that grew among them formed a low, winding corridor, and Tall Boy had to climb down from the horse to get through.

Hidden Canyon was just as I remembered it. The yellow cliffs rose on all sides. The spring flowed from the rock and made a waterfall that the wind caught and spun out over a meadow. On the far side of the meadow was the grove of wild plums, where I had picked many handfuls of fruit. The trees now were covered with white and pink blossoms.

But I had forgotten the cave. Tall Boy saw it at once.

"A good place," he said, and went off to explore it.

The cave was on the face of the western cliff, where the morning sun shone first. It was about thirty feet from the ground and twice that many feet in width. To reach it, there were handholds cut into the soft, yellow stone; but some were worn away, and I had never tried to use them. Indians had lived there a long time ago and left; no one knew why.

Tall Boy started to chip away at the handholds, using the knife I had found at Bosque Redondo. He dug out four of the holds and tried them. I held my breath; I feared that he would never be able to make his way up the face of the cliff. Even with two good hands it was not easy. But he went up and came down without trouble.

"See," he said to his son, "it is easy. Before long you also will be able to climb. For your mother we will stretch a rope that she can hold on to."

Clouds were gathering, and he started working on the handholds again. While I watched him, my black dog pointed his ears; and I heard a small noise. It came from the far side of the meadow, near the wild plum trees; and I walked toward it.

I had not gone far when out of the tall grass I saw a ewe looking at me. She turned away as I reached her but did not flee. Her coat was thick and full of burrs. Beside her was a lamb, not more than a few days old.

I took my son from his carrying board and held him up so that he could see the lamb. He wanted to touch it; but with both hands he was grasping a toy that his father had given him, a willow spear tipped with stone. Tall Boy had made up a song about the Long Knives and how the spear would kill many of them. Every night he sang this song to his son.

I took the spear and dropped it in the grass and stepped upon it, hearing it snap beneath my foot.

My son touched the lamb once before the two moved away from us. He looked up at me and laughed, and I laughed with him.

Rain had begun to fall. It made a hissing sound in the tall grass as we started toward the cave high up in the western cliff. Tall Boy had finished the steps and handholds and now stood under the cave's stone lip, waving at us.

I waved back and hurried across the meadow. I raised my face to the falling rain. It was Navaho rain.

DISCUSSION

1. What did Tall Boy think had happened to the sheep that were left in the Canyon de Chelly? What did the sheep that he saw later look like?
2. Why did Bright Morning think it was not wise to ask her husband too many questions?
3. What was the song about that Tall Boy sang to his son every night? What action by Bright Morning did this song bring about?
4. What did Bright Morning mean by asking Tall Boy if he were an old woman?
5. Why do you think Tall Boy would change his mind and do something else if Bright Morning asked too many questions?
6. How did the Long Knives kill the peach trees in the canyon? Why did they do so?
7. How did Bright Morning and Tall Boy learn that soldiers were on their trail? Do you think this could be done in a busy city? Why or why not?
8. What reason did Tall Boy give Bright Morning for going back to the canyon? Do you think he had another reason for going back? Why do you think that?
9. Why do you think Bright Morning walked quietly, even though she felt like shouting and dancing? If you had been Bright Morning, could you have controlled your emotions? Why or why not?
10. What do you think Bright Morning meant when she said the falling rain was "Navaho rain"?
11. Who do you think had the stronger character, Bright Morning or Tall Boy? Why do you think that?

AUTHOR

Scott O'Dell has written seven books for young readers, the first of which, *Island of the Blue Dolphins,* won the Newbery Medal as well as seven other literary awards. It is one of the few children's books that has been made into a movie. Three others, including *Sing Down the Moon* from which "Navaho Rain" was taken, were Newbery Honor books. In addition to being a Newbery Honor book, *Sing Down the Moon* was chosen to receive the American Library Association's Notable Children's Book Award. In 1972, Mr. O'Dell had the distinctive honor of being the recipient of the Hans Christian Andersen Award. This award, given every two years by the International Board on Books for Young People, brings worldwide recognition to one author for his entire body of work.

All of Mr. O'Dell's novels have a historical aspect to them. *Sing Down the Moon* was written after the author spent a summer in Navaho country. He was so impressed by the history of this area that he "wanted to write a modest tribute to the Navaho women and to the courage of the human spirit." The result is the story of Bright Morning and her sheep.

Mr. O'Dell grew up in California "never far from the sound of the sea." He attended Occidental College and Stanford University in California and the University of Wisconsin. His career has not been limited to writing children's books. He worked for a time in the motion-picture industry as a technical director, then as a technical cameraman. He became a newspaperman and book reviewer and wrote both fiction and nonfiction for adults.

FROM THE BOOKSHELF

A CANDLE IN HER ROOM, *by Ruth M. Arthur*
An evil wooden doll influences three generations of a Welsh family until one girl has the courage to destroy this evil influence.

DARK VENTURE, *by Audrey White Beyer*
Demba, a twelve-year-old African boy who is captured and put on a slave ship to the New World, learns the horrors and hardships of slavery.

A ROOM MADE OF WINDOWS, *by Eleanor Cameron*
Lonely Julia Redfern discovers that she is destined to become a writer.

WHERE SPEED IS KING: STORIES OF RACING ADVENTURE,
edited by Phyllis R. Fenner
The stories revolve around man's love of speed. Primarily, they concern auto racing, but tales of horse racing, balloon racing, and railroad racing are also included.

RED HAWK'S ACCOUNT OF CUSTER'S LAST BATTLE,
by Paul and Dorothy Goble
The story of Custer's Last Stand is told from the point of view of a fifteen-year-old Sioux boy.

WHO DISCOVERED AMERICA?, *by Patricia Lauber*
Here is a scientific story that tells of the search for clues of the earliest Americans.

A FLOCK OF WORDS: AN ANTHOLOGY OF POETRY
FOR CHILDREN AND OTHERS, *compiled by David MacKay*
This collection contains poems from many countries and many centuries.

PULGA, *by S. R. van Iterson*
Pulga, a puny, ragged street urchin of Bogotá, Colombia, gains self-respect and self-discovery when he is hired as a truck driver's helper.

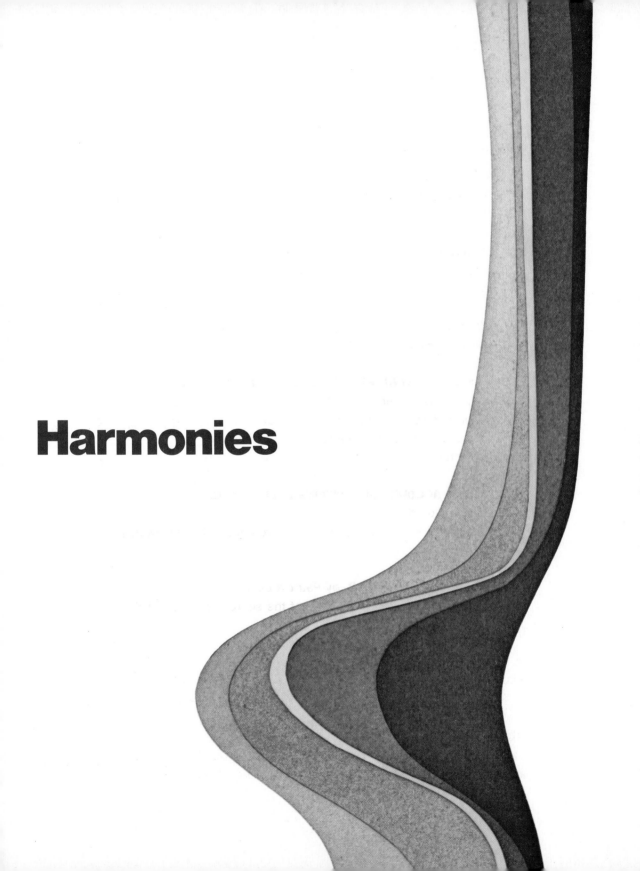

Harmonies

Contents

Harmonies

BEAT THE QUEEN

by William Pène du Bois

There were two rich birthday cakes at Pat O'Sullivan Pinkerton's birthday party — one all for him and the other for his ten best friends. Pat O'Sullivan Pinkerton was finishing his cake, licking the frosting off the tiny pink feet of the thirteen candles, when the two short-legged chairs he was sitting on broke beneath him. His best friends snickered, giggled, then bellowed with laughter. He hated being made fun of, particularly at his own party, and he stomped out of the dining room. In his fury he forgot to walk sideways like a crab, and he stuck fast in the doorway. Purple with anger, he charged forward, cracking two walls and taking the door frame with him. He puffed and panted upstairs and flung himself face down on his double bed. His bed collapsed with a thunderous crash.

"That does it!" said Mrs. Pinkerton.

"Boarding school?" asked Mr. Pinkerton hopefully.

"Boarding school!" exclaimed Mrs. Pinkerton.

Pat O'Sullivan Pinkerton howled from the wreckage of his own birthday party. It was a sad cry, like that of a wounded jungle beast. "Oh no, no, no! They'll *starve* me!"

He was exactly thirteen years old, and his whole life was about to change.

The boarding school that Mr. and Mrs. Pinkerton had picked was President Coolidge School for Boys on Lake Brown Bear near the Canadian border. It was known to boys as a hockey school, which is to say that it was famous for its hockey teams. Its big rival across the frontier, Queen Mary School, was in the south of Canada on Lake Black Otter.

His mother and father had not picked a school famous for hockey because Pat was fast on ice. Not at all. They picked President Coolidge School because it was the only school they had written to that hadn't asked to see a photograph of their son. The school application form didn't go into such things as appetite or whether he was a normal-sized boy. The school asked little more than "to send your son along with plenty of warm woolen clothing."

Mr. and Mrs. Pinkerton loaded Pat in the back of their padded half-ton truck and drove north on opening day. It was an hour's trip, so they gave Pat a suitcase full of Southern fried chicken for company. Pat sat thinking only blue thoughts.

Whenever Pat O'Sullivan Pinkerton saw something for the first time, it looked like something to eat. He had to rub his eyes and shake his head to tune in the true picture. When he first looked at the main building of President Coolidge School, it looked like a giant strawberry shortcake — heavy on the strawberries and light on the shortcake. It was a lovely sight. It made him feel better. He then crossed his fingers and shook his head for a second look. The school turned into a severe building of red brick with white cement trim. He felt blue all over again.

It seemed to take his mother and father only a minute to join their hands, reach their arms around him, and kiss him goodby. Now he was all alone, abandoned along with 170 other boys.

He was assigned to Room No. 4 in C Dormitory. His first impression was that his room was made of pistachio ice cream with two fat chocolate cookies in the middle. He then noticed something he hadn't thought about — a roommate, who seemed to be a skinny chicken in a turtleneck sweater.

He rubbed and shook himself again and found he was in a plain apple-green room with two small polished brown tables. His roommate jumped to his feet, gave Pat O'Sullivan Pinkerton a rather curious look, then introduced himself. "My name is Jim Finger. My friends nicknamed me One-Point-Two-Five. I was going to take the lower bunk, but on second thought I'll take the upper. Welcome aboard. What position do you play?"

"I don't play any position," said Pat.

"I'm a second-year man," said Jim Finger. "You didn't ask, but they call me One-Point-Two-Five because I play goal on the hockey team. I'm the best goalie this school has ever seen. That's what they tell me. I allowed only a hair over one goal per game last season. One-Point-Two-Five average. Get it? Up Coolidge! Beat the Queen!" he shouted. And he danced a crazy jig, ending up with a split.

"What time is dinner?" Pat O'Sullivan Pinkerton asked.

"When the gong bongs," Jim Finger answered. "What's your name?"

"Pat O'Sullivan Pinkerton. I have no nickname," he added, blushing red at the lie. From babyhood he'd been called everything from Fats to Piggy, Tubby, Porky, and Amplegut.

"Porko von Popbutton," Jim Finger announced, grinning. He turned and stared out the window. "Great name. Rhymes with Ludwig van Beethoven, rhymes with Baron von Richthofen. Is there a touch of the Teuton in your ancestry?"

"My name is not Porko von Popbutton." Pat stamped his foot in anger. "It's Pat O'Sullivan Pinkerton! And there's no touch of anything. . . ." The gong bonged, and he lost his train of thought.

"Follow me, Porko," said Jim Finger. "I'll lead you to the horse trough."

The dining hall was in a pretty, white wood building with white shutters. It first looked to Pat O'Sullivan Pinkerton like a moist coconut layer cake, and he was so hungry he didn't bother to shake off the picture and correct it.

Then a terrible thing happened. Just as Pat reached the dining hall, the boys turned right and ran around to the back of the building and up a nasty, steep hill that was slippery and gnarled with roots. The top of this hill overlooked Lake Brown Bear. Once at the top the boys lined up facing the lake. There was a hushed silence; then they bowed and shouted, "BEAT THE QUEEN!" The cheer bounced off surrounding mountains, echoing three times:

BEAT THE QUEEN!
BEAT THE QUEEN!
BEAT THE QUEEN!

They plummeted down the hill helter-skelter — tripping, rolling, tumbling, screaming — picked themselves up, and barreled around the white building and back up the hill. They repeated the run not once, not twice, but three times. Pat O'Sullivan Pink-

erton, who had been up front at first, was now grunting and gasping, far behind. He was with four other new boys — all chubby, all red with rage, all fit to be tied.

The tables in the dining hall seated nine — eight boys, four on either side, and a master at the head. When the boys finally came to a stop at the dining-room door, they were assigned to their seats for eating. The fastest arrived first and, being the best athletes, they had the privilege of sitting at what was known as "Tilly's Table." Mr. George Tilghman was both headmaster of President Coolidge School and head coach of the hockey team. This was his table, and it was raised a step higher than the others. Jim Finger sat at "Tilly's Table," and he and the seven other boys wore superior faces as they looked down at the lesser tables filling up.

Pat O'Sullivan Pinkerton and the four bulgy leftovers — all shiny with sweat — were seated last. They were assigned to a table at the head of which sat Mademoiselle Régime, a French nurse who was head of the infirmary and supervisor of the kitchen. She looked tall and strict. She sat straight as a West Pointer, and she had a proud nose. Watching Pat O'Sullivan Pinkerton pull out two chairs to sit on, she slowly shook her head and said in an accent as French as soft Camembert cheese, "Zees weel nevair do, *mon ami.*[1] We must queekly theen

---

[1] **mon ami** (mŏn ä-mē′), my friend.

you down to one chair!" To Pat it sounded like the voice of doom.

Mademoiselle Régime served the boys. She gave Pat a dry lettuce leaf, a raw carrot, and an apple for dessert. He sneaked a look at other tables. A welcome-to-school dinner of steak with French-fried potatoes, salad, and pie à la mode was being eaten with a contented clicking of silverware. He quickly checked on the less fat fellows at his side. They were crunching the same miserable dinner as he — rabbit food. He, Pat O'Sullivan Pinkerton, was sitting at the *diet table!*

"How can I send a telegram?" Pat asked Jim Finger up in their room.

"Telegram?" One-Point-Two-Five asked. The grin spread across his thin face. He turned and looked out the window again. "Go see Mademoiselle Régime at the infirmary. She'll send one for you." He turned around to see Pat's reaction.

Pat stood up. He sat down. He grabbed his sheet of paper, and with a trembling hand he wrote in angry letters:

Dear Mom and Dad,

I warned you they'd starve me! Well, they're starving me! If you love me, send FOOD! Quick! Yours in haste, haste, HASTE!

Pat

He stuffed the note in the envelope, slobbered on the glue, pounded it shut, and waddled off to look for a mailbox.

When he came back, Jim Finger had finished unpacking and was hanging pop-art posters on the walls of the room, each with the message BEAT THE QUEEN! Pat noticed that Jim had selected the dresser with the uncracked mirror and had chosen all the wooden hangers in the closet, leaving Pat a few bent wire ones with sloping shoulders.

Young One-Point-Two-Five had unrolled an oilcloth diagram — six feet wide and four feet high — and had tacked it on the far wall of the room opposite the window. It represented the opening of a hockey-goal cage. He fastened a big bell to the wall in each corner of the diagram and attached two smaller bells — one just where the goalie's head would be when he was bent over in head-on position, the other where his skates would be in center-goal position. Each bell represented a difficult spot to defend in goaltending. Jim Finger then slowly put on his goalkeeper's equipment, all twenty-eight pounds of it — body pads, shoulder pads, arm pads, overstuffed leg pads, mammoth gloves — the works, except for skates. He took his stick and practiced a few splits in front of the diagram of the cage. He felt the limits of the diagram with his great gloves. Pat O'Sullivan Pinkerton was trying to ignore all this but without much success.

Jim Finger took six beanbags from his bottom dresser drawer, tossed them to Pat, and said, "O.K., Porko Baby, try ringing a bell with one of

these beanbags. Stand over there by the window. Wing 'em in, Fats Baby. Sneak up on me if you want. Wing 'em in. Be cunning, be fast, be mean! Ring those bells, Popbutton Baby, *ring those bells!*"

"What kind of beans are in these bags?" Pat asked.

Jim Finger exploded. "Well, that beats all!" he screamed. "You eat one of my bags, and I'll stick you like a pig, understand?"

"What do you think I am?" Pat O'Sullivan Pinkerton asked.

"You are what you are, all ten tons of you," Jim shouted back. "What kind of beans?" he muttered under his breath. "That's gotta beat all!"

At that exact moment Pat O'Sullivan Pinkerton had built the most ferocious anger of his entire life. He wound up like a windmill and started underhanding beanbags at Jim Finger as hard as he could.

One-Point-Two-Five, talking aloud to himself, stopped everything. He blocked the first beanbag with his body, quickly freezing it to his chest with his gloved hand. He stopped a low one with a half split, smothering it on the floor when it bounced out before him. He followed every move Pat made, keeping an eye on the beanbag. When Jim sidestepped or sideglided across the mouth of the goal, he shifted his stick instantly to have a quick hand free to cover the portion of the goal left open.

"Watch him, Jim Baby, watch that position," Jim Finger said aloud to himself, keeping up the steady chatter. "Don't lose it, Baby; he's fat but he's fast; he's dumb but he's dangerous; great stop, Jimbo Baby; great hands, great movement. Let that one go, Jimbo," he said of a poor throw. "He's mad and he's bad; can't even hit the cage. He's a child and he's wild. He's sneakin' up on you, Jimbo Baby. Position; *eyes!* He's up close; watch 'im, Jimbo, *stick check!*"

Pat O'Sullivan Pinkerton let out a howl.

From way up close he'd tried to fling one into a low corner. Just as the beanbag left his hand, Jim Finger batted it with his goalie stick, sending it off to one side of the room, and also batting four of Pat's fat fingers, including the thumb.

"Sorry about that, Porko," Jim Finger said.

Pat's face was a map of pain. He was shaking, wringing, and twisting. Nothing seemed to help.

Jim Finger went to his dresser, opened the top drawer, and pulled out a box with a bright Confederate flag on its top. "Here, Fats Baby, my old Uncle Mint Julep airmailed me this as a good-by present. It's two whole pounds of genuine rich pralines imported from the very heart of the Southland."

Pat O'Sullivan Pinkerton snatched the box with his sore red fingers and ran grunting out of the room.

"Phew!" Jim Finger said aloud to no one. "Some of those fat babies are fast. He must have pitched softball."

Pat O'Sullivan Pinkerton returned a few minutes later with brown sugar rounding out the corners of his mouth. His hand seemed better, but now he was limping. On his way out of the building he had run into a frantic indoor hockey game up and down one of the wider linoleum halls. The players were using small hockey sticks with felt-covered blades and a light wooden puck. They wore sneakers. He'd tried to dance his way through but had been whacked on the shins a few times.

"What kind of a dumb school is this anyhow?" he asked Jim Finger.

"Watch your tongue, new boy," Jim Finger said from his upper bunk. "This just so happens to be *the* school that this year will beat *the* unbeatable Queen Mary School. And we're going to beat those Canadian babies on the shimmering fields of Grand Old Lake Black Otter. That is to say, we're going to beat those Canadian babies right in their own shimmering backyard. The game is away this year."

"How'd you make out last year?" Pat asked.

There was silence from the upper bunk.

"I said, how did we make out last year against the Queen?" Pat repeated.

"Listen straight, Porko, and try to get it right the first time. We don't speak about that game, understand? We played eight games last year and won seven. They call me One-Point-Two-Five, and I told you why.

"I had seven shutouts; then we played the Queen. Now button your lip, Popbutton, you're spoiling my daydreams."

A bell rang and the lights went out. Pat O'Sullivan Pinkerton undressed and went to bed. Slowly his brain pondered the problem in arithmetic. It wasn't exactly his best subject; he had no best subject. He finally figured out President Coolidge had lost 10–0 — *ten to zero!*

And the school hoped to win this year?

What a dumb school!

And who cared anyway?

Jim Finger held daily beanbag sessions with Pat O'Sullivan Pinkerton in their room. Pat found them boring, but he was now totally under Jim Finger's thumb — his fat slave. Jim was two years older than Pat but shorter. Jim also had the second-highest marks in the entire school, which did not seem to make him more amiable.

If Pat claimed to have no nicknames his first day at school, he now had the biggest collection on the campus. Porko von Popbutton was the most used. Mademoiselle Régime called him Ben Appetite or Freddy Fromage, depending on her mood. His English teacher, who happened to be English, called him Sir Cumference Girth. Some boys tried on Ample Andy for size — the name lasted two weeks. It was followed by Blimpy Splitseam, Mack O'Roany,

Fatty Unbuckle, John Swillerton Hogwash, and Oink-Oink Morchow.

Late one afternoon — feeling sad and fed up, walking alone, kicking the devil out of some poor stone in his path — he heard a soft voice call out, "Pat."

He had become so unused to hearing his own name, he didn't even think to turn around.

"Pat Pinkerton," he heard, louder.

He still didn't react.

"Pat O'Sullivan Pinkerton," the voice came back. His complete name tweaked his brain. He turned slowly, suspiciously, and to his great embarrassment found he was being spoken to by Mr. George Tilghman, the headmaster.

He straightened up quickly and blushed. "Excuse me. I didn't recognize my own name, sir, I guess."

"Poor Pat," Mr. Tilghman said, "has it come to that?"

"I beg your pardon, sir. What do you mean, sir?"

"Oh, nothing, Pat," said Mr. Tilghman. "I have been going over a list of prospects lately and have decided you'd make a fine manager for the hockey team."

"Me?" Pat asked aghast, pointing to himself as if still not certain who he was.

"I know you could do it," said Mr. Tilghman. "Anyway, you'd be shown as you went along. Would you like the job?"

Pat stood quite stunned, then broke into a half-moon grin. "Would I!" he shouted. "Oh thank you, thank you, thank you!"

"You are welcome. And if you do your job well, you'll get your letter at the end of the season just like any other good player."

"Thank you again, sir. I'll do my best," Pat said. He waddled off, walking on clouds, blimplike, to tell Jim Finger. He found him in his upper bunk.

"Guess who's the new hockey manager," he boomed.

Jim Finger squirmed uneasily in his bunk, as though his entire life had been disturbed by the dumbness of the question. "Some clown, no doubt," he sighed, without bothering to look up from his magazine. "Tilly always picks a pathetic boobnick who feels sorry for himself." He rolled over in his bunk, facing the wall. "Now button it, Porko. You bore me." He yawned outrageously.

Pat came crashing back to earth with a thump. He looked as sad as a broken umbrella. He walked over to the window and stared blankly into space. The low winter sun hit him squarely in the eyes and made him turn around. He then saw an amazing thing. His shadow was cast on Jim Finger's diagram of a hockey goal cage, and it completely filled the opening. He looked at Jim Finger, who was still facing the wall, deep in his magazine. He tiptoed up close to the goal cage, moving his arms up and down and his legs out sideways. His shadow shrunk quite a bit, but it still left little space for a player to shoot at. He sat at his table and scribbled a letter home. He asked his parents to send him a complete set of goalie equipment in his size.

"Another S O S for CARE packages?" Jim Finger asked, rolling over in the upper bunk.

"Maybe," Pat O'Sullivan Pinkerton answered. He sealed the envelope rather secretly — like a spy — and sneaked off to mail it special delivery.

The package arrived the day after hockey practice started. Pat rushed up to try it on. He stood admiring his shadow against Jim Finger's hockey-goal diagram. The pads fattened him out even more. He was busy testing the moves he'd seen Jim Finger make so often when Jim walked in, totally unexpected. He took one look at Pat and pretended to faint. He reeled around the room, grasped his throat, and crumpled upon the floor, moaning, "Good grief, it's the Blob, the Blob lives, the Blob *lives!*"

"Very funny," Pat said. Then in a tough voice, protected by some thirty-five pounds of padding, he added, "O.K., One-Point-Two-Five, get your beanbags. Stand over there by that window and wing 'em in. Come on, Jimbo Baby, *ring those bells!*"

"You?" Jim Finger shouted scornfully. "Porko von Popbutton? Don't waste my time, you manager!" Then he paused.

He looked curiously at Pat standing there in front of his goal diagram. He looked at him with that circular motion of the head that Pat had noticed when he first met Jim. He pulled open his bottom dresser drawer, took out the beanbags, and said simply, "Ready, Porko?"

"Ring those bells, Jimbo Baby." He bent over in position — knees flexed — limbering up, fat and loose. "Be fast, be mean!"

Jim fired the first six in rapid succession. Pat looked clumsy, but no bells rang. Jim threw six more. Still no bells. Six more. Six sloppy stops but no bells. Pat O'Sullivan Pinkerton started the chatter. "Great moves, Pat Baby. He's got class and he's fast, but he can't pass the mass. Position, Patsy Boy. Eyes. He's quick and you're slick." He did a seam-ripping split and flopped on a beanbag. "Fall on it, Pinky Baby. That's the way. Smother it, Pinky Boy. . . ."

"Watch that Pinky stuff," Jim Finger interrupted. "There's just one Finger in hockey, and that's old One-Point-Two-Five."

"Sorry, Jimbo Baby. Sorry, Jimbo Boy. Wing 'em in, Baby!"

"I'm sneakin' up, Fats," said Jim. He tried two up close, but somehow Pat managed to block them. He covered so much of the area he didn't have to move much. Just then Jim cocked his head and asked no one, "Didn't I hear the gong bong?" Pat turned sideways for a second. Beanbags whizzed past him. Four bells rang — one in each corner of the goal cage.

"See that?" said Jim Finger. "No concentration. You'll never make it!"

"Never make what?" Pat grumbled, furious with himself.

Jim slowly put the beanbags away, shaking his head from side to side. He vaulted into his upper bunk. "You'll never make it," he repeated. He let out a huge yawn of boredom and snuggled his head in his pillow. "No concentration. Some kid will peel a chocolate bar up in the audience and zing, *red light,* score!" He pretended to sleep for a while, then leaned out of his bunk. "Say, Porko, can you skate?" he asked.

"I get by," Pat answered.

There was another pause.

"What I mean to say," said Jim, "is that there are two little ponds with grass pushing up through the ice in the woods beyond the lake. They're known as the Cub Ponds. You might want to sneak up there by yourself and break in that great goalie stuff. It looks too new the way it is, too stiff."

"Thanks, I will," said Pat.

"And I'll work you out some more here," Jim added.

Pat felt overwhelmed. It was the first nice thing Jim Finger had ever said to him. It made his day. He removed his new pads, took a tin of plum pudding from his secret store of goodies, and shuffled off to celebrate.

The hockey season followed the pattern set the year before. The first seven games were played against the five toughest school teams in the United States and two college freshman teams. President Coolidge School swept them all impressively.

Pat O'Sullivan Pinkerton made an adequate manager. Jim Finger gave him severe shaping-up talks in their room the morning of each game away from school, making certain none of the players' needs would be overlooked — from complete uniforms to soap and towels. Hockey players are tough to get along with the day of a game. Pat made a fine fat target to pick on, great for relieving tension. He took a beating from the whole team every game. He became fair at packing and unpacking the team bus. He got a secret thrill out of packing his own goalie equipment along with the team's, but that was as close as he ever got to the ice. One bonus the job offered that he hadn't known about was that he was responsible for providing sweet hot tea with lemon and hot chocolate between periods for the players. He was also in charge of energy boosters for players during the game — glucose candy bars, fig newtons, raisin crackers, and oatmeal cookies. Considering he was a nonplayer, he managed to cram enough energy boosters down himself each game for a person to ride up the Eiffel Tower on a bicycle. He liked games away from school because there was usually a good meal served, without Mademoiselle Régime.

For weeks President Coolidge was building up its fever pitch to meet Queen Mary. BEAT THE QUEEN had been carved in snow in letters huge enough to cover their biggest mountain. Bonfires and pep rallies, flags, posters, painted bed sheets — everything proclaimed that this was to be *victory* year. This was curious because in the twenty-nine-year history of the encounter, Queen Mary had won twenty-nine games, President Coolidge zero. Twenty-nine drubbings. Twenty-nine shutouts!

The team was greeted at Queen Mary School with politeness and indifference. One of the Canadian youths who acted as guide asked, "What's the name of your school again, old boy? President Coolidge? Curious name. That must be in the States, eh, old boy? We thought you chaps only played *field* hockey down there." The visitors, already angry enough, got boiling mad.

Pat O'Sullivan Pinkerton ate the biggest meal of his lifetime. With all the fattening food at his table left untouched by his teammates, he let himself go all out. He was munching on his eleventh cream puff when a voice behind him with a French accent said, "Zee cream poofs are *délicieux,*[2] are zey not, *mon ami?*" Thinking Mademoiselle Régime had suddenly appeared to haunt him, he coughed a mouthful halfway across the dining hall. He turned to find a small, smiling French-Canadian boy. He decided he'd eaten enough and leaned back to catch his breath.

---

[2] **délicieux** (dā'lĭ-syû), delicious.

The setting for the game was magnificent and the ice surface perfect. The sun was on one end of the rink because this was the last game of the season; winter was nearly over and the sun was higher in the sky. The days were also getting warmer. It was just about freezing temperature in the sun and not much cooler in the shade.

In a display of rash contempt for President Coolidge, Queen Mary sent a four-man line up front from the first face-off, leaving only a defenseman and the goalie to protect its goal. The team's style of play was European. It passed beautifully in fast patterns, avoiding much body contact. In the first period the puck was entirely at the President Coolidge end of the rink. When the American boys got the puck, the Canadians were able to skate backward as fast as the Americans could bring it up the ice. President Coolidge had a tough time even bringing the puck to midrink. As soon as it had, Queen Mary would quickly take it away and mount its dazzling four-man attack.

Jim was having a busy afternoon. Not only was he being bombarded from all angles, but his defensemen were backed up near the mouth of his cage, making it difficult to follow the puck.

And Jim Finger was superb!

He was having a brilliant *on* day. Not only did he handle every shot, he never lost control of the puck after a stop. Then, just as the horn blew ending the first period, an accident

144

happened. A low, stinging shot bounced from his stick to the point of his jaw, right on the button. Jim Finger fell forward, flat on his face and on the puck. He was out cold. Gus, the team's trainer, worked feverishly on him behind a circular hedge of players, then signaled for a stretcher. A spontaneous standing ovation by both schools escorted poor Jim Finger off the ice.

As he was carried near Headmaster Tilghman, Jim Finger stirred on his stretcher. He raised his head slightly and muttered in a raspy voice, "Send in Porko von Popbutton."

Headmaster Tilghman looked at him sadly, then looked at the trainer. "Take good care of this fine boy, Gus!" he ordered.

Seeing his message wasn't getting through, Jim Finger propped himself up on his elbows and repeated forcefully, "Send in Pat O'Sullivan Pinkerton." He fell back flat on the stretcher from the effort.

It was the first time Pat had heard Jim say his real name. He opened his mouth, and out fell a huge oatmeal cooky he'd managed to wedge in. "He knows my name," Pat mumbled stupidly.

Headmaster Tilghman looked from Jim to Pat, then back to Jim again. Then he, too, gave Pat that curious circular look, his eyes rolling around Pat's outline. "Have you pads, Pat, by any chance?" he asked.

"Yes, sir," Pat O'Sullivan Pinkerton answered.

"Well, get 'em on fast," the headmaster said. "Help him," he shouted to two players.

Pat went to the locker room. He was too nervous and excited to put on his thirty-five pounds of goalie equipment all by himself. On this winter day in Canada sweat was streaming off his round face. "I've got to hold 'em for Jim," he muttered aloud. "Got to lock it up tight for Old Jimbo." Then he warmed up his patter, still sitting there on a locker-room bench, two players struggling with his skates, one working feverishly on each of his fat feet. "Great moves, Pat Baby. Great eyes, Pat Boy. They're quick as a jet, but they can't find the net. *Position,* Patterino. They've got class and they're fast, but they can't pass the mass. Great stop, Patsy Baby. Smother it, Patsy Boy! *Concentrate!*" he screamed. At his feet his helpers looked at each other and slowly shook their heads in total disbelief. The one-minute warning whistle blew. Too stunned to move, the two players sat on the floor and watched Pat waddle off into the bright outdoors, his wobbly ankles flopping inward then outward, the steady chatter pouring from his lips.

An explosion of Canadian laughter greeted his appearance.

The President Coolidge School boys, used to seeing Pat, were at first puzzled by the laughter, then furious. They'd been badly outplayed in the first period. They'd been kidded from the moment they hit the Queen Mary campus. Their star goalie, to whom they owed so much, had been knocked cold. The players headed for their positions with fire in their eyes.

The first time the four-man Canadian line streaked toward the American goal, two body checks sent two Canadians off their feet, crashing into the rink boards. Seconds later the puck was at the Canadian end for the first time in the game. The President Coolidge team was clicking and playing with all-out fury. It kept the puck at the Canadian end and got off a few fine shots but didn't score.

Pat O'Sullivan Pinkerton, that great hot blob of calories, stoked with energy, eyes fixed on the puck, was radiating steamy clouds of chatter in the brisk Canadian air. "Jim Finger knew my name all the time!" he shouted aloud to nobody. *"Eyes,* Patsy Baby. *Position,* Patsy Boy! *Concentrate!"*

Suddenly from the mess of players around the opposite goal, that four-man Canadian line appeared, flying down the rink, zipping the puck in clicking passes, one to three to two to four, as they charged forward to test Pat O'Sullivan Pinkerton.

Pat's defensemen backed up in front of his cage, and the American forward line scrambled back in panic. A defenseman blocked the first shot; then Pat stopped three hard ones in a row before flopping on a fourth, which he gathered up under him like a fat hen squashing a chick. "Smother it, Pat Baby. Freeze it, Pat Boy!" Following the face-off he received a barrage of vicious slap shots from up close that stung him — arms, body, and thighs. He stopped them all. He was as clumsy as ever, splitting, flopping, side-sprawling, and shrieking to himself. The ice under him and in the goal crease — a small outlined area in front of his cage — was turning to slush from his great heat.

They didn't score.

President Coolidge finally stole the puck and nursed it to the Canadian end of the rink with passes and desperate skating. Then a whistle stopped the game. A referee had noticed a bit of snow piled up in front of the American goal. It wasn't Pat's fault. He wasn't even aware of it, but it was against the rules. A Canadian boy skated out with a snow shovel and cleared the mouth of the goal. Pat O'Sullivan Pinkerton found himself standing in a slight indentation, down a bit lower than the other players.

After the face-off the Americans kept the puck up at the Canadian end for a long time. Pat O'Sullivan Pinkerton — soaked with sweat, alone at his end of the rink, chatting wildly to himself in the sun — was startled by an ominous *thunk* sound right under his feet. At the same time he seemed to feel his right leg grow somewhat longer than his left. He looked to the audience on either side of the rink. All eyes were on the action at the Canadian end. He kept up the chatter.

Pat withstood one more long assault on his goal before the horn blew, ending the period. He sighed with relief, happy to skate out of the sun, rest his sore ankles, and grab a well-earned snack.

After the face-off the Queen Mary School players grabbed the puck and sent all five men up the ice, leaving only their goalie alone, standing back in Pat's indentation. The third period rapidly became a repeat of the first period — all the action at Pat's end. The American boys, swamped by the faster-skating Canadians, didn't seem able to put anything together to get the puck up the ice. Pat was taking terrible punishment. His patter became gibberish. He was flopping and floundering in his cage like a wounded sea lion.

But they didn't score.

Then it happened.

There were just seconds to go, and Headmaster Tilghman sent in his best front line with shouted instructions to get the puck out of there!

They did.

Three body checks sent three Canadians sprawling. Suddenly the whole American team was scrambling up the rink toward the sunlit goal. An easy shot went wide of the goal. The Canadians chased back up to their own end. Eleven boys were fighting up there in the sunshine. It was the Canadian goalie's turn to take a pounding. There was a free puck in front of the goal. A Canadian player shot it toward the American end. It bounced off another player and came to a stop midrink. There was a thunderous crack. The Canadian goalie, two Ca-nadian players, the American center, and the left wing slowly went down together on a raft of ice into the dark waters of Lake Black Otter. The referee and linesmen rushed to help. There was another roaring crack, and down they went too. Players scattered off the ice, vaulting the rink boards like panicky bullfighters. The sunken players and officials pushed each other back up on the ice and wriggled to the rink boards, where they were hauled in.

But out there, with his eyes still fixed on the puck, was Pat O'Sullivan Pinkerton. He was alone — just Pat, the puck, half a rink, and a great sunny hole he'd helped melt. The clock showed seven seconds to go.

Bruised and battered, Pat O'Sulli-van Pinkerton continued his patter, softly at first, then louder and louder. "Come on, Pat Baby. Come on, Pat Boy. Win it, Pat Baby. Take all the marbles, Pat Boy." Skating on those ridiculous wobbly ankles, a look of ferocious concentration on his shiny sweaty face, he headed up the rink, ice cracking in spider-web patterns beneath him. "Do it, Patsy Baby. *Do it, Patsy Boy!*" With the taped heel of his clumsy goalie stick he caressed the puck, lining it up with the Queen Mary goal. He shot the puck — a flip shot. There was a *whack* and a *splash,* and Pat O'Sullivan Pinkerton went straight down like a stone. All eyes watched the puck as it followed a rainbow course, wobbling end over end off the ice, over the water, and

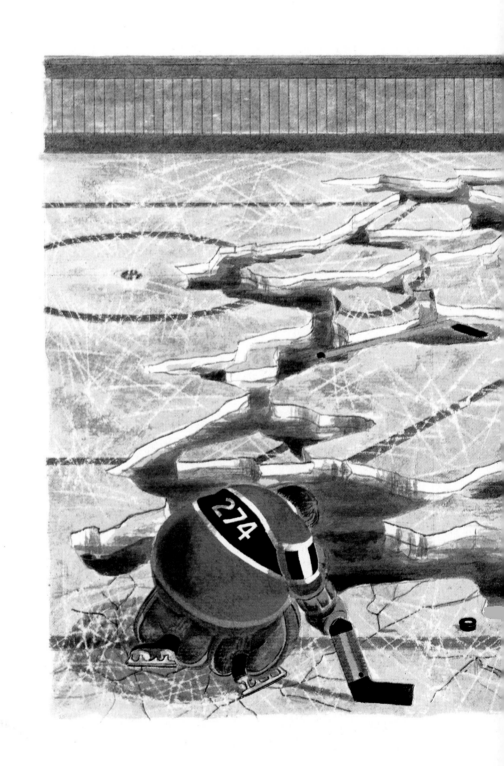

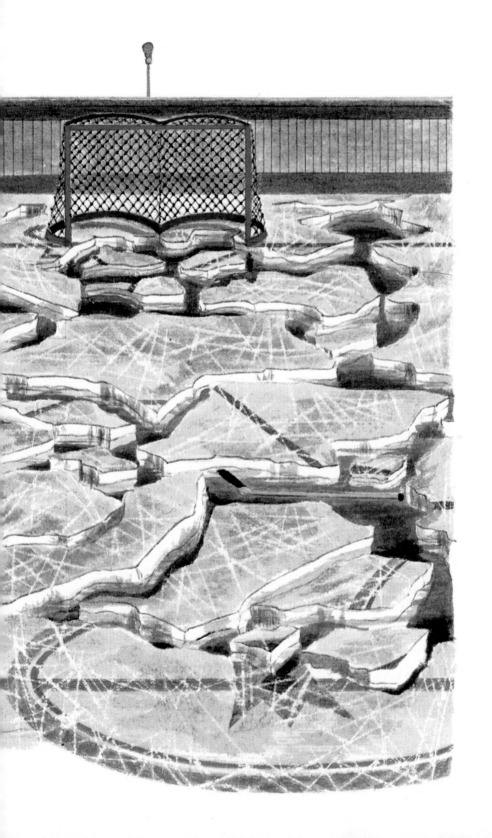

right into the net. The cage slowly leaned over backward, the soles of its icy feet rising above the surface. It sunk to the bottom of Lake Black Otter, carrying in its net one regulation hockey puck.

The horn blew.

The game was over.

President Coolidge School — 1.

Queen Mary School — 0.

The audience, open-mouthed and strangely silent, turned to look for Pat O'Sullivan Pinkerton.

There he was, floating in the lake, tummy up — spouting ice water like a whale, cool at last!

Deafening applause disturbed his comfort, and at that moment Porko von Popbutton was no more.

Pat O'Sullivan Pinkerton arrived at President Coolidge School early the following year. Since the afternoon of his triumph on Lake Black Otter his whole life had changed. He now thought and dreamed only of hockey. He had lost 125 pounds and was down to a fairly trim 150. He was assigned to Room No. 8 in B Dormitory. He hung his suits on the wooden hangers in the closet and put his shirts, bean-bags, and other things in the dresser with the good mirror. He hung an oilcloth diagram of a hockey goal with six bells on the wall opposite the window. He tacked up some bright posters saying BEAT THE QUEEN in art-nouveau lettering on the walls. He chose the lower bunk for his own, and he was lying there considering his status when in walked a tiny, skinny chap, looking quite frightened.

Pat jumped to his feet and introduced himself. "My name is Pat O'Sullivan Pinkerton. My friends nicknamed me Number One. Welcome aboard. What position do you play?"

"I don't play any position," the small chap said nervously.

"I'm a second-year man," said Pat O'Sullivan Pinkerton. "You didn't ask, but they call me Number One because I play goal on the hockey team. I'm the best goalie this school has ever seen — except for the great Jim Finger. That's what they tell me. I was the first goalie ever to score a goal. I was the first and only player ever to score against Queen Mary, on the first team ever to beat Queen Mary. Number One, *El Numero Uno* (ĕl nōō′mā-rō ōō′nō), get it? Up Coolidge! BEAT THE QUEEN!" he shouted. He danced a crazy jig, ending up with a split. "What's your name?"

"Billy Putnam Rigby. I have no nickname," he added, blushing red at the lie. From babyhood he'd been called everything from Gnat to Mouse to Shrimp.

"Teeny Puny Digby," Pat O'Sullivan Pinkerton announced, grinning. He turned and stared out the window. "Great name. Rhymes with Lilliputian Pigmy, rhymes with Peewee Button Twiggy. Is there a lick of the limey in your lineage?"

"My name is not Teeny Puny

Digby." Billy stamped his foot in anger. "It's Billy Putnam Rigby! And there's no lick of anything. . . ." The gong bonged.

"See that?" Pat interrupted. "I didn't even twitch. I used to jump at the sound of that bell like a punchy boxer. I'm cured. Follow me," he said. "I'll show you to the horse trough."

DISCUSSION

1. Why had Pat's parents chosen President Coolidge School for Pat?
2. What job did Mr. Tilghman offer Pat? What was Pat's reaction to the offer? What was his reaction after he had told Jim about it?
3. What did Pat notice that made him decide to ask his parents for a set of goalie equipment?
4. What gave Pat the opportunity to score the winning goal?
5. What was Pat's nickname the second year? Why?
6. In what ways did Pat imitate Jim the second year? In what other way had Pat changed?
7. What did Jim mean when he said, "Watch that Pinky stuff. . . . There's just one Finger in hockey. . . ."?
8. Why do you think Jim encouraged Pat to practice with his new goalie outfit?
9. Why do you think the guide from Queen Mary School asked, "What's the name of your school?"
10. When did Pat first find out that Jim knew his real name? Why was that fact important to the story?
11. What two factors were involved in weakening the ice in front of Pat's goal?
12. Jim would not talk about last year's game with Queen Mary School. Why? Do you agree with Jim that we should not discuss our failures or disappointments? Why or why not?
13. Why do people use nicknames so much of the time? How did Jim's nickname and the fact that his team had scored seven shutouts before the Queen Mary game enable Pat to figure out the score of last year's game?

14. Pat imitated Jim when he played goalie. How might the constant chatter be of help to a goaltender?

15. Do you think Pat's parents were glad they had sent Pat to President Coolidge School? Why do you think that?

AUTHOR

William Pène du Bois has been a writer and an illustrator of children's books for over thirty years. The son of the well-known American painter and art critic, Guy Pène du Bois, and Florence Sherman du Bois, a designer of children's clothes, Mr. du Bois was educated in France. Later when he returned to America, he hoped to go to Harvard University. When he learned there was not money enough for him to go to *any* college, he announced calmly that he would spend his life writing and illustrating children's books. And he has done just that! At nineteen his first book, *Giant Otto,* was published. Since then he has not stopped writing and illustrating his own books and illustrating those of other authors. The day he went into the army, he gave his publisher a book; and the day he came out, five years later, he presented his publisher with *The Twenty-One Balloons,* which won the Newbery Medal in 1947.

"Beat the Queen" was adapted from Mr. du Bois's book, *Porko von Popbutton.* The third in his series of books on the "seven deadly sins," it is a hilarious tale about gluttony. The theme of his latest and fourth book in the series, *Call Me Bandicoot,* is stinginess.

THE GOALIE
WHO SCORED A GOAL

by Stan Fischler

Ever since R. F. Smith drew up the first rules for hockey in the late 1800s, it has been generally accepted that a goalie's place is in that abbreviated area between the posts. In fact, just about every man who has ever laced on the forty-pound leather pads has done his goaltending in close proximity to the cage. There is, however, an exception to this, and the following brief story tells of a goalie who ranged far afield with a rather spectacular result.

Chuck Rayner, who tended goal in New York — first for the old Americans and later for the Rangers — harbored an obsessive desire to spring away from his nets, dipsy doodle through the enemy's defense, and score a goal against his opposite number on the other side of the rink.

During World War II, Rayner's fantasy was realized. Playing for an all-star Royal Canadian Army team, he was guarding the goal when a ten-man scramble developed behind his net. Suddenly the puck squirted free and slid temptingly in the direction of the other goal. What's more, there was nobody between Rayner and the puck.

The bush-browed goalie got the message. With a five-stride head start on his pursuers Rayner charged down the ice. His opponents were so startled by the maneuver that they just stopped in their tracks to watch. What they saw was a phenomenon: Rayner skated to within firing distance and whacked the puck into the net. A goalie had scored a goal! As of this writing, the feat has never been duplicated in big-league hockey.

GOOD SPORTSMANSHIP

Good sportsmanship we hail, we sing,
 It's always pleasant when you spot it.
There's only one unhappy thing:
 You have to lose to prove you've got it.

RICHARD ARMOUR

The Dolphin Girl

by Ethel Parton

The wild slopes of Mount Pelion (pē′lē-ŏn) fall away into the wilder crags of the coastline, and these in turn at one end drop sharply to the curving dip of a long beach. Just there, upon a shelf of rock, stood two cottages, one firmly built and comfortable, the other a tiny wattled hut. In front of them two men were seated and a young girl stood, each busy in a different way. They were working fast before the late afternoon sun would sink behind the ridges and the golden light change suddenly to purple shadows. Asphalion (äs-fä′lē-ŏn), the old fisherman, was mending a net. Scyllias (skĭl-lē′ŭs), the diver, was splicing the handle of a knife. Hydna (ē′dnə), his daughter, twirled a distaff, and, as she sang, her voice floated out clearly across the low waves lapping on the shore and the shining water beyond. She sang:

Dolphin, Dolphin, strong the tide —
Dolphin O! Dolphin O!
O good Dolphin, let me ride —
Strong the waters flow.
Far and long the homeward track;
Take me, Dolphin, on your back —
Dolphin, Dolphin O!

Old Asphalion chuckled: "Hear to that girl of yours! — if you can call her a girl at all when you've brought her up like a boy. Spin she can, but she can't even do that woman fashion. Has to twirl her thread to a comical old song the sailors sing. *She's* no girl. How do you expect to find a husband for her?"

"I don't want a husband," said Hydna, laughing. "I'm going to be Father's partner."

"And a good little partner too, Asphalion," said Scyllias. "If the gods had left me either my wife or my son, it would have been different. Her mother would have wished her brought up like other girls, I suppose, and I couldn't have said her nay. But she died and then my three boys the same year — such a year! I couldn't bear the place where it all happened any longer. I left Scione (skē-ōn′ē) and came here with only my girl. But from the day her last brother went, the child declared she was going to take his place. She couldn't do that — nobody could — but she's been as much son as daughter to me ever

157

since. She's happier that way, and so am I."

"Surely you didn't mind my joking about her, Scyllias; you know I'm almost as fond of her as I am of my own Chloe (kloi). She's a good child and a sheer wonder in the water. She'll be as good a swimmer as you before long."

"She's as good a swimmer now and diver too, as far as her strength allows. There's no other difference," said Scyllias. "She has the skill."

Hydna flushed with pleasure. Her father did not often praise her, and he had never given her such praise as that, for he was known far and near as Scyllias of Scione; and in all the lands of Greece there was no such famous diver and swimmer as he.

The purple shadows swept swiftly from the west. She stepped indoors to leave her distaff, then leaped lightly down the rocks to meet Chloe, Asphalion's thirteen-year-old grandchild, who was coming along the beach carrying a shrimp net in one hand and a basket in the other. She flourished the shrimp net and quickened her pace as Hydna strolled to meet her.

The two girls, chattering as they walked along, had been occupied with each other rather than anything less close at hand; but when they climbed to the flat rock before the cottages, they saw that both Scyllias and Asphalion were gazing intently out to sea. They also looked.

"Oh!" cried Chloe. "What is it? What is it? I never saw so many ships!"

"Very many and coming fast, but I think they are not all in sight," said Scyllias. "No, not yet. I wish there were no more."

"A fair breeze and from the right quarter," said Asphalion. "We shall soon know."

"Soon, now," said Scyllias through tightened lips.

"Is it the Persians?" asked Hydna, but she knew even before Scyllias answered her.

"Yes, it is the Persians, the great fleet of their great King Xerxes (zûrk'sēz), coming to conquer Greece. Neither his army by land nor his ships by sea will touch us here in Magnesia (măg-nē'zhə), for the state gave earth and water in token of submission when he sent his herald to demand them. But every Grecian state and city that refused, he will plunder and destroy if he can and, most of all, Athens."

"Yes," agreed Old Asphalion, "we are safe here, but I should not be proud of that safety if I were younger."

"I am not proud of it," said Scyllias. "No, I am not proud of it. I wish I were with the Athenians. They will fight."

The Persian ships, stately as a flock of great golden swans, numerous as a school of monstrous

golden fishes, with the beams of the setting sun full on their glistening sides and brilliant sails, swept splendidly on, heading straight toward the watchers across a golden sea. More and more and again more they came, and still they came. Asphalion, checking off on shaking fingers, tried to count them and could not. Hydna tried too.

"There are hundreds," she said at last in a voice of awe. "More than five hundred — six — seven — I lost count."

"Look, Asphalion!" Scyllias exclaimed. "Surely those nearer ships are standing in so close they can only mean to cast anchor. The others too, I think, or they would bear away more to the south."

Even as he spoke, one ship that had outdistanced all the others let go her anchor with a rattle and a splash. It was a good place to anchor for the night, off the one stretch of sandy shore in many miles of rough and dangerous coast. The voices of the sailors and the sharp commands of officers rose clearly to their ears. Dusk came and darkness and stars, and out on the water, lights that seemed as many as the stars before the ships lay each in its assigned place. One inner row of vessels was drawn up close and moored to the shore. The rest swung at anchor, eight long rows of them, one beyond the other, reaching far out upon the soft blackness of a sea as quiet as a pond, for the breeze had gone down with the sun.

At last Asphalion and Chloe turned in upon their rough beds of heaped dried seaweed inside the little hut where old Eunoe (ĕv-noi′), Chloe's grandmother, too dim of sight and dull of hearing to understand what was going on, had settled herself long before and was snoring placidly. Remembering what a terrible danger to Greece lay in that great fleet outside, Chloe sighed and thought sorrowfully that with such a worry on her mind she would never, never get to sleep — and fell asleep at once.

Hydna, too, troubled as she was, was young and soon slept. She waked to feel the hut quivering, Scyllias pulling her by the shoulder, and to hear the high screaming of a great wind.

"Wake! Wake!" her father shouted to her. "Leave your bed, child — up and out! The gods themselves are fighting for the Greeks — with tempest and hurricane they are fighting. Never again will there be such a sight to see. Already a score of the Persian ships are broken away, and well I know the reefs on which they will be shattered — the Ovens and the Three Fangs and a nameless hundred more! It is the Great Wind from the Hellespont[1]

---

[1] **Hellespont** (hĕl′ĭs-pŏnt′), the ancient name for the Dardanelles.

that is blowing. Many a northeast gale have I known but none such as this!"

Outside, under a ragged sky, the black, wild night changed slowly to a gray, wild dawn. The shrieking wind never stopped for a moment, and for miles and miles the rocks and reefs of a fierce lee shore lay waiting, smothered in foam. The best hope, almost the only hope, for the Persians was to ride out the tempest where they were, if only anchors would not drag and ropes would hold. The sailors, by frantic labor, had beached most of their inner line of ships and a few others before the storm had reached its full fury and had drawn them far up on the sand. But the greater number still strained at their moorings. Some had thrown over extra ropes and anchors and lay doubly held, head to the gale, with a fair promise of safety. Some were breaking loose and scudding like leaves before the blast. In almost a moment they passed beyond the long stretch of yellow sand and whirled to their crashing doom on distant rocks. More would go. But most were yet holding fast.

"A knife!" shouted Scyllias suddenly. "Not for nothing am I Scyllias the Swimmer! A slash of my blade across those taut ropes, and they will snap like threads!"

He sprang back into the cottage and was out in an instant. Beside him came Hydna, and in her hand, too, a knife flashed.

"No, no!" said Scyllias.

"Partners, Father!" answered Hydna, and together they ran to an overhanging rock, and together they leaped — leaped with a long, clean dive that carried them, like otters, far under and out before they rose.

In their terror and confusion the Persian crews did not discover this new enemy. The two sleek, dark heads moving among the heaving waves and straining ships were not easily noticed and were mistaken when they were seen for those of two sailors swept overboard. Rope after rope parted from the ships that had seemed securest, but still they were not discovered. The cut was never made on the surface of the water. There was no gleam of a bright blade. Even the dark heads were seldom seen. They swam underwater, struck, and vanished.

At first they were together, but that was only for a short time. In the dimness of the dawn and the wildness of the sea, they would have been separated even if they had been unwilling; but it was soon clear that if they were able to do their dangerous work at all, they could do more by each acting separately. They spared no breath to tell each other so; when each lost sight and knowledge of the other, neither sought for the partner who was missing but kept doggedly on alone, counting on no further help. Nor would Scyllias let himself wonder if his daughter had vanished forever under the waves, nor Hydna if her father, the strong swimmer, the Diver of Scione, had gone down for the last time and was rolling limp and helpless among churned sands and tattered seaweed deep below the screaming turmoil. Such thoughts might weaken hearts that needed all their courage. Hydna only knew she was alone in a gray, fierce world of wind and water and warships, all in violent and frantic motion, and that she was fighting: fighting every instant for her own life and for something greater than her own life, for Greece, and that she must keep on fighting to the end.

Every moment brought its own peril, and there was no pause. As she cut the cable of one ship, another, torn loose by the storm or freed by her father's knife, bore down upon her so furiously that she was almost caught and crushed between the two. Only by a desperate dive did she escape, and even then the ships came thunderously together, the crashing keels scarcely farther from her upflung feet as she dived than the low roof of her cottage home from its floor. When she came up gasping, both ships were gone. Nothing was left of them but fragments on the waters, and of the sailors none remained. Few indeed were the Persians who could swim,

and many were they that day who had need of swimming, although indeed swimming would hardly have saved them unless they had such art and skill above the common as Scyllias and his daughter. For Hydna was like a fish more than a girl or any creature born to live on land. Her swift and slender body seemed to move upward or downward or in a flashing forward rush or in an instant, check and turn like the darting silver shape of a deep-sea fish, answering to the perfect living rudder of tail and fin. She was the Dolphin Girl indeed.

Yet with all her skill it seemed again and again that she was lost. Other drifting ships she only just avoided. Once a taut rope, snapping back as it was severed, almost curled about her and drew her down. Pieces of floating wreckage threatened her; the racing current tore at her young strength; often the salt-flying spray blinded her eyes, and the salt foam was in her mouth.

How long it all lasted she never knew, but toward the end she knew that she was growing weary and that meant the greatest danger of all. She came up after a long dive close to a small, battered ship that lay tugging at a rope that was pulled as tight as a bowstring. At that moment the captain and crew had forgotten their own danger, for a comrade vessel, one of the largest and most splendid in the fleet, came rushing past them, doomed and helpless. A stately man in rich robes, a prince in his own land, stood with an arm round the mast, calmly facing his fate. As the two ships came abreast, he waved a hand in farewell; and from the crews of both broke shouts of anguish and long despairing cries. Unnoticed, Hydna gripped the low, broken gunwale of the nearer ship and clung there, tossing as it tossed, yet resting a little and drawing long deep breaths.

The great ship with its wailing crew and princely commander passed and was gone. Hydna's rest was over. Someone noticed her. Someone gripped her wrist. Like every other Persian who had seen her as she swam, he thought she must be a Persian too, a lad fallen overboard, and no enemy — for what enemy would be expected at such a time and place? Then he saw her long hair, whipped now from its close-wound braids and spreading out behind her on the water like fronds of fringed-brown seaweed whenever a swelling wave lifted it from her shoulders. A girl, he saw — but how could a half-drowned girl be an enemy? He tried to pull her aboard and called another man to help him.

That must not be! Hydna had no mind to be wrecked in a Persian ship should the rope part, nor should it hold, to be a captive, who would be slain or enslaved when it was found she was no Persian.

Unexpectedly she seized the other wrist of the stooping sailor who held hers and with a strong, jerking motion flung her body outward. Taken by surprise, he could not resist the sudden pull. Hydna did not go aboard the Persian vessel; instead, her captor became her captive and plunged headlong with her into the sea. At once she let go her hold; so did he, but only to grasp her anew with both arms in a convulsive clasp. She tried to break his hold and thrust him away, but she could not. They went down together. Swimming for both, for her own arms were free, she made a tremendous effort and reached the surface again but still in the grip of the desperate Persian. She could not free herself and thought they both must drown together when good fortune brought help in great need. A floating galley oar, long and heavy, whirled down upon the struggling figures just as they were sinking. The girl it did not touch, but it struck the clutching man a stunning blow as it glanced by. His hold relaxed. Hydna broke away, came up, drew in a lungful of good air, and knew that she need not yet give up hope. She could do no more, for her knife was lost, and she was close to the limit of her powers; but she might yet swim back to safety.

Almost exhausted, but refusing to despair, she let herself drift toward the end of the long, sandy beach,

swimming only a little to spare her strength. Beyond the last of the beached Persian ships, she headed in for a small protected cove. She could hardly have come through the surf alone even there; but the fishermen from the village, with two of their best swimmers tied to a rope held by the others, ran in, wading and swimming, and seized her and carried her to land. There on the sands lay Scyllias, safe too, though weak with weariness and sick with anxiety, watching and hoping for his partner's return.

The fishermen, who had gathered on the beach, looking with awe and wonder upon the havoc of the storm, had seen Scyllias homing through the waves and helped him in; and he had begged them to keep a watch for Hydna. They had promised readily, but in pity rather than hope, for none of them expected ever to see the Dolphin Girl again, alive. Those hardy men understood well what the bold pair had been doing. But the Persian sailors close by, crouching, drenched and dazed among the beached vessels, never knew or guessed.

The hurricane blew itself out, and the heaving waters slowly quieted. On the fourth day, after a moonlit night, a windless morning dawned. The Persian captains could draw breath and count their losses. Besides many transport and provision craft, more than four hundred ships of war were missing from the mighty fleet of the Persian king.

His power was not yet broken. Land battles were yet to come and a great sea battle at Salamis (săl'ə-mĭs), but those were things far away from the two little cottages above the sandy, yellow beach.

Before the Persian ships sailed away, their captains had learned who lived in the cottage on the cliff and had employed the famous diver for salvage work among the wrecks. Scyllias did their work and took their pay readily but only until he could plan how to escape. If they had known he was unwilling, he would have been watched; and they would not have let him leave. But by biding his time and by daring to swim out to a little boat that lay in readiness, he got away before they guessed he meant to go and

carried to the Athenian admiral the welcome news of the great hurricane and the disaster it had wrought on the enemies of Greece. After that he served, and served well, in the gallant navy of Athens and her allies.

His fame had become, since the hurricane, greater than ever; but now people spoke not of Scyllias alone but of Scyllias and his daughter. Hydna, too, had become a famous person. Not only praise, but also great honor were accorded to Scyllias of Scione and his daughter. It was decreed that two bronze statues should be made of them by a famous artist and should be placed as a memorial to the brave swimmers and a thanks offering to the gods among the treasures of the great Temple of Apollo at Delphi (dĕl'fī).

DISCUSSION

1. What had happened to make Scyllias and Hydna especially close to each other?
2. According to Scyllias, what one thing made him superior to Hydna as a swimmer? Did the story prove him right or wrong? Why do you think so?
3. Why did the Persian fleet decide to cast anchor off the coast of Magnesia?
4. What stroke of good luck saved Hydna's life when the Persian sailor held onto her in the water?
5. How did the fishermen of Magnesia help Scyllias and Hydna?

6. What did Scyllias mean when he said, "The gods themselves are fighting for the Greeks"?

7. Why do you think Hydna was called the "Dolphin Girl"?

8. What was the author's purpose in including Asphalion and Chloe in the story, since they were not involved in the main action?

9. Why do you think so few Persian sailors could swim, let alone swim in the midst of a furious storm?

10. Why do you suppose the Persian sailors and captains never suspected what had caused the destruction of their ships?

11. Do you think the honor accorded to Scyllias and Hydna was an appropriate one? Why or why not?

12. If Scyllias and Hydna were alive today, which do you think would be more important to them: what is good for their state or what is good for their country? Why?

AUTHOR

Despite the fact that her parents died when she was very young, Ethel Parton, author of "The Dolphin Girl," had a happy childhood. She was brought up by her Aunt Ellen and Uncle James Parton. It pleased them both that when she was old enough, she legally changed her name to Parton. Until she was eleven years old, she was taught by James Parton, biographer, lecturer, and essayist.

Even before she graduated from high school, she wrote articles and stories, which were accepted for publication. After graduation she decided against going to college and remained at home as secretary and literary assistant to James Parton. During this time she wrote stories and ballads for several young people's magazines. Later, Miss Parton was employed as an editor and a writer for *Youth's Companion,* where she worked for more than forty years.

The Mule of the Parthenon and Other New Stories of Ancient Greece, from which "The Dolphin Girl" was taken, was Miss Parton's first book. It was followed by *Melissa Ann* and *Tabitha Mary.* Her most famous book, *Melissa Ann,* was not published until she was sixty-nine years old. At the age of eighty-two Miss Parton died in Newburyport, Massachusetts, where she had spent most of her life.

SKILL LESSON 3

VARYING READING RATE

When you read an informative selection, you often have a particular purpose in mind. You may read an article to find a particular piece of information, such as a name, a place, or a date. You may want just a general idea of what information an article or book contains so that you can decide whether it will help you in preparing a report. If you are reading to study for a test, you probably pay close attention to items and ideas that you consider important enough to remember. The rate at which you read informative material should vary according to your purpose for reading.

Assume that your purpose in reading the following paragraph is to find the answer to this question: *What was the name of the colony founded by the Puritans?* How will you read the paragraph, very rapidly, very slowly, or at a moderate rate of speed?

Plymouth Colony, founded by the Separatists, had a neighbor. It was a colony founded by English people known as Puritans. The Puritans did not wish to separate from the Church of England, as the Separatists did, but wanted to change or "purify" the Church. But like the Separatists, they were persecuted by the English government for their religious beliefs. Most of the Puritans were well-to-do, middle-class Englishmen. They were members of a trading company called the Massachusetts Bay Colony, which had been granted land and a charter by the king.

They said, "If the Separatists can make a success of a colony in the New World, so can we. Why not buy out those company members who do not wish to go to America and move our whole Massachusetts Bay Colony and its charter across the Atlantic Ocean to Massachusetts?" And this is just what they did.

Did you skim the selection rapidly until you came to the particular information that answered your question? What answer did you find?

As you read, do you vary your rate according to the purpose for which you are doing that reading? A good reader uses various rates, depending on his purpose. He reads rapidly when his purpose is to get an overview of a selection. He also reads rapidly when he is looking for a specific piece of information or an answer to a specific question. In that situation he reads quickly until he finds his answer; then he slows down to assure himself that he has found and will understand the information he is looking for.

If your purpose for reading informational material is to thoroughly understand and remember all the information given about a certain topic, you should adjust your reading rate to a much slower pace. You may have to reread certain parts to plant them firmly in your mind and, for longer selections, take notes and prepare an outline to aid you in recalling the information.

If the purpose for reading the paragraph concerning the Massachusetts Bay Colony was to remember everything it said about the Puritans, would you read quickly or slowly? Reread the paragraph for that purpose now.

Take a brief test to see how much you remembered. You may *not* look back for answers.

1. *How were the Puritans different from the Separatists in their feelings about the Church of England?*
2. *Why did the Puritans decide to leave England for the New World?*
3. *What did the Puritans have to do before they could move their colony to Massachusetts?*

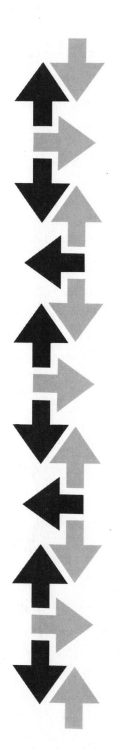

You probably realize now why the two different purposes for reading the paragraph on the Massachusetts Bay Colony require different reading rates. When you read the paragraph the first time to find the answer to just one question, you read it rapidly. Your second purpose, that of reading to find all the information it gave about the Puritans, caused you to read at a slower rate.

At times you read a paragraph or a passage to find out what the material is generally about. You would read neither at a very fast or a very slow rate, but probably at a moderate rate of speed. Read the following paragraph for the purpose of finding out what it is generally about. Then think of a topic for the paragraph.

Wars can be costly in terms of human and economic loss. At the close of World War I both the victors and the defeated were exhausted. France, for example, owed tremendous war debts. Parts of the country were ravaged by heavy equipment used for combat. Industry was in a shattered state, with many factories and railroads destroyed or closed. Numerous families were separated or made homeless. Reorganization of city and community life was a major, immediate problem.

You have learned that you should adjust your rate of reading according to the *purpose* for which you are reading. Your rate should also be adjusted according to the *difficulty* that the reading matter has for you. Think of how much time you would waste if you read comic strips and cartoons at the same rate needed to read a chapter in your science textbook.

If your purpose for reading two different articles is to remember all the information contained in them, you would read at a slow rate. However, if one article is much more difficult than the other for you to understand, the more difficult article should be read even more slowly.

Read the following paragraph as slowly as you need to in order to understand and remember all the information it gives about its topic:

THE WHITE HOUSE

The White House is the home of the President of the United States. It has one of the best-known addresses in the world — 1600 Pennsylvania Avenue. It was the first public building ever built in Washington, D.C. John Adams was the first President to make the White House his home. Since then the White House has been enlarged several times.

Can you answer the following three questions without looking back at the article?

1. *What is the White House used for?*
2. *What is the address of the White House?*
3. *Who was the first President to live in the White House?*

Below is another paragraph. Read it as slowly as you need to in order to understand and remember all the information it gives about its topic:

AMENDMENTS TO THE CONSTITUTION

The Congress, whenever two thirds of both houses shall deem it necessary, may propose amendments to the Constitution. An amendment may also be made on the application of the legislatures of two thirds of the states. In order to ratify an amendment, either of two methods may be used. First, the legislatures of three fourths of the states must act affirmatively on the amendment. Second, conventions in three fourths of the states must agree to the proposed amendment. No amendment, however, can deprive a state of its equal suffrage in the Senate.

Can you answer the three questions at the top of the next page without looking back at the selection?

1. What are the two methods for proposing amendments to the Constitution?

2. What are the two methods for ratifying an amendment?

3. How are states' rights protected?

Which of the two paragraphs was the more difficult for you to read? Your reading rate for the more difficult paragraph required a slower rate than you used in reading the other selection. What caused one paragraph to be more difficult for you than the other? How was your reading rate affected?

When a reading selection is complicated and contains unfamiliar words, difficult sentence structure, and is heavily loaded with ideas, you must read it slowly enough to understand its meaning. This slower rate may also apply to subject areas that you find difficult in school. Whenever you read a selection, always adjust your speed to the difficulty that the material has for you.

Discussion

Help your class answer the following questions:

1. Why do you vary your rate of reading?
2. How are rate of reading and purpose related?
3. Under what conditions do you read rapidly?
4. For what reasons would you read at a slow rate?
5. When would you read at a moderate rate?
6. What effect does the difficulty of material have on the rate of reading?
7. What did you decide was the topic of the paragraph you read on page 170?

On your own

Read the following paragraph for the purpose of finding a specific answer to the question *What major function does the thyroid fulfill?*

The thyroid is a large gland located in the lower part of the neck. The gland is larger in women than in men and, on the average, weighs about one and one-half ounces. The thyroid is an organ of great importance. Its major function is to keep the body and the mind functioning in a normal way. Removal or impairment of the thyroid can cause mental disturbance or muscular disorders.

Read the following paragraph for the purpose of finding what the paragraph is generally about:

Teen-agers have become one of the biggest groups of money exchangers in the United States. Billions of dollars are spent each year on amusements and sporting equipment. Skiing and underwater sports are particular favorites of teen-agers. Records and tapes account for a large expenditure of the spending money of young people. Travel, because of lower costs, is proving attractive to more and more teen-agers. The effect of all this has changed the approaches of advertising people in the many industries that serve young people. Many radio and television commercials are aimed directly at teen-agers. Advertisers in magazines, too, are appealing more and more to the buying power of the young.

Read the following paragraphs for the purpose of remembering as much information about study habits as you can:

Two very important factors in developing good study habits are organization and discipline. Organization means, for one thing, having clearly in mind just what you are to study. It also means that you have an effective study strategy. An effective way to study written material is to quickly get an overview of the information that the material contains. You do this by turning the pages of the material rapidly to find the main headings and the subheadings or by quickly reading through the material. Once you

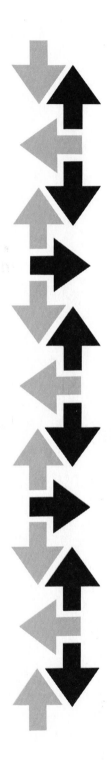

have an overview of the material, you read the material again, this time slowly, making sure that you understand the information. Another part of your study strategy might include making notes about the information, particularly if there are specific points or answers to questions that you need to know. Notes can be very effective because they will help you recall the information even at a much later date.

Discipline really means self-discipline. You plan a time for study and you stick to that plan. You make sure that interruptions will be at a minimum, that you have allowed enough time for study, and that you will not let yourself be distracted in any way.

Checking your work

If you are asked to do so, tell the rate at which you read the first paragraph and what the function of the thyroid gland is. Then, if asked, tell the rate at which you read the second paragraph. What was the general idea of that paragraph? Lastly, tell at what rate you read the last two paragraphs. What information did the paragraphs contain?

THE MYSTERIOUS JINX
of the
HOPE DIAMOND

by James Stewart-Gordon

In the Hall of Jewels of the Smithsonian Institution in Washington, D.C., a long line of Sunday sightseers passed in front of a bullet-proof glass case. There, glittering brighter than the spring light outside, was possibly the most famous, certainly the most notorious, jewel on earth. On its rope of sixty-two smaller matched diamonds, the spotlighted Hope Diamond stared back at me like an enormous, malevolent blue eye. And if the Hope was not alive itself, it seemed to be holding something imprisoned in itself that *was* alive. Finally, I managed to move on — and, like everyone who has ever looked at the eye inside the Hope, I found myself unable to resist turning and staring back.

The original stone, of which the 44½-carat Hope is — as far as can be determined — a portion, was first discovered in India over 300 years ago. It was then more than two and a half times larger. Although cutting has reduced its bulk, the Hope somehow still manages to give a feeling of magnitude, as though nothing that man could do could diminish it. Its unique qualities set it apart from other huge diamonds and make it a top attraction at the Smithsonian.

It is flawless — no lines, cracks, or other impurities can be detected. (While stones of one carat or a little more, as in engagement rings, are frequently flawless, this is unusual for a stone as large as the Hope.) Even more unusual is its color — an incredible gun-barrel blue. Twice when it has left the Smithsonian — once to be exhibited at the Louvre and once to be shown in South Africa — it has been insured for $1,000,000. However, as an official of the Smithsonian said to me, "How can you place a value on an irreplaceable object?

The million dollars might make you feel better about losing it, but it wouldn't take the place of the Hope. Nothing can do that."

For the Hope has a unique history. Legend says that it has brought more bad luck to its owners than just about all the witches' curses ever intoned.

The stone came to Europe after Louis XIV suggested to Jean Baptiste Tavernier (bä-tēst′ tä′vĕr′nyā′), a French jewel merchant, that he trade emeralds in India for any gems the rajahs might want to part with. Tavernier came back in 1668 with a $330,000 collection that included what is now presumed to be the Hope, 44 other large diamonds, and 1,122 smaller ones. The Hope then weighed 112½ carats, and it was officially designated as "The Blue Diamond of the Crown." Because it had been crudely cut in India, Louis had it recut into a heart-shaped 67⅛-carat stone.

Soon after, trouble began to plague Louis. His favorite grandson, the Duc de Bourgogne (bōōr′gô′nyə), died suddenly. The battlefield glories of his early days began to go sour, and he made the mistake of marrying Madame de Maintenon (măn′tə-nŏn), a religious fanatic who made him miserable. His agent, Tavernier, was later reported torn to death by wild dogs in Russia.

After Louis XVI got the stone, he and his queen, Marie Antoinette, also got the French Revolution — and the guillotine. In 1792, during the Revolution, the French Treasury was looted and the Hope disappeared until 1830. During this time Goya painted a picture of Queen Maria Luisa of Spain wearing a gem very much like it. The supposition is that either the French Royalists got the stone out of the country into the hands of the Spanish, or the Spaniards bought it from thieves.

It reappeared in the hands of a Dutch diamond cutter named Wilhelm Fals, who cut it to its present shape — possibly to make it as difficult as possible for the French government to claim the stone. Fals's son Hendrik soon stole the Hope from his father and took it to London, where he committed suicide.

A few years later the stone was sold for $90,000 to gem collector Henry Philip Hope — whence its present name. Henry Thomas Hope, so the story goes, inherited the diamond when his uncle died in 1839. This Hope subsequently exhibited it in the Crystal Palace

Exhibition of 1851, where it was much admired, although no one yet seemed concerned about its role as a carrier of bad luck. At the turn of the century the diamond and other items of the Hope collection were sold to a dealer named Jacques Celot (zhäk sə-lō′), who quickly committed suicide. It was then bought by a Russian named Kanitovski (kän-yē-tŏv′skē), who was stabbed to death.

The next owner of record was a merchant named Habib Bey, who drowned with his family off Gibraltar. Legend has it that the stone was then sold to Simon Montharides (mŏn-thär-rē′dēs), who in turn sold it to Abdul Hamid II, Sultan of Turkey. Simon, still counting his profits, took his wife and child for a drive — and the car hurtled over a precipice, killing all three occupants. Sultan Abdul was deposed by "Young Turks" in 1909.

The Hope turned up again in Paris, this time in the hands of jewel merchant Pierre Cartier (pyâr kär-tyā′), who sold it to Evalyn Walsh McLean of Washington, D.C. She was the daughter of mining tycoon Thomas F. Walsh and the wife of Ned McLean, son of the publisher of the Washington *Post* and the Cincinnati *Enquirer*. She paid $154,000 for it, and newspapers estimated that it would cost the McLeans an additional $24,000 a year upkeep, mainly for insurance and guards.

With the famous diamond the McLeans also got a large share of misfortune. In 1918, while they were attending the Kentucky Derby, their eight-year-old son, Vinson, at home in Washington, escaped from his bodyguards (kidnaping had been feared), ran out into a road, and was killed by a car. Not long thereafter Ned McLean lost his reason and his newspapers, and a daughter died suddenly. And in December 1967, with the curse of the Hope seemingly still virulent, Mrs. McLean's granddaughter and namesake, twenty-five-year-old Evalyn McLean, was found dead in her Texas home.

After Mrs. McLean died in 1947, jeweler Harry Winston bought her gem collection, valued at more than $1.1 million. Winston sent the big stone on tour with others of his most famous jewels. In nine years the Hope traveled 400,000 miles, was seen by 5,000,000 people, and raised over $1,000,000 for charities.

In 1957, Winston began negotiating with the Smithsonian Institution to give it the Hope as the center piece for a collection of jewels similar to the Crown Jewels in the Tower of London. The Smithsonian accepted, and on November 8, 1958, the blue diamond was placed in a suede-covered box, wrapped in brown paper, and taken to New York City's General Post Office to be mailed to Washington. (Diamond dealers believe that this is the best and safest way for stones to travel.) Specially marked and sealed, it was placed in a vault in the post office's Registry Section, which is under constant surveillance by postal inspectors and armed guards. From there it proceeded, still under armed guard, to its destination. Insured for $1,000,000, it cost Winston $145.29 to mail. Fortunately, the jinx did not affect Harry Winston during the nine years he possessed the Hope.

DISCUSSION

1. What are two things that make the Hope Diamond unusual?
2. For the most part this article tells of the bad luck supposedly brought about by the Hope. What good has it brought about?
3. What is believed to be the safest way to transport valuable stones?
4. What do you think made the author "unable to resist turning and staring back" at the Hope?
5. Do you think that the Hope is really responsible for the bad luck that its owners have had? Why do you think that?
6. How might a collection of jewels in the Smithsonian Institution be like the Crown Jewels in the Tower of London? How might the two be different?
7. Why do you think people like to own precious jewels when there always exists the danger of theft or loss?

A Day for Antonio

by John Figueroa

The young boy, asleep on the fire escape, turned over on the thin mattress as the summer sun edged its way over the East River. The sun spread a soft, gray light down into the canyons between the New York tenements and touched the boy's face. His eyes opened quickly, hurrying sleep away, but he lay still a moment, smelling and hearing the morning all around him.

Across the alley Mrs. Morales (mō-rä′lĕs) was preparing breakfast. Frying *chorizos,*[1] perking *Café Bustelo* (bōōs-tĕ′lō) — sharp, strong, sweet smells — made his mouth water. He thought of the cold milk and cheese-cake he would buy later that day when he finished the job and got his pay from Joe.

Upstairs Jimmy Loco's *abuelita,*[2] Doña Pilar (dōn′yä pē-lär′), hummed her song to the quiet morning. It was a nameless tune, soft and pretty. It was the tune she had always hummed to her chickens back in Puerto Rico. As she hummed, the boy pictured her in front of her open window watching the sun rise, as she had done ever since he could remember. She was a nice old lady. She gave him nickels. He smiled.

---

[1] **chorizos** (chō-rē′sōz), pork sausage.

[2] **abuelita** (ä-vwĕ-lē′tä), grandmother.

The soft sound of a pigeon cooing came from inside his apartment. The boy scrambled to his feet. "Petey!"

He rolled up his mattress, threw it over his shoulder, and climbed through the open window into his apartment. The house was dark, and he tiptoed around the couch where his mother was still asleep. He dropped the bedding and hurried over to a box-coop nailed to a window sill in the next room. Petey was moving around inside. The boy talked gently to the pigeon, then reached under a chair for the bird's feed. He tossed some of the grains into the cage and bent to watch the bird peck rapidly at the kernels. When Petey finished eating, the boy reached into the box and pulled him out. He examined him, first one wing and then the other. The wings were whole again. Petey was ready. Today the boy would turn him loose.

The boy gently returned the bird to the box, threw some more feed inside, and went back into the living room. His mother was awake now.

"Tony? You up? Turn on the light."

He felt for the light string somewhere over his head, found it, and pulled.

"What time is it?" his mother asked.

"About five," he said.

"The coffee made?"

"No, I just got up."

"Well, go make it — and hurry up. I don't want you to be late. Joe wants you on the job at six, sharp."

Tony lit the burner under the coffeepot, then went to his room. He put on his patch-pocket army pants and a T shirt, slid into his sneakers, and went back to his mother. She was tying her robe.

"He's ready, Ma."

"What?"

"Petey."

"Oh, that."

"His wings are all grown again. I'm going to let him out before I go."

"You sure he's ready?"

"It's been three weeks, Ma."

"Well, I hope you're right. I hate to think of you throwing away thirty-five cents on a pigeon, even if you did get money from Doña Pilar."

"He'll come back."

He went over to the open window, climbed out onto the fire escape, looked up at the brightening sky, then jumped back into the room.

"It's going to be a nice day, Ma. Hot, too, so he'll —"

"Quit fooling around, Tony. Get yourself ready to go."

"I was just going to say, he'll come back. Don't worry. Besides, he's got to come back to eat."

His mother stopped dressing and looked sternly at him.

"Stop worrying about it now. Go wash up. And hurry up, so you can eat something before you leave."

"I'll take some bread and butter to eat later. I'm not hungry now." He went into the bathroom, washed his face and hands, rubbed his finger over his teeth, and hurried back to the coop.

Tony removed the pigeon, held him for a moment, then set him lightly on top of the box. He watched Petey move to the outer edge of the cage and stop. Petey looked around and up a moment, stretched, and flew off. Tony saw him climb and break past the parapets, out of sight. He gazed at the sky for a long moment.

His mother was drinking coffee when he returned to the kitchen.

"He's gone, Ma."

"So quick?"

"Yeah." He laughed weakly. "He took off like he maybe had some-place else to go."

"He'll come back, Tony. Don't worry about it." His mother smiled.

He nodded, kissed her on the cheek, and left the house.

The bus left Tony two blocks away from the address his mother had given him. As he walked, he thought of Petey. Where would the bird be now? He hoped Petey was smart enough to avoid the big flocks of pigeons some of the guys sent up. Petey would be trapped if he didn't stay away from them. He'd join a flock and circle and circle with the other birds until it was time for them to come down and feed. Then Petey would land with them, and the guy who owned the flock would take Petey to a pet shop and sell him. Tony would never see him again. He forced the possibility out of his mind. Petey was smart. He wouldn't get caught.

Tony stopped at the door of the horse barn. Inside the dark building he could see many horses drawn up to wagons. Men were moving around, making large piles of clothes and junk. He watched for a few moments, then went in. He asked a large, red-faced junkman for Joe. The man pointed to someone at the far end of the barn. Joe was busy hitching a horse to a beat-up wooden wagon.

"You Joe?" Tony asked as he came up to the man.

"That's me," Joe said, turning and looking down at Tony.

"My name's Tony. Antonio Ramírez (än-tō′nyō rä-mē′rĕz). My mother said that ——"

"So you're Rosa's boy, eh?"

"That's right. I'm supposed to work for you."

Joe looked him up and down.

"I know. But say, your mother didn't tell me you were so young."

"I'm old enough," Tony said. "Don't worry. I can do it."

"How old are you?"

"Thirteen."

Joe stopped to think. The waiting made Tony nervous. Finally Joe spoke.

"Ah, the heck with it. Even if you are just a kid, a promise is a promise." He pointed to the wagon. "Hop on. Let's get going."

The sun seemed brighter than ever as the old horse pulled them out of the dim barn. Tony closed his eyes against the glare as Joe inched the cart into traffic and headed uptown. They crept along in silence for a while before Joe pointed to a cowbell hanging between them over the seat.

"See that string?" he asked. "Pull on it. That tells the people we're coming."

Tony did as he was told, and as they plodded along, he grinned at the people on the street. They turned to stare at the wagon as he pulled the bell cord with all the energy of his thirteen-year-old arm. Soon Joe held up a hand to Tony and pulled over to the curb.

"What's wrong?" Tony let go of the bell cord. "Did I do it too loud?"

"No, no, son," Joe said, looking at the buildings around them. "You did just fine. Thought I heard somebody calling, that's all. Look around. See if you can spot him."

Tony looked. On the fourth floor of a gray building he saw a woman leaning out of her window, waving. He pointed her out to Joe.

"Let's go," Joe said, tying the reins to the brake and climbing down from the wagon.

They went into the building and up the four flights. The woman and
two shy little girls met them at the landing. Joe and Tony followed them
into an apartment. Inside, the woman pointed to a pile of old sheets and
toys.

"How much can you give me?" she asked, as Joe walked over and
inspected the bundle.

"Fifty cents," he said.

"Fifty cents?"

Joe nodded.

"Why, mister!" The woman raised her voice. "That stuff's worth a
lot more. Least three dollars. Fifty cents is nothing."

Joe shook his head and, nodding to Tony to follow, started out of the
apartment. The woman stopped Joe.

"Wait. Wait a minute, mister. Give me a dollar and the stuff's yours."
She pulled at his arm as he stood in the doorway. "Look, my husband's

sick, been in the hospital two weeks — two whole weeks. I've got to buy some food for my little ones. Please, mister, give me a dollar."

Joe shook his head but said nothing. Tony watched silently. Then, moving away from behind Joe and going over to the pile, he pulled out a toy rifle from among the broken toys. He looked at it closely, clicked the trigger, and ran excitedly back to Joe.

"Joe. Hey, Joe!" he said. "Look! Here's a good rifle. Look at it. It's almost new. I got one just like it. Cost more than a dollar. It's worth more than fif —"

Joe looked down at Tony holding the rifle before him. "Put it back, Tony," he said, his voice angry, his face red.

The woman grabbed the rifle from Tony. "He's right, mister. This belongs to my nephew. He got it for a present just a couple of weeks ago. Now you got to give me a dollar. This boy told you the truth."

"I said fifty cents. Now take it or leave it."

The woman looked at the floor, at the pile of junk, and then at Tony. He turned away.

"Okay, mister," she said finally. "Take the stuff. You win."

Joe took the rifle from her and paid her fifty cents. He made two bundles out of the things, so he and Tony could carry them down the stairs.

"Hey, Joe! Just a minute." Halfway down the first flight Tony stopped.

"What's wrong now?" Joe said looking up at him.

Tony put down his bundle and turned back up the stairs. "I've got to do something back there. Is it okay if I leave the stuff here a minute?"

Joe rested his load on the banister. "Like what? What you going to do back there?"

"Just something, that's all."

"Sure. Go ahead."

Tony ran back to the apartment. He was gone a few moments.

"Okay," he said. "Let's go."

"What did you do in there?" Joe asked, swinging his full sheet over his back.

"Oh, nothing. I had some bread and stuff, that's all. I gave it to the kids."

Joe's face was blank as he looked long and steadily at Tony. Finally he smiled and headed down the stairs. Tony followed. Out on the street they dumped their loads into the back of the wagon and climbed up. They were pulling away when Tony finally spoke.

"Wasn't that stuff worth more than fifty cents, Joe?" he asked as Joe pulled into the traffic.

Joe didn't answer. They went about half a block, Joe gazing straight ahead.

"Ring the bell, Tony." Joe broke his silence with a smile.

Tony smiled back and rang, his question forgotten in the noise of the bell's tones. He was still pulling heavily on the cord when two blocks later a man ran in front of them. The man spoke to them in Spanish.

"*No comprendo.* You speak *muy*[3] quick." Joe was ready to drive on when Tony stopped him.

"Wait, Joe. I understand him. I'm Puerto Rican too. He says he's got something to sell to you."

Joe drew the wagon over to the curb, and they followed the man to a storefront. As they walked toward the back, a woman, dressed in a flowered housedress, stopped them.

"*¡No le haga caso* (nō lĕ ä′gä cä′sō)*!*" she screamed. "*¡Esta loco* (ĕs-tä lō′cō)*!*"

"She says he's crazy, not to pay attention to him," Tony said to Joe.

Joe shrugged at the woman and continued after the man, with Tony walking behind. There were three beds crowded in the back room, a double and two folding cots, side by side.

The man pointed to one of the cots. "*Pregúntale cuanto me da por una de las camas chiquitas* (prĕ-gōōn′tä-lĕ kwän′tō mĕ dä pôr ōō′nä dĕ läs kä′mäs chĕ-kē′täs)."

"He wants to know how much you'll give him for one of the cots," Tony told Joe.

Joe pulled up the mattress on the nearest cot. The man watched him closely.

"Tell him one-fifty," Joe said to Tony.

Tony felt a tug at his arm. It was the woman. She spoke rapidly to him and then began to cry.

"You really want to buy it, Joe? I mean, the lady just told me he wants the money for the lottery. They've got five people living here. I mean —— "

---

[3] **muy** (mwē), very.

"Tell him, Tony. One-fifty." Joe's tone was firm.

The man answered loudly.

"He says he wants four bucks, Joe. But . . . uh, I don't think you ought to buy it at all. The lady says they need the bed. Tell him you changed your mind, Joe."

"Look, Tony. Just tell him what I tell you. Stay out of all the rest. Don't get into their lives. Now, tell him one-fifty is all. That's final."

Tony hesitated but then gave the man Joe's terms.

"He says four, Joe. Nothing less."

"Come on, let's go." Joe brushed past the man.

They were just leaving the storefront when the man called to Tony.

"He says okay, Joe."

Joe stopped, pulled out his money purse, and handed a dollar bill and two quarters to Tony.

"Here. Give it to him. I'll wait outside."

"I'm very sorry, *Señora,*" Tony whispered to the woman.

Almost crying himself, Tony helped push the cot onto the wagon. He didn't ring the bell. He didn't talk. After they had gone a block, Joe reined in the horse and moved over to the curb. He tied the reins to the brake and turned to Tony.

"How old did you say you were, son?" he asked softly.

"Thirteen. Almost fourteen."

"What would you be doing today if you weren't with me?"

Tony shrugged. "I don't know. Cooling off in the water from the hydrants, maybe. Or waiting for my pigeon. I turned him loose this morning. Why, Joe?"

Joe shook his head. "I don't know. Just curious, I guess. I been thinking about when I was your age. Started comparing things . . ." He was silent a moment, deep in thought. Finally, he spoke again. "Listen, Tony. How'd you like to do me a favor?"

"Sure, Joe," Tony answered eagerly, "anything."

Joe reached into his pocket and pulled out two one-dollar bills. He pushed them toward Tony.

"Take this," he said.

"What's that for?"

"Never mind. I want you to take this money. Don't tell your mother about it. It's for you. I'll tell her I didn't use you."

188

"But, what — why?" Tony started to object, but Joe put the money into Tony's pocket.

"Don't ask questions," he said. "Just take it. Go to the beach or something. Do anything you want but take it."

"But I don't want it, Joe. I've only been with you a little while. It's too much."

Joe smiled. "You've earned it, Tony. Don't worry."

"Was it something I did, Joe? Did I do something wrong? Is that why you want to get rid of me?"

Joe put his hand tenderly on Tony's shoulder. "No, Tony. It's nothing you did. You're all right."

"I don't understand, then, Joe. Why?"

"Now, look, Tony. I don't have time to argue with you. Just take the money. I can't waste time arguing with you over two crummy dollars."

Tony was about to answer, but Joe's sharpness stopped him. He gave Joe an angry look, then jumped off the wagon to the sidewalk.

"Okay, okay," he said. "If that's the way you want it, I'll go."

"That's the way I want it," Joe said, starting to move. But he stopped and twisted around to look at the boy standing at the curb. He smiled.

"Bye, Tony," he said. "Don't be mad. Maybe someday you'll understand." He waved.

Tony watched him go until the wagon disappeared around a corner. Blinking back tears, he ran with all his might to a bus stop.

"I'll never, never, work for Joe again."

A short while later Tony forgot his anger. All thoughts of the bad experience with the junkman were gone. He was caught up in the festive air of a crowded, swaying railroad car on a train headed for Coney Island.

He ran all the way from the station to the boardwalk, stopping only to buy popcorn. He stopped at last at the rail overlooking the beach and ocean. For as far as he could see, people were sitting, lying, playing, jumping, or running in the sand and water. The happy buzz of thousands of voices floated to his ears.

He watched the scene for a minute, then turned and ran along the long boardwalk until he reached a flight of wooden steps leading down to the sand. He jumped down them two at a time and raced toward the edge of the beach. He stopped before the water's edge and ripped off his sneakers and shirt. Wearing only his army pants, he ran into the water.

The bright sun had just begun to dip over the horizon when Tony, tired but satisfied, dragged himself up onto the beach. A moment of worry crossed his mind. He shouldn't have stayed in the water so long. His mother would be mad if he got home too late. And Petey. The bird would be home as soon as the sun set. He jumped up quickly, gathered his clothes, and, dressing as he went, ran toward the rides. "I'll go home as soon as I have a hot dog and go on a couple of rides," he promised himself.

But Tony didn't keep his promise. Instead, he wandered through the noisy amusement park, all thoughts of home and Petey forgotten in the excitement of Coney Island.

From the beginning he had saved some money for two things: his carfare home and a hot dog. He had tucked the forty-five cents inside his sneaker and now and then would jam a finger into the soiled shoe to feel around for the money. Then, satisfied it was there, he would rush to another ride or watch another game.

His last ride of the night, before heading home, was the Hammer. He hung on tightly, yelling playfully as the machine looped and dived, almost tumbling him head over heels. When the ride was over, he jumped off quickly, took a moment to shake off his dizziness, and then made a dash toward the closest hot-dog stand.

He felt for the money but it wasn't there. He took off his shoe and felt around inside. Finally, he pulled the shoe back on and ran back to the Hammer, the only place he could have lost the money. The man who ran the ride didn't pay any attention to his yells at first.

"Hey, mister!" Tony yelled again.

The man looked down at him from the entrance platform. "What's that?" he said.

Tony asked him if he had just picked up some money.

The man shook his head. "You lost any money on this ride, it's probably scattered all over the place by now."

Tony began to look for his money. He looked at the ground around the platform and found nothing. He crawled underneath and found a penny, but that was all.

"Don't feel bad." The man smiled. "More than I've found around here. Keep it."

"But I haven't got any money to get home with," Tony said. He was close to tears. He was about to say more when a man came up to them.

"What's going on, son?" he asked Tony in Spanish. He was an old man, dressed in a sweater and baggy pants.

"Kid's lost some money on the ride," the man who ran the Hammer said, and turned away.

"You sure you lost it on this ride?" asked the old man.

"Yeah. I had it in my sneaker till after I got off."

The old man looked around the ground near them. "Did you look for it?"

Tony told him he'd already searched the ground.

"Well, then we'll just have to fix it up," the old man said, reaching into his pocket. He took out some coins and held them out to Tony. "Here," he continued, "this'll get you home."

Tony started to reach out for the money; then he slowly shook his head. "I don't want the money."

"Take it, take it!" The old man smiled at the boy.

"But it isn't fair," Tony said. "Besides, I don't know you and ——"

"Antonio Sandoval (sän-dō-väl′), *su servidor,*"[4] the man introduced himself, bowing slightly from the waist. "What's your name?"

"Tony — Tony Ramírez."

"Okay," the man began, "now I know your name and you know mine. So take the money. You can pay me back."

"And how can I do that? I don't know where you live."

The man pulled out a piece of paper and wrote on it. "Here. Take this. It's the address of my shop."

Tony took the paper and read it aloud. "Antonio Sandoval, Pet Shop." He looked up. "It's on 109th and Lexington."

The man smiled proudly. "That's right. Best pet shop in the whole neighborhood."

"I live around there too," Tony said, holding onto the paper.

"Good. That makes it easy for you to pay me."

Tony thought it over a minute, and finally the need to get home right away won him over. "Okay," he said. "I'll take it — as a loan. I'll pay you back, you'll see."

---

[4] **su servidor** (sōō sĕr-vē-dôr′), at your service.

Sandoval handed over the coins. "Now you better go. Your family is going to be worried about you."

Tony was already running when he yelled back his thanks. He saw the man standing there, smiling at him and shaking his head.

He ran all the way home from the subway station in Puerto Rican Harlem. He had spent the trip uptown from Coney Island worrying. When he got on the train, he had started to think about what would surely be waiting for him at the apartment. His mother would be angry — but there was nothing new in that. She'd been angry before and he could get around that.

But his pigeon, Petey, that was something to worry about. Surely the bird had returned and was already pecking at the corn in the coop. All his thoughts had been on the bird.

When he got to his building, he ran inside and up the stairs two at a time. He fumbled at the door with his key and almost fell into the house. His mind heard the soft, welcome cooing of the pigeon. Reaching the coop, he flung himself at it; then he began feeling frantically around it, calling out the bird's name.

But the pigeon wasn't there.

Tony hung halfway out the window and called into the darkness around him for his pigeon. He half heard his mother's voice behind him in the room.

"Tony," she shouted, "stop this foolishness right now. It's gone, and there's nothing you can do about it!"

The boy threw himself on the bed.

"But how, Ma — why? I mean, I trained — "

"I told you not to waste thirty-five cents on it, didn't I? If you'd listened, this wouldn't have happened."

"He wasn't a waste . . . he . . . was . . . my friend, *Mamá*. I . . ."

His mother sat next to him. "I'm sorry, Tony," she said. "I didn't mean to yell. But listen, it's not the end of the world. Maybe he'll come back sometime tonight — we don't know he won't."

Tony straightened. "You think maybe he might?"

"*¿Quién sabe?*[5] Pigeons have their own ways," she said. "He's got food here, so maybe . . ."

---

[5] ¿Quién sabe? (kyĕn sä′vĕ): Who knows?

The boy sat up. "I know what," he said excitedly. "I met somebody today, somebody who owns a pet shop. He'll know what I should do. He'll know if Petey'll come back — or if he won't."

His mother tried to keep Tony's hopes up. "If anybody knows, that man should. Go see him."

"He's a nice man; I met him at the beach."

"The beach?"

Tony nodded. "I went there — with the money Joe gave me."

"But Joe told me you didn't work today. He didn't use you."

"He gave me two dollars," Tony said, as he remembered the morning and his hurt and anger. "He told me not to tell you. He told me just to leave the wagon, just like that. I didn't do anything wrong."

"Why'd he do that, I wonder?" She frowned.

"I don't know." He paused, trying to guess what his mother was thinking before he said what he wanted to. "*Mamá*," he said.

"Hmmmm?" She was deep in thought.

"I spent it all," he blurted out finally. As it came out, he knew the only way to get around her anger would be a quick explanation. "But only because he got me so mad. He made me feel like I was nothing — the way he told me to get off his wagon and all. I was . . . so . . . so mad I just went and spent the money. I'm sorry, *Mamá*."

She looked at him a long time. Finally, she smiled. She pulled him to her, hugging him. "That's okay, *mi hijo*,"[6] she said gently. "Don't worry about it. I'll get you another job — a job you'll like. But if I do, don't you go spending all the money in one place, okay?"

He smiled for the first time since he had gotten home. "No, Ma. I promise. Anything I make'll be for the house."

"Fine," she said. "We understand each other." She got up from the bed. "*¿No tienes hambre?*"[7]

"No, I'm not hungry."

"Get to bed then. It's getting late." She leaned down, kissed him on the forehead, and walked out of the room.

With a final look around in the dark outside, he undressed and got into bed, sure that Petey would come home during the night.

---

[6] mi hijo (mē ē'hō), my son.

[7] ¿No tienes hambre? (nō tyĕn'ĕs äm'brĕ): Aren't you hungry?

But the pigeon didn't return. The next morning Tony jumped out of bed and ran to the window. No Petey. He dressed quickly and hurried into the kitchen. He gulped down the breakfast his mother had left for him. Then he went to a place behind the kitchen stove where he kept the empty bottles, gathered them up, and ran out of the house down to the Morales' store. At the store he cashed in the bottles and walked quickly to the address Mr. Sandoval had given him.

The pet shop was small, and as Tony stepped inside, his ears rang with the sounds of the many animals. Mr. Sandoval wasn't in sight, so he walked toward the back of the store, looking into the cages and stalls where the animals were kept. He stopped only at the pigeon coop to admire the hundreds of pigeons housed there.

At the back of the store he reached a thick curtain. Calling the owner's name, he pushed it aside and stepped into a small, furnished room. Sandoval was seated at a small table drinking coffee.

"Antonio," the man said, smiling broadly. "Come inside. Nice to see you."

"I came to pay you back," Tony said.

"Pay me?" the man began. "Oh, *sí, sí*. The carfare — ah, *muy bien,*[8] *muy bien*. You're an honest boy." He pointed to a chair. "*Pero siéntate, siéntate.*"[9]

Tony sat down across the table from him and placed the money on the table. Without a word Sandoval took it and dropped it into a cigar box near his hand. Then he smiled.

"*Gracias,*[10] Tony."

"*A usted,*"[11] Tony replied.

"And how did it go?" Sandoval continued. "*¿Llegaste bien a tu casa?*"[12]

Tony replied that he had gotten home all right, thanks to Mr. Sandoval.

"I came to ask you something," he said hurriedly during a pause in the conversation.

"Ask it," Sandoval said, and sat back.

---

[8] bien (byĕn), good.

[9] Pero siéntate, siéntate. (pĕ′rō syĕn′tä-tĕ syĕn′tä-tĕ): But sit down, sit down.

[10] Gracias (grä′syĕs): Thanks.

[11] A usted (ä ōōs-tĕ′): You're welcome.

[12] ¿Llegaste bien a tu casa? (yā-gäs′tĕ byĕn ä tōō cä′sä): Did you get home all right?

Tony told him all about Petey and how the bird hadn't come back.

Sandoval listened silently. When Tony finished, he asked him a question. "Tell me," he said, "the bird — where did you buy it?"

"A pet shop on Second Avenue. But the man told me he was a good —"

Sandoval interrupted. "I'm asking you because sometimes some people sell you a bird that was already trained for too long at another place. Even if you clip the wings, the bird goes back to the place it came from. It's very hard to train those kind. Maybe your pigeon was one of those."

"You think that happened with Petey?"

Sandoval smiled. "Maybe. If he didn't come back by this morning, something must have happened."

"Maybe he'll come back later," Tony said hopefully.

"I don't think so. But look, why don't you buy another one? I have some young ones. Nobody has ever trained them. I'll sell you one right now. I have a very good young one. . . ." He stood up. "I'll get it." He stopped when he saw the look on the boy's face.

"You can't?" he asked the boy.

Tony shook his head. "Even if I had the money, my mother wouldn't let me buy it. We need the money for food."

Sandoval shrugged, trying to appear unconcerned. "Well, it's not important. Some other time . . ." He smiled again. "But why don't I show you the animals. You like animals, no?"

Tony's eyes sparkled and he jumped up. "*Sí* — I'd like that."

During the rest of the day Sandoval guided Tony expertly through the shop, talking to him about the animals. He taught Tony how to feed and bathe them. He showed him how to use the adding machine and let him wait on customers.

Toward sunset Tony suddenly became aware of the time. After waiting on a customer, he hurried over to Sandoval, who was busy feeding the canaries.

"I . . . ah . . . I'm going now, Señor Sandoval," Tony said, stammering, his voice registering his disappointment at having to leave.

Sandoval turned to him. "So soon? My goodness, I didn't realize the hour! It is late. You've been here a long time."

Tony didn't quite know how to ask the next thing on his mind. "Ah, could," he began, then blurted it out, "could I come back tomorrow?"

Sandoval set the bag of feed he was carrying on top of a cage and took the boy by the shoulders. "You don't have to ask," he said. "You come any time you want. I like your company. You learn quick. Yes, come tomorrow. You can help me around the store again. Would you like to do that — help me?"

Tony's eyes shone. "Yeah, would I! I can do anything you want, you'll see. You just teach me and ——"

Sandoval pushed him toward the door. "Okay, come tomorrow, but now, get going! You've been here all day. Your mother's really going to worry today."

Tony started for the door. "I'll see you tomorrow," he said as he went.

But Sandoval stopped him. "Wait, Tony. *Espérate un momento.*"[13]

Tony stopped. Sandoval went to the pigeon cage, stuck his hands in, and took out a light blue-gray homing pigeon.

"I forgot to show you this one," he told the boy. "Was your Petey like this?" Sandoval asked.

"No," Tony said with his new knowledge of birds. "I had a flight pigeon. This one's a homer."

"You remember what I told you — about which birds are best to train?"

Tony nodded. "Sure. Homers. That's what you said."

"*Sí.* Homers." He held the bird out toward Tony. "You like it?"

Tony nodded vigorously.

Sandoval thrust the bird at him. "Good. Take good care of him. He's yours."

Tony could only stare.

"Take him," Sandoval insisted, "before I change my mind."

Tony didn't need any further encouragement. He grabbed the bird and, thanking Mr. Sandoval, hurried out of the store.

The people who noticed the young boy running wildly down the crowded streets stopped and stared at him. None could know, of course, that the boy was running with all the joy his thirteen-year-old body could have. He was headed home to show his mother the greatest pigeon in the world! This one would soon be trained and would return home time after time.

---

[13] **Espérate un momento.** (ĕs-pĕ′rä-tĕ ŏŏn mō-mĕn′tō): Wait a moment.

And certainly no one could tell that the boy had found out today that some men sold things that made people happy . . . or that he found out yesterday that some men bought things that made people unhappy . . . or that he was Antonio, getting to know the great world.

DISCUSSION

1. Why had Tony let Petey go? What did Tony think might have happened to Petey? What did Mr. Sandoval think probably had happened?

2. How did Joe earn his living? What did Tony do that made Joe decide he did not want him as a helper?

3. How did Tony happen to meet Mr. Sandoval? On what conditions was Tony willing to accept his offer of carfare?

4. What represented Tony's first earnings for working in Mr. Sandoval's store?

5. Why was helping Joe not a good job for Tony? Why was helping Mr. Sandoval a much better job?

6. What did Joe mean by saying, "Don't get into their lives"? Do you think Joe was hardhearted? Why do you think that? Do you think Joe should have been willing to pay more for the things he bought? Why do you think that?

7. Why was Tony so angry when he left Joe?

8. How did Mr. Sandoval and Joe differ in their attitude toward people?

9. How would you have acted and felt if you had been working for Joe? Would you have been as angry as Tony was at being dismissed? Why?

10. Name at least two things Tony did that proved he was basically honest. Do you think he was completely honest when he told his mother why he had spent all the money? Why do you think that? Do you think most people are honest most of the time but not always? Why do you think that?

11. Tony's mother said that she would get him another job, one that he liked. Is it better to get your own job or have someone get it for you? Why?

12. What do you think the author meant by describing Antonio as "getting to know the great world"?

AUTHOR

John Figueroa, the author of "A Day for Antonio," was born in New York City and subsequently moved to California, where he went to high school and college.

Mr. Figueroa has been interested in writing for many years. His interest started at the age of thirteen when he bought an old typewriter and wrote two short stories, which he sold for five dollars. His writings are based primarily on his own experiences. Through his writing he hopes to show the pride, tragedy, love, warmth, and common experiences of his people, the Puerto Ricans.

Mr. Figueroa has written articles and stories for several magazines, including *Con Safos,* and has contributed to various anthologies of ethnic writers. He has also written a half-hour television drama, "No More Mañanas," which was televised in April, 1971.

Mr. Figueroa is married and has three children. At the present time he is Project Director of Model Cities Youth Agency in Los Angeles, California.

AFRICA

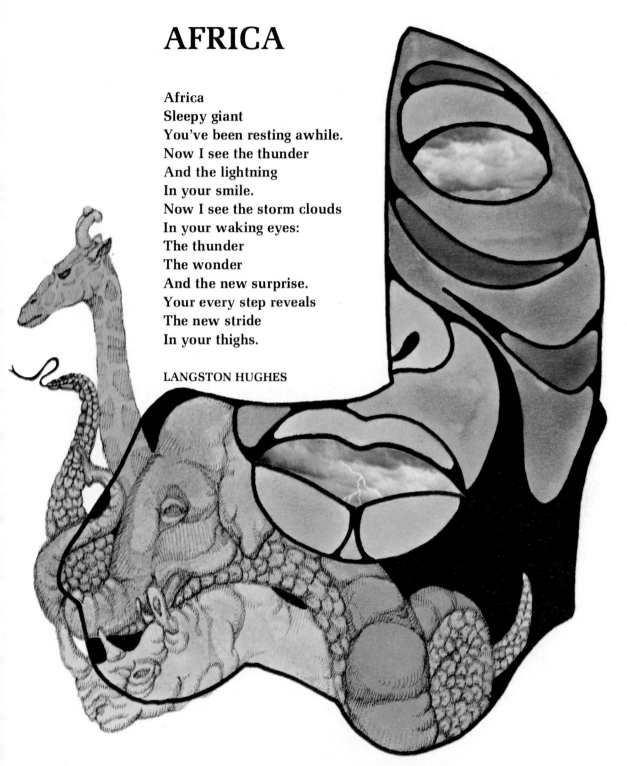

Africa
Sleepy giant
You've been resting awhile.
Now I see the thunder
And the lightning
In your smile.
Now I see the storm clouds
In your waking eyes:
The thunder
The wonder
And the new surprise.
Your every step reveals
The new stride
In your thighs.

LANGSTON HUGHES

SECURITY CHECK

by ARTHUR C. CLARKE

It is often said that in our age of assembly lines and mass production there's no room for the individual craftsman, the artist in wood or metal who made so many of the treasures of the past. Like most generalizations, this simply isn't true. He's rarer now, of course, but he's certainly not extinct. He has often had to change his vocation, but in his modest way he still flourishes. Even on the island of Manhattan he may be found, if you know where to look for him. Where rents are low and fire regulations unheard of, his minute, cluttered workshops may be discovered in the basements of apartment houses or in the upper stories of derelict

shops. He may no longer make violins or cuckoo clocks or music boxes, but the skills he uses are the same as they always were, and no two objects he creates are ever identical. He is not contemptuous of mechanization: you will find several electric hand tools under the debris on his bench. He has moved with the times: he will always be around, the universal odd-job man who is never aware of it when he makes an immortal work of art.

Hans Muller's workshop consisted of a large room at the back of a deserted warehouse, no more than a vigorous stone's throw from the Queensborough Bridge. Most of the building had been boarded up

Copyright 1957 by Fantasy House, Inc. Reprinted by permission of the author and the author's agents, Scott Meredith Literary Agency, Inc., 580 Fifth Avenue, New York, New York 10036.

awaiting demolition, and sooner or later Hans would have to move. The only entrance was across a weed-covered yard used as a parking place during the day, and much frequented by the local juvenile delinquents at night. They had never given Hans any trouble.... Hans was on good terms with everybody. Being a peaceable citizen, that suited him very well.

The work on which Hans was now engaged would have deeply puzzled his Bavarian ancestors. Indeed, ten years ago it would have puzzled Hans himself. And it had all started because a bankrupt client had given him a TV set in payment for services rendered....

Hans had accepted the offer reluctantly, not because he was old-fashioned and disapproved of TV, but simply because he couldn't imagine where he would find time to look at the darned thing. Still, he thought, at least I can always sell it for fifty dollars. But before I do that, let's see what the programs are like....

His hand had gone out to the switch: the screen had filled with moving shapes — and, like millions of men before him, Hans was lost. He entered a world he had not known existed — a world of battling spaceships, of exotic planets and strange races — the world, in fact, of Captain Zipp, Commander of the Space Legion.

Only when the tedious recital of the virtues of Crunche, the Wonder Cereal, had given way to an almost equally tedious boxing match between two muscle-bound characters who seemed to have signed a non-aggression pact, did the magic fade. Hans was a simple man. He had always been fond of fairy tales — and *this* was the modern fairy tale, with trimmings of which the Grimm Brothers[1] had never dreamed. So Hans did not sell his TV set.

It was some weeks before the initial naïve, uncritical enjoyment wore off. The first thing that began to annoy Hans was the furniture and general décor in the world of the future. He was, as has been indicated, an artist — and he refused to believe that in a hundred years taste would have deteriorated as badly as the Crunche sponsors seemed to imagine.

He also thought very little of the weapons that Captain Zipp and his opponents used. It was true that Hans did not pretend to understand the principles upon which the portable proton disintegrator was based, but however it worked, there was certainly no reason why it should be *that* clumsy. The clothes, the spaceship interiors — they just weren't convincing. How did he know? He had always possessed a highly

---

[1] **Grimm Brothers** (grĭm): Jacob and Wilhelm, well-known German writers of *Grimm's Fairy Tales.*

developed sense of the fitness of things, and it could still operate even in this novel field.

We have said that Hans was a simple man. He was also a shrewd one, and he had heard that there was money in TV. So he sat down and began to draw.

Even if the producer of Captain Zipp had not lost patience with his set designer, Hans Muller's ideas would certainly have made him sit up and take notice. There was an authenticity and realism about them that made them quite outstanding. They were completely free from the element of phonyness that had begun to upset even Captain Zipp's most juvenile followers. Hans was hired on the spot.

He made his own conditions, however. What he was doing he did largely for love, notwithstanding the fact that it was earning him more money than anything he had ever done before in his life. He would take no assistants, and would remain in his little workshop. All that he wanted to do was to produce the prototypes, the basic designs. The mass production could be done somewhere else — he was a craftsman, not a factory.

The arrangement had worked well. Over the last six months Captain Zipp had been transformed and was now the despair of all the rival space operas. This, his viewers thought, was not just a serial about the future. It *was* the future — there was no argument about it. Even the actors seemed to have been inspired by their new surroundings: off the set, they sometimes behaved like twentieth-century time travelers stranded in the Victorian Age, indignant because they no longer had access to the gadgets that had always been part of their lives.

But Hans knew nothing about this. He toiled happily away, refusing to see anyone except the producer, doing all his business over the telephone — and watching the final result to ensure that his ideas had not been mutilated. The only sign of his connection with the slightly fantastic world of commercial TV was a crate of Crunche in one corner of the workshop. He had sampled one mouthful of this present from the grateful sponsor and had then remembered thankfully that, after all, he was not paid to eat the stuff.

He was working late one Sunday evening, putting the final touches to a new design for a space helmet, when he suddenly realized that he was no longer alone. Slowly he turned from the workbench and faced the door. It had been locked — how could it have been opened so silently? There were two men standing beside it, motionless, watching him. Hans felt his heart trying to climb into his gullet, and summoned up what courage he could to challenge them. At least, he felt thankfully, he had little

money here. Then he wondered if, after all, this was a good thing. They might be annoyed. . . .

"Who are you?" he asked. "What are you doing here?"

One of the men moved toward him while the other remained watching alertly from the door. They were both wearing very new overcoats, with hats low down on their heads so that Hans could not see their faces. They were too well dressed, he decided, to be ordinary holdup men.

"There's no need to be alarmed, Mr. Muller," replied the nearer man, reading his thoughts without difficulty.

"This isn't a holdup. It's official. We're from — Security."

"I don't understand."

The other reached into a portfolio he had been carrying beneath his coat, and pulled out a sheaf of photographs. He riffled through them until he had found the one he wanted.

"You've given us quite a headache, Mr. Muller. It's taken us two weeks to find you — your employers were so secretive. No doubt they were anxious to hide you from their rivals. However, here we are and I'd like you to answer some questions."

"I'm not a spy!" answered Hans indignantly as the meaning of the words penetrated. "You can't do this! I'm a loyal American citizen!"

The other ignored the outburst. He handed over the photograph.

"Do you recognize this?" he said.

"Yes. It's the inside of Captain Zipp's spaceship."

"And you designed it?"

"Yes."

Another photograph came out of the file.

"And what about this?"

"That's the Martian city of Paldar, as seen from the air."

"Your own idea?"

"Certainly," Hans replied, now too indignant to be cautious.

"And *this?*"

"Oh, the proton gun. I was quite proud of that."

"Tell me, Mr. Muller — are these all your own ideas?"

"Yes, *I* don't steal from other people."

His questioner turned to his companion and spoke for a few minutes in a voice too low for Hans to hear. They seemed to reach agreement on some point, and the conference was over before Hans could make his intended grab at the telephone.

"I'm sorry," continued the intruder. "But there has been a serious leak. It may be — uh — accidental, even unconscious, but that does not affect the issue. We will have to investigate you. Please come with us."

There was such power and authority in the stranger's voice that Hans began to climb into his overcoat without a murmur. Somehow, he no longer doubted his visitors' credentials and never thought of asking for any proof. He was worried, but not yet seriously alarmed. Of course, it was obvious what had happened. He remembered hearing about a science-fiction writer during the war who had described the atom bomb with disconcerting accuracy. When so much secret research was going on, such accidents were bound to occur. He wondered just what it was he had given away.

At the doorway, he looked back into his workshop and at the men who were following him.

"It's all a ridiculous mistake," he said. "If I *did* show anything secret in the program, it was just a coincidence. I've never done anything to annoy the FBI."

It was then that the second man spoke at last, in very bad English and with a most peculiar accent.

"What is the FBI?" he asked.

But Hans didn't hear him. He had just seen the spaceship.

DISCUSSION

1. Why are there fewer individual craftsmen these days? How have they become modernized?
2. What gift changed Hans's life? How did it do so?
3. What new work did Hans find himself engaged in? What made his ideas outstanding?
4. What reason did Hans's two visitors give to get him to go with them? What misunderstanding did this lead to?
5. How were the two visitors dressed? Why were they dressed that way?
6. Do you agree with the statement that the individual craftsman will always be around? Why?
7. Hans was described as "on good terms with everybody . . . a peaceable citizen." Do you think one can always be on good terms with everybody? Why do you think that?
8. Do you think Hans should have gone with the men without requiring identification from them? Why or why not?
9. What TV show do you think has authentic and realistic sets? Why do you think so? What shows do you feel have sets that could be improved? Why do you think so?

AUTHOR

"Security Check," which you have just read, is from Arthur C. Clarke's fourth volume of short stories, *The Other Side of the Sky.*

Mr. Clarke was born in England. He graduated from King's College, London, where he won First Class Honors in physics and mathematics. In World War II, as an RAF officer, he was in charge of the first radar talk-down equipment, which was then in its experimental stage.

Mr. Clarke is a member of several scientific organizations, including the Academy of Astronautics and the Royal Astronomical Society. He has written many books in the field of space, some of them pioneers in the literature of space flight. Three of his books about space and the modern age are *The Exploration of Space, Profiles of the Future,* and *Voices from the Sky.*

In addition to nonfiction he has written many science-fiction books and more than three hundred magazine articles and short stories. Over five million of his books have been sold in twenty languages, including more than one hundred paperback editions. With Stanley Kubrick he wrote the book and screenplay *2001: A Space Odyssey.*

In 1962, UNESCO awarded Mr. Clarke the Kalinga Prize for science writing; and in 1963, the Franklin Institute presented him with a gold medal for proposing the use of communication satellites, which he had suggested as early as 1945.

Mr. Clarke's hobby is underwater exploration, particularly along Australia's Great Barrier Reef and off the coast of Ceylon, where he spends much of his time.

THE LESSON
of the
LEMMINGS

by Ola and Emily d'Aulaire

A few years ago, while hiking through the dwarf-birch stillness of the mountains of eastern Norway, we were startled by a sound resembling a short-wave radio run amok. It was coming from a furred animal about the size of a field mouse, haunched on a patch of reindeer moss. When we approached for a closer look, the creature bounded at us, his long yellowish teeth bared. As we hiked on, more of these agitated little creatures kept popping out of the moss to scold us. Suddenly they were everywhere. One small fellow sprang up and down like a miniature riveting hammer, clearly beside himself with rage. "Lemmings," our guide explained. "1970 is a lemming year."

The lemmings' aggressive behavior was more of a surprise to us than their large numbers. We knew of the lemmings' population explosions every few years, and of how, at least according to legend, they hurl themselves off cliffs into the sea in mass suicides. Scientists are looking into the matter and beginning to separate facts from the age-old myths. They have become especially interested in the animals in light of the exploding human population. Perhaps better knowledge of the lemmings can help man to avoid a similar biological disaster.

There are five species of lemmings. Two species, including the most common, *Lemmus lemmus* — usually called the Norwegian lemming — are found in Norway, Sweden, Finland, and northern Russia. The other three species inhabit mostly the northern parts of Greenland and North America. Members of the hamster family, all lemmings measure about five inches from whisker to tail-tip, weigh less than four ounces, and have tawny-and-black streaked fur. The lemming's legs and tail are short; and underneath his shiny, thick coat is a layer of fat which, together with his furred paw pads, enables him to withstand the hard northern winters.

Lemmings everywhere appear in large numbers every three or four years. At the beginning of their population cycle only a few lemmings are around, and they are shy animals, afraid even of other members of their own species. They hole up in their burrows, feed on roots and bulbs, and rarely show themselves.

So far, too, their reproduction rate is lazy. But in the second year of the cycle it builds up, and in the third or fourth year it becomes brisk. Females are almost continuously with young. They are ready to breed when only twenty-five days old, and since they do not hibernate, they can reproduce in winter as well as in summer. With a gestation period of only twenty-one days and five to eight young to a litter, a single pair can be responsible for 16,000 descendants in the fourth year of the lemming cycle!

It is now, at the end of the cycle, that this shy, retiring rodent turns so aggressive. The pressure of such sharply increased numbers causes millions of lemmings to leave their overcrowded habitat in a frantic search for Lebensraum.[1] And in Norway the lemmings quickly become victims of topography. In this land of jagged, narrow river valleys that run into other narrow valleys and in turn into narrow fjords, the valleys are the only available paths of flight; and as these merge, so do the teeming swarms of rodents.

The mad rush goes on until the army finds its way barred by water. Since the creatures do not gladly swim, they rush back and forth along the bank in search of some dry way of crossing. In central Norway during 1966, traffic was halted for almost an hour as a chattering horde of animals surged across a bridge connecting Dovre and Dombaas. A snowplow had to be brought to clear the span. There are times, however, when the lemmings can find no bridges and must take to the water. Although they are fair swimmers, even small waves can flip them over, and eventually they all tire and drown.

When an army of lemmings hits the sea, it sometimes forms a carpet covering one or two square miles. Once, years ago, the captain of a passenger ship on Trondheim Fjord (trôn'hām fyôrd) reported steaming through a solid raft of the animals for a full fifteen minutes. Fishermen frequently report sighting patches of lemmings. At times they will

---

[1] **Lebensraum** (lā'bəns-roum'), living space.

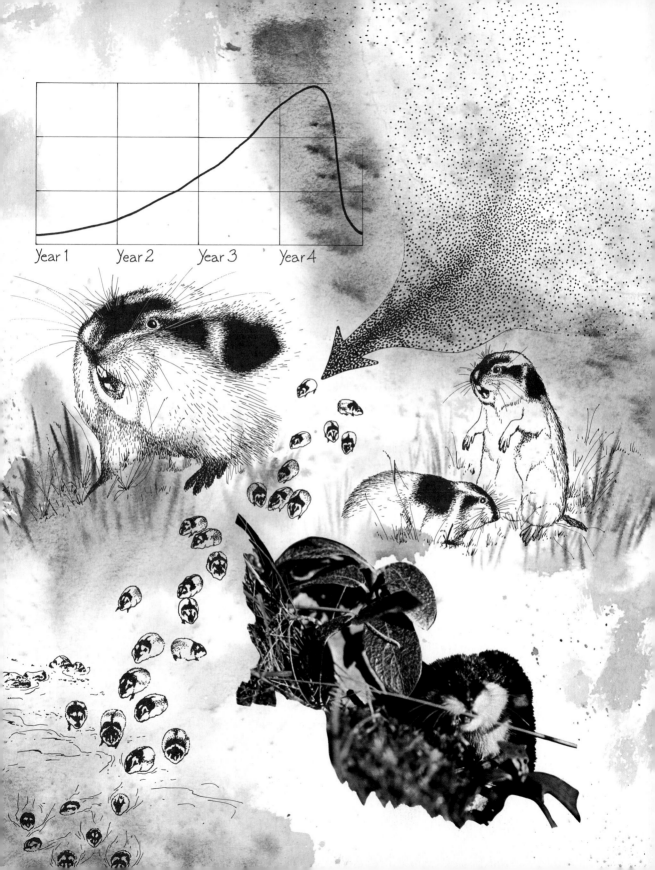

Year 1 Year 2 Year 3 Year 4

clamber up the nets, spill into the boats, and then, as more lemmings follow, splash back over the side again.

Sometimes lemming hordes blunder into towns. The havoc these animals can cause was demonstrated when Vadsø (väd′sû′), one of Norway's northernmost outposts, was inundated in 1955. The creatures began tumbling down from the barren hills like a living avalanche. Soon they were dying in nearby streams in such numbers that they polluted the community's water supply. "I remember it vividly," says Anders Aune, Vadsø's member of Parliament. "Lemmings streamed across the roads. Whenever I drove, I couldn't help but crush hundreds of them." The invasion lasted two weeks, then disappeared as suddenly as it had come.

A lemming army on the march can be troublesome even away from human habitations. Since lemmings must eat their own weight in food every twenty-four hours, they rip through farmland, denuding everything in sight. When the greenery is gone, they work on the root stocks. "Four-legged mowers" the farmers call them.

Despite the havoc these invasions can cause, men have been able to do nothing to forestall them. For although zoologists can precisely predict the coming of a lemming year, it is impossible to pinpoint where the armies will form or where they will head once they have done so. The whole process is as nervously random as the behavior of the individual lemming at migration time — it's dash, weave, pause, and sniff; then off again on another heading. As with locusts the only way to stop the plague is to prevent the animals from breeding. With lemmings this has not proved practical.

But though man has lagged in devising means of muffling the lemming explosions, there is an impressive line-up of natural predators who do their bit. When the lemmings are running, for instance, sea gulls add them to their usual menu of fish. Owls, hawks, eagles, weasels, ermines, and foxes also seem to relish them. Somehow they seem in tune with the lemming cycle. As if in anticipation, snowy owls have been observed laying more eggs than usual in a lemming year, and foxes may throw an additional pup or two.

But despite the predators and the suicidal rushes into lakes, rivers, and sea, teeming multitudes of the animals are still left over. Then, wondrously, the cycle comes to an abrupt end. The little creatures begin dying as fast as they multiplied. Why? Arne Semb-Johansson, professor of zoology, and his coworkers at the University of Oslo think that, at the end of the population cycle, the adrenal glands of the lemmings become overactive. These glands secrete adrenaline — the substance that, in humans, makes our hearts beat faster when we react to fear. Eventually, the lemmings' overtaxed glands collapse and the animals die. Other researchers claim that there is a poisonous substance in the bloodstream of lemmings that causes no harm until the end of the cycle when, for reasons as yet unexplained, it attacks and destroys the central nervous system.

Whatever the actual physical causes of the lemmings' abrupt end, researchers agree that the trigger is overcrowding. It is only under conditions of overpopulation that the lemmings' chemistry goes out of kilter and the lemming population shrinks eerily to where the little creatures again become scarce and unseen.

Scientists began to investigate the lemming only a few years ago, and the chances are that it will be some time before they find anything of benefit to the human condition. Nonetheless, the aggressive rage of *Lemmus lemmus* as he fights to survive crowding is likely to strike a responsive chord in many people — at least in anyone who has, for example, attempted to squeeze into a bus during rush hour.

DISCUSSION

1. Why have scientists recently become much more interested in the lemmings?
2. In what ways are the lemmings victims of Norway's topography?
3. Why is it that men cannot forestall the havoc wrought by "the lemming year"?
4. What happens to natural predators during the lemming explosion?
5. What is the relationship between the lemming explosion and people crowding on a bus during rush hour?
6. Do you think a study of the lemmings will prove helpful to man? Why do you think that?

SKILL LESSON 4

USING A DICTIONARY

Sometimes you can figure out the meaning of a strange word by using the context in which you meet the word. When the context does not give you the help you need, you should use a dictionary. You may also use a dictionary to determine such things as the pronunciation and spelling of a word and where to break a word at the end of a line. Whatever your reason for using it, a dictionary is a valuable source of information about words in our language.

To find a word in a dictionary, think of the order of the alphabet, because the words are arranged alphabetically. The word *balky* will be found near the beginning of a dictionary; the word *larghetto,* near the middle; and the word *veil,* near the end. To locate a word as quickly as possible, you open the dictionary to the approximate location of the word according to the alphabetical order of its first letter. To locate the following words, where would you open a dictionary, near the beginning, the middle, or the end of the dictionary?

sycamore	impoverish	picot
amalgamate	vulcanize	glib

When you open a dictionary to the approximate location of a word, you then need to locate specifically the entry for the word you are looking for. GUIDE WORDS at the top of a dictionary page help you in the rapid location of words. On the opposite page is a dictionary page. The two guide words are *paintbrush* and *pallet,* so *paintbrush*

paint·brush (pānt′brŭsh′) *n.* A brush for applying paint.

paint·er[1] (pān′tər) *n.* A person who paints, either as an artist or as a workman.

pain·ter[2] (pān′tər) *n.* A rope attached to the bow of a boat, used for tying up.

pain·ter[3] (pān′tər) *n.* A mountain lion or other North American wildcat.

paint·ing (pān′tĭng) *n.* **1.** The art, process, or occupation of working with paints. **2.** A picture or design in paint.

pair (pâr) *n.* **1.** A set that contains exactly two members, especially if they are somehow matched or associated in function or form: *a pair of boots.* **2.** One object consisting of two joined or similar parts dependent upon each other: *a pair of binoculars; a pair of trousers.* **3. a.** Two persons joined together in marriage or engagement. **b.** Two persons, animals, or things having something in common and considered together: *a pair of scientists; a pair of oxen.* **c.** Two mated animals. —*v.* **1.** To arrange in sets of two; couple: *Pair the synonyms in the two columns.* **2.** To provide a partner for: *She paired John with Alice.*

pais·ley (pāz′lē) *adj.* Having a colorful pattern of curved shapes and swirls: *a paisley dress.*

pa·ja·mas (pə jä′məz) *or* (-jăm′əz) *pl.n.* A loose-fitting outfit of jacket and trousers worn to sleep in or for lounging.

pal (păl). *Informal. n.* A friend; chum. —*v.* **palled, pal·ling.** To associate as friends.

pal·ace (păl′ĭs) *n.* **1.** The official residence of a royal person. **2.** Any splendid residence.

pal·at·a·ble (păl′ə tə bəl) *adj.* **1.** Acceptable to the taste; agreeable enough in flavor to be eaten: *palatable food.* **2.** Acceptable to the mind or sensibilities; agreeable: *a palatable way of handling the problem.*

pal·ate (păl′ĭt) *n.* **1.** The roof of the mouth in vertebrates, forming a complete or partial separation between the mouth cavity and the passages of the nose. **2.** The sense of taste.

pa·la·tial (pə lā′shəl) *adj.* Of or like a palace; spacious and magnificent: *a palatial hotel.*

pa·lav·er (pə lăv′ər) *or* (-lä′vər) *n.* **1.** Idle chatter, especially that meant to flatter or deceive. **2.** A parley between two groups, especially a parley formerly held between explorers and representatives of local populations in Africa. —*v.* To chatter idly.

pale[1] (pāl) *n.* **1.** A stake or pointed stick; a picket. **2.** A limit or boundary. —*v.* **paled, pal·ing.** To enclose with pales; fence in.

pale[2] (pāl) *adj.* **pal·er, pal·est. 1.** Whitish or lighter than normal in complexion, often because of a poor supply of blood to the skin, as in weakness or some illnesses. **2.** Containing a large proportion of white; not intense; light: *a pale blue.* **3.** Not bright; dim; faint: *a pale moon.* —*v.* **paled, pal·ing. 1.** To lose normal skin coloration; turn pale. **2.** To become pale: *The sky crimsoned, then paled.*

pa·le·on·tol·o·gist (pā′lē ən tŏl′ə jĭst) *n.* A scientist who specializes in paleontology.

pa·le·on·tol·o·gy (pā′lē ən tŏl′ə jē) *n.* The scientific study of fossils and ancient forms of life.

pal·ette (păl′ĭt) *n.* A thin board, often with a hole for the thumb, upon which an artist mixes colors.

pal·ing (pā′lĭng) *n.* **1.** One or more of the pales or pickets forming a fence. **2.** A fence made of pales or pickets.

pal·i·sade (păl′ĭ sād′) *n.* **1.** A fence of stakes, forming a fortification. **2. palisades.** A line of high cliffs, usually along a river.

pall[1] (pôl) *n.* **1.** A cloth covering, often of black velvet, for a coffin or tomb. **2.** A coffin being borne to a grave. **3.** A dark, gloomy covering: *a pall of smog over the city.* **4.** A gloomy atmosphere: *The bad news cast a pall over the household.*

pall[2] (pôl). *v.* To grow dull or tiresome: *a clever idea that begins to pall by the end of the movie.*

pal·let (păl′ĭt) *n.* A narrow, hard bed or straw-filled mattress.

ă pat/ā pay/â care/ä father/ĕ pet/ē be/ĭ pit/ī pie/î fierce/ŏ pot/ō go/ô paw, for/oi oil/o͞o book/
o͞o boot/ou out/ŭ cut/û fur/*th* the/th thin/hw which/zh vision/ə ago, item, pencil, atom, circus

Adapted from The American Heritage School Dictionary, *published by American Heritage Publishing Co., Inc. and Houghton Mifflin Company. Reprinted by permission.*

is the very first word listed on that page, and *pallet* is the last word listed. The other words on that page come alphabetically between *paintbrush* and *pallet*. Would you expect to find the word *palm* on that page? Would you expect to find the word *pain* on that page?

Once you have located the word you are looking for, you will find that it is first spelled by syllables. This separation of the word into syllables tells you where the word may be divided when you cannot write the entire word at the end of a line. Look at the word *pajamas* on the dictionary page. You will see that the word is spelled by syllables, pa•ja•mas. The word may be divided after the first syllable *pa,* or after the first two syllables *paja.* What punctuation mark do you use at the end of a line to show that a word has been divided?

Where may you separate the following words at the ends of lines?

palatable	palette
palaver	palisade

The second spelling of a word in a dictionary entry is a SPECIAL SPELLING that uses symbols to stand for the sounds in the word. The purpose of this respelling is to aid you in pronouncing the word. A PRONUNCIATION KEY is used to determine the sounds represented by the symbols. For example, the word *palette* is respelled **păl′ĭt**. By referring to the key that appears at the bottom of the dictionary page, you see that the symbol ă stands for the sound of *a* in *pat.* The symbol ĭ stands for the sound of *i* in *pit.* The heavy black slanted line (′) after the first syllable is called a STRESS MARK. It tells you that you should put more stress on the first syllable than on the second syllable when you say the word. Pronounce the word *palette* softly to yourself.

On the dictionary page use the special respelling of the word *palatial* and the pronunciation key at the bottom of the page to help you pronounce that word. Look at the special spelling of the word *palisade.* Notice that it has two stress marks. The heavier stress mark (′) that follows the last syllable is called a PRIMARY STRESS MARK; the lighter stress mark (′) that follows the first syllable is called a SECONDARY STRESS MARK. A syllable that has a primary stress mark in a word is spoken with the most force; a syllable that has a secondary stress mark is spoken with medium force; a syllable that has no stress mark is spoken with the weakest force.

Find the following words on the dictionary page and use the pronunciation key to help you pronounce the words:

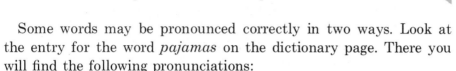

1. paisley
2. palaver
3. paleontology
4. pallet

Some words may be pronounced correctly in two ways. Look at the entry for the word *pajamas* on the dictionary page. There you will find the following pronunciations:

(pə **jä′**məz) *or* (**-jăm′**əz)

In the first pronunciation the symbol ä stands for the sound of *a* in *father,* and the *m* sound is a part of the third syllable. In both pronunciations the first syllable is pronounced the same way. In the second pronunciation the symbol ă stands for the sound of *a* in *pat,* and the *m* sound is a part of the second syllable. Pronounce the word both ways.

When you find two pronunciations for a word, you should pronounce the word both ways. Both pronunciations are correct, although the first may be somewhat more common. Use the pronunciation that seems more familiar to you or that sounds more like the way words are pronounced in your area.

Following the pronunciation of a word, you will often find an abbreviation for the part of speech of the word. Abbreviations of this kind include *n.* for *noun, v.* for *verb, adj.* for *adjective,* and so on. The letter *n.* in the entry for *pair* indicates that the meanings that follow will define *pair* as a noun. Farther on in the same entry you will see -*v.* That indicates that the meanings that follow will define *pair* as a verb. As what part or parts of speech can the word *pal* function? *Palatial? Palaver?*

If there is more than one meaning for a word as a particular part of speech, the meanings are numbered. How many noun meanings for the word *palaver* are given on the dictionary page? How many meanings for that same word as a verb? Find three examples of words with only one meaning.

Because many words have more than one meaning, you often need to decide which meaning of a word is the one you are looking for. Use the dictionary page to help you decide which meaning is the correct one for each italicized word in these sentences:

1. The *paling* surrounds the garden and the pool.
2. Linda has a new *pair* of gloves.
3. Jim enjoys *painting* in his spare time.
4. The new wallpaper is *pale* green.

To help you further understand the meanings of words, a dictionary may provide examples that show how a word is used in context. These examples follow the meanings that they illustrate, and they are often printed in italic type to show that they are examples, not meanings. On the dictionary page notice the examples that are given for some of the meanings of the word *pair*. Notice, too, that an example may be just a short phrase, or it may be a whole sentence.

Separate entries occur for words that are spelled alike but have different meanings and different origins. On the dictionary page find the two entries spelled *pall*. In *pall*¹ the word *pall* functions as a noun and has four meanings. In *pall*² the word *pall* functions as a verb and has one meaning. Notice that the meanings of *pall* as a noun are quite different from the meaning of *pall* as a verb. What other words spelled the same way have more than one entry?

Why are words spelled the same way so different in meaning? The ETYMOLOGY of the word provides an answer to that question. The etymology of a word is its origin and development, a kind of history of the word. Here is what one dictionary tells about the etymology of the two words spelled *pall*.

pall¹⁻²
Pall¹ *was Old English* pæll, *which was borrowed from Latin* pallium, *"cloak."* **Pall**² *is shortened from* **appall.**

How does the meaning "cloak" for the word from which *pall*¹ came relate to the present meanings of the noun *pall*? *Pall*² may not seem to have much to do with the word *appall* from which it came; however, *appall* came from a word meaning "to grow pale," and that meaning does bear some relationship to the word *pall* as a verb.

On the dictionary page you will find three words spelled *painter*. Are the three words quite different in meaning? Here is what a dictionary tells about the etymology of those three words.

painter¹⁻²⁻³

Painter¹, *obviously, is from* **paint**. **Painter**² *probably comes from Old French* pentoir, *"clothesline, hanging rope," from* pendre, *"to hang."* **Painter**³, *an Americanism first occurring in the late colonial period, is a variant of* **panther.**

Is there a relationship between the meaning of each word spelled *painter* and the origin of the word? In the following sentence which meaning of the word spelled *painter* is the correct one? *A large painter was seen prowling around the deserted farmhouse.*

There are two words spelled *pale* on the dictionary page. How do the two words differ in meaning? Do they function as different parts of speech? Information about the origin of each word is given this way in a dictionary.

pale¹⁻²

Pale¹ *is from Latin* pālus, *"pointed stick"; it is related to* **palisade** *and to* **pole**². **Pale**² *is from Latin* pallidus, *"pallid."*

Is there a relationship between the present meaning for the first word spelled *pale* and the original meaning, "pointed stick"? How does the present-day meaning of the second word spelled *pale* compare with the original meaning, "pallid"?

As you know, you may find in a dictionary two or more words spelled the same as the word you are looking for. Even though the words are spelled the same, their meanings may be quite different. To ensure that you find the correct word and the correct meaning that you need, you should read through all the entries for the words that are spelled the same.

Notes adapted from The American Heritage School Dictionary, *published by American Heritage Publishing Co., Inc. and Houghton Mifflin Company. Reprinted by permission.*

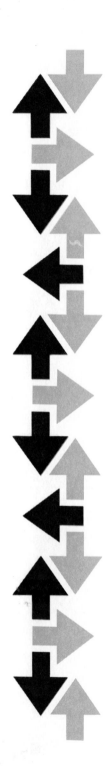

Discussion

Help your class answer these questions:
1. In what order are words listed in a dictionary?
2. What is the purpose of guide words?
3. Why is it helpful for you to know how a word may be broken into syllables?
4. How does a dictionary show how a word should be pronounced?
5. What are the two stress marks called? How do they help to tell you how to pronounce a word?
6. How does a dictionary indicate the part of speech of a word?
7. If there are several meanings for a word, how do you decide which meaning to use?
8. What is meant by the etymology of a word?
9. Why are there sometimes separate entries for words that are spelled the same way?
10. How would you pronounce the four words listed on page 217?
11. What is the meaning of each italicized word in the four sentences on page 218?

On your own

In the glossary at the back of this book you will find the words that are italicized in the following sentences. Copy the number of each sentence on a sheet of paper and write the meaning of the italicized word as it is used in the sentence.

1. In the first *quarter* my brother came home from college only once.
2. At the end of the first *lap* Dave was far ahead of all the other runners.
3. Some people consider air pollution a national *blight*.
4. The *hulls* had to be removed before we could eat the berries.
5. The judge will *render* her decision on Thursday.
6. What was your *score* on the test?
7. I thought the last speaker would *drone* on forever.
8. Did you see that great *pivot* the left forward just made?
9. My aunt accepted a position on the *faculty* of Atlantic College.

10. Such a *brilliant* scholar will certainly go far.
11. Before you leave the country, you should *convert* some of your dollars into foreign money.
12. Sarah didn't realize how late it was until she heard the church bells *toll* at midnight.

Checking your work

If you are asked to do so, read aloud the meanings you found for the italicized words in the sentences in On your own. Check your paper as others read their answers. If you made a mistake, find out why you did so.

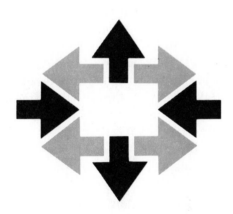

An Unpredictable Japanese Lady

by Monica Sone

The author, Monica Sone, whose Japanese name is Kazuko Monica Itoi (kä-zōō-kō män-i-kə e-tō-ē), recalls some humorous episodes of her childhood in the early 1930's on the Seattle waterfront, where her father ran the old Carrollton Hotel.

Mother was different from Father in that she was not always right, but she was a lot of fun. Unlike Father, who took life with the unwavering calm of a philosopher, Mother vibrated on a higher frequency. In fact, she rattled the sensibilities of some of the more correct women in the neighborhood. It was because Mother had come to the United States at the wrong age, when she was a curious seventeen-year-old on whom the cement of Japanese culture had not yet been set. Mother tried hard. She cultivated a gentle and soft-spoken manner and even managed a poker face when the occasion demanded, but underneath, Mother was a quivering mass of emotions.

We were satisfied with her just as she was. I was glad that she wasn't like slow-as-molasses Mrs. Kato, chubby Jiro's mother. Once Mother and I went downtown with Mrs. Kato. Just as we were about to board the Second Avenue streetcar, the three of us became separated in the swarming crowd. The car door opened and people surged inside, but all of a sudden the movement stopped. The bottleneck was slow-motion Mrs. Kato smiling and bowing graciously to Mother, who was submerged in the crowd. "*Sah, Itoi-sama,*[1] *dozo osaki ni* (sä ē-tō-ē-sä-mä dō-zō ō-sä-kē nē). Please, after you."

---

[1] **Itoi-sama,** endearing term for Mrs. Itoi.

I screamed at Mother to tell Mrs. Kato to please get in and dispense with the ceremony. Mrs. Kato was standing hesitantly, waiting for Mother to emerge from the tight crowd. Mother's voice floated out to her in Japanese, "Please go ahead; we're right behind you."

Reluctantly, Mrs. Kato climbed up into the car and bowed to the conductor as she dropped a token into the box. All this time people were turning and staring at us, attracted to the Japanese dialogue.

When we neared our destination and should have been moving toward the rear door, Mrs. Kato again started bowing and urging Mother to go ahead. Mother, firmly wedged between a mountain of a woman clutching two shopping bags of groceries and a crotchety old man, declined the invitation. "Iiye (ē-ē-ĕ) . . . dozo. After you."

I suppressed a scream, fought my way through the packed bodies, and leaped off the streetcar first, not caring whether Mrs. Kato made it or not. Mother emerged successfully, but we lost Mrs. Kato then and there.

One of Mother's many consuming desires was to learn to speak the English language well. Mother's younger sister, Kikue (kē-kōo-ĕ), had the opportunity to attend high school, and in a short time Kikue was able to speak fluently. Mother had been married too soon and missed out on this chance, but she was determined to master the language with whatever facilities she had. If her four children could learn to speak it, there was no reason why she couldn't. Still, we felt something was amiss whenever we were welcomed home by Mother with a beaming smile, "Well, did you guys have a good time?"

Mother was really too busy, and we were too impatient to sit down and teach her in a systematic way. It was mostly a trial and error method . . . a great trial to us while she made the errors. She drove us frantic by asking us the meanings of odd phrases to which she was invariably attracted. She liked the lilt of a phrase in a song which she had heard over the radio "nothing but a nothing." She repeated it over and over to master the difficult "th" sound. We told her it meant nothing at all and that no one ever talked that way, really, so there was no sense in memorizing it.

Father had no practical need to learn a polite version of the English language because his contacts were with skid row men, and it was better for him to speak to his rambunctious guests on equal earthy terms. But Mother simply could not get away with a similar dialect. She had to attend teas, P.T.A. meetings, and festivals at school and carry on conversation with our teachers. Many Japanese mothers never appeared at these functions, they being such excruciating experiences.

Those who did show up remained close to their children, smiled tirelessly, and said, "Yes," "No," "Thank you," and laughed at the wrong time. But Mother was not satisfied with just a spiritual evening of good will. Although I was secretly proud that Mother showed spunk in wading into a full-sized conversation, I often wished that she was not quite so spirited with her words. As she chatted with my teacher, I listened in agony, for it was always a mangled dialogue in which the two parties never seemed to be talking about the same thing at the same time. Miss Powers would smile at Mother, "So you are KaZOOko's mother." Miss Powers could never remember that there is no accent on any syllable in pronouncing my Japanese name. "You seem so young, Mrs. Itoi; you look more like her big sister."

"Yes, I am, thank you." Mother smiled back, more intent on being gracious at the moment than on the subject matter. Miss Powers remained unruffled.

"Did KaZOOko tell you we're having a special program for the May Festival soon?"

"Oh yes, it was very nice. I enjoyed program so much." Mother nodded her head enthusiastically. I curled inside. I had not yet told Mother about the May Festival, and I knew she had become lost after the words "special program." Mother was speaking about the Christmas program. Miss Powers's blue eyes fluttered, but she quickly figured that Mother was thinking about last year's May Festival.

"Oh yes, we had a nice time all right, but KaZOOko wasn't in my class then. This year she's going to be one of the crocuses, and we want her in a real pretty costume ... a lavender skirt and purple petal hat made from crepe paper. Do you think you could help us make the dress if I sent the instructions home with KaZOOko?"

"Oh yes, I make them all the time." Mother smiled with great assurance. It was a bare-faced lie. Mother had never made a single crocus costume for me nor had she ever seen one; but Mother did make lots of pretty dresses for me for which she thought Miss Powers was complimenting her. I had to bolster this crippled dialogue.

"Mother can help with the costume, Miss Powers. She made this for me," I said, holding out the skirt of my new dress. It was a flaming, candy-red taffeta dress, crawling with dainty ruffles according to my tyrannical specifications. Miss Powers was back on the track, and she gushed politely, "Did she really? My what a wonderful seamstress you are, Mrs. Itoi. And I love that color! It's as lovely as can be."

"Oh, no, it's not so good," Mother said modestly. She could have said, "Thank you," at this moment, but I was content that Mother was talking about the same thing as Miss Powers. All of a sudden Mother burst out, "It's too red, but my daughter, she likes red. I think it's *lousy!*"

A tense silence followed. Miss Powers was struggling to keep a straight face. I felt as if I were standing inside a furnace. I managed to tug at Mother's elbow and whisper, "*Kairo* (kä-ē-rō), Mama, let's go home."

I thought, miserably, as I walked home with Mother, how much the other teachers would laugh when Miss Powers told them about Mother's *faux pas.*[2] I pointed out to Mother in a tearful, disgraced-for-life voice that she had made a terrible mistake. "Mama, you should have said, 'loud, loud!' not 'lousy!' 'Lousy' is a vulgar word, a bad word like 'hell.' "

"Soh? I didn't know. I heard you children using it all the time, so I thought it was perfectly all right." Mother didn't sound at all sorry. I fell into a morose silence the rest of the way home, wondering how I was ever going back to school and face my teacher. But when I saw her next, she seemed to have forgotten all about the episode.

Mother's haphazard way with the language did not always work against her. I remember once she became involved in a switch of identity and lived for a day like

---

[2] **faux pas** (fō-pä′), a social blunder.

royalty, suddenly swept into high society. It happened when Sumiko (sōō-mē-kō) and I were rabid fans of Mickey Mouse and members of the Mickey Mouse Club at the Coliseum Theater, which met every Saturday morning. We sang Mickey Mouse songs; we saw Mickey Mouse pictures; we wore Mickey Mouse sweaters; we owned Mickey Mouse wrist watches. Because the club had the endorsement of the Parent-Teacher Association, Father and Mother raised no objections to our latest craze.

One Saturday there was to be a very special party to which we could invite our mothers. There would be a Mickey Mouse drawing contest for the members and refreshments for everyone. Mother said although she would like to be there, she was too busy Saturday morning. Sumiko and I wept.

"But, Mama, everybody else's mother will be there. We'll be the *only* ones without a mother. People will think we're orphans."

Fortunately, a few days before the event, Mother went to a P.T.A. meeting at Bailey Gatzert School, at which time Miss Mahon, our school principal, pleaded with the Japanese mothers to go to this particular party with their children. Women of different nationalities would be there, and Miss Mahon wanted to see the Japanese represented. Miss Mahon stirred Mother's conscience. Mother decided to go. Su-

miko and I knew it was going to be one of the biggest, happiest parties we would ever attend.

That bright Saturday morning Sumiko and I put on our best red coats and matching red berets. We bounded down the long flight of stairs, clutching our Mickey Mouse sketches, and ran all the way downtown. Mother had promised that she would follow later, as soon as she had finished the hotel chores. We had drilled Mother on the location of the theater building. With a thick red crayon we printed the name of the theater, its address, and the name Pike Street, the block where she was supposed to get off the streetcar, on a big sheet of paper, so Mother could not lose it or herself.

Having taken these precautions, Sumiko and I relaxed. At the Coliseum Theater we pushed our dimes through the box-office window, deposited our drawings in a large chest in the foyer, and slid into our seats, breathless with hope that one of us would win a prize. The meeting started off as usual. The same double-chinned master of ceremonies greeted us, shook with laughter at his jokes, and raved a great deal about what a wonderful time we were going to have. He introduced a bouncy, Dutch-bobbed, five-year-old girl named Patsy, who tap-danced and sang for us. Later the lights were dimmed, the words of songs were flashed on the screen, and Patsy led us in singing our Mickey Mouse songs. Soon it was time for the judging of the picture contest. Sumiko and I also thought it was time for Mother's appearance. We went to the lounge where we had agreed to meet her. No one was there. Little Sumiko's lips started to tremble. I said, hastily, "She'll be here soon. Let's wait."

We sank deep into the luxurious low sofa and waited silently. Hours seemed to pass and still there was no Mother. We hurried back to our seats to see what was going on, but it was hard to keep our attention focused on the stage. We learned that the pictures were still being judged upstairs. Everyone was getting restless, and two boys started wrestling in the aisle. Soon a team of usherettes swooped down the aisles, distributing ice cream in Dixie cups, and cookies. While we thoughtfully ate our refreshments, the master of ceremonies suddenly appeared and announced the names of three contest winners. Our spirits sagged when neither of our names was mentioned; and worse than that, Mother was lost.

The party over, the auditorium, hallway, and lounge soon filled with chattering boys and girls and their smiling, bright-eyed mothers. We made one last inspection of the theater without success. Maybe Mother was wandering downtown, lost and bewildered. Or maybe she had just decided not to attend.

We headed back home with an ache lodged deep in our throats. How could Mother have failed us after she had promised us a dozen times! We climbed heavily up the hotel stairs, made our way to our living quarters with solemn expressions on our faces, all set to reprove Mother. The rooms were empty. We scurried through the dim labyrinth of halls until we found Father in the last room at the other end of the hotel. He was busily making the bed. Indignantly I asked, "Papa, where is Mama? Why didn't she come to the party?"

"*Nani?*[3] Why, Mama left about half an hour after you both had gone. I was afraid she would be late, so I told her to take a taxi. Where could she have gone?"

We were thoroughly alarmed. Sumiko burst out crying. Father, looking harried, put the finishing touches on the bed, picked Sumiko up, and led me out of the room.

"Now, now, don't start that. Mama's all right, wherever she is. She's been downtown before by herself. Maybe she just walked into the wrong place. If Mama isn't home in an hour, I will call the police."

At the word "police" I started to cry too. Father sighed and took us into the kitchen, where he tried to stifle our sobs with cookies. "Now, why don't you two go back to the

---

[3] **Nani?** (nä-nē): What?

parlor and play a while. I have a little more work to do."

No, we didn't feel like it. We wanted to be with him. We trailed after him with wet faces and damp cookies, really feeling like orphans now. As Father pushed the carpet sweeper carefully over the frayed edges of the rug, he asked questions about the party. Between sniffles and bites we managed to give Father all the boring details. Then, all of a sudden behind us we heard the sweetest voice in the world. It was Mother.

"Ka-chan, Sumi-chan,"[4] she said happily, "wasn't that a lovely party?"

Father stopped sweeping. Sumiko and I stared at her, wondering what party she had attended. Mother was still glowing with excitement. She looked exquisite and beautiful in her best gown of pale lavender silk velvet. Delicate floral patterns were traced in velvet, woven over a background of sheer voile. A huge butterfly rhinestone pin held the drape on the side of the skirt. Mother also had on a close-fitting helmet over her freshly marcelled black hair. The long length of hair was coiled into a low, thick bun at the nape of her neck. She looked pretty and out of place, standing in the doorway near the mop and the laundry pile. She turned brightly to Father, "By the way, what does 'consul's wife' mean?"

"Consul's wife? What in the world . . . why, that's the wife of a *ryoji* (rē-ō-jē). Why do you ask?"

"Arra!" Mother shrieked in horror. "A *ryoji's* wife! *Doshima sho!*"[5]

Mother clapped her hand to her mouth, then to her head as if she didn't know what to do next. Sumiko and I jumped all over her, trying to get her attention.

"Mama, Mama, what happened? Where were you anyway? We waited for you all morning."

Mother then burst into hysterical laughter, and the only words we could get out of her were, *"Mah, iyayo! Tondemo nai kotoyo."*[6]

We went back to the parlor and waited impatiently for Mother to subside. Father scolded her, "Where were you all this time? The children have been crying for you all morning."

With tears of laughter in her eyes Mother told us the whole story. She had gone to our Mickey Mouse party. The taxi driver had delivered her to the front of the Coliseum Theater. Just as soon as she had stepped out of the cab, a suave,

---

[4] **Ka-chan, Sumi-chan** (kä-chän su̱-mē-chän), endearing terms for Kazuko and Sumiko.

[5] **Doshima sho!** (dō-shē-mä shō): What shall I do!

[6] **Mah, iyayo! Tondemo nai kotoyo.** (mä ē-yä-yō) (tōn-dě-mō nä-ē kō-tō-yō): Oh, my! This is ridiculous.

beautifully groomed woman pounced on Mother and escorted her into the theater. "We're so glad you could come, Mrs. Saito (sä-ē-tō). We're having quite a party this morning."

Mother felt slightly overpowered with this warm reception, but she smiled politely back at the nice lady as if she were quite used to such cordiality.

"Thank you. I'm late little bit. I'm so sorry."

"It doesn't matter in the least, Mrs. Saito. You're in time for the important part of the program."

Mother didn't completely understand what the woman was saying, but she realized she was being addressed as Mrs. Saito. She corrected her new friend, "I'm Mrs. Itoi."

"Oh? Er . . . you're the Japanese consul's wife, aren't you?"

Mother didn't know what she meant, but she knew very well she should be agreeable at all times. She said, "Yes, thank you."

Obviously, the hostess had been assigned the special task of taking charge of the Japanese consul's wife, Mrs. Saito. The eager hostess had stepped out of the theater door several times; and when at last a beautifully gowned Oriental woman had stepped out of a cab, she thought the quarry was safe in her hands. The woman trilled to Mother, "Oh, Mrs. Saito, I wonder if you would do us the honor of acting as one of the judges for our Mickey Mouse drawing contest?"

"Yes, yes," Mother answered absent-mindedly, wondering why the woman kept calling her Mrs. Saito. "I'm Mrs. Itoi."

"I beg your pardon, Mrs. Itoi." The hostess paused for a moment and then began again, "You *are* the consul's wife?" This time she asked the question slowly and loudly. "Yes!" Mother replied, almost snapping. The woman was certainly asking a lot of questions. The hostess finally seemed satisfied with Mother's positive reply.

Just then, a woman walking in front of her stumbled. Her high heel had caught the edge of the carpet and both heel and shoe came off. Mother dove for the torn heel and shoe. She had fixed many a broken heel. The woman with the broken heel said, "Dear me, it would happen now."

"I fix for you," Mother assured her.

The hostess's eyes widened, "Please, Mrs. Saito, er, Mrs. Itoi, the maid will do that." She turned in desperation to the woman, "I'd like you to meet Mrs. Saito, the Japanese consul's wife."

The introductions were made; but Mother ignored them both, adjusted the heel into the nail holes, kneeled down, and pounded it back into place on the marble floor.

"Fixed now, I think." Mother returned the shoe to the pink-faced

woman while the hostess made high-pitched sounds.

Mother was led upstairs to a luxuriously furnished room, glittering with shiny mirrors and elegant crystal chandeliers, the like of which Mother had never seen. The room was filled with the subdued murmurs of distinguished-looking guests. The hostess introduced Mother to many gay, enchanting people. Mother caught words like "Swedish . . . English . . . German" and heard the same mysterious expression, "consul's wife," over and over again. Soon everyone was addressing Mother as Mrs. Saito, and Mother let it pass amiably. Far be it from her to continue correcting these lovely people. Nobody seemed to mind that Mother hardly said anything except, "I'm glad to meet you," and "Yes, thank you," whenever refreshments were offered to her and "I think so," when she couldn't understand the topic of conversation.

Mother sipped delicious coffee from a tiny, doll-sized cup and nibbled at dainty sandwiches of all shapes and colors. On the tables were gleaming silver platters of bonbons, cookies, and assorted nuts. Mother felt as if she were part of a movie set.

Soon the hostess came up to Mother again and closeted her in a small, adjoining room with three other smartly dressed women who spoke English with heavy foreign accents. No one understood what the other was saying, but somehow they picked the prize pictures of Mickey Mouse. They went back to the reception room again for some more polite chatter and laughter. Half an hour later the party drew to a close. Mother bade farewell to her new acquaintances, the French consul's wife, the English consul's wife, the German consul's wife, and a few more. They all shook her hand cordially. "Goot-by, Mrs. Saito. It was just loavely meeting you. . . ."

What charming manners! What delightful ladies! The same attentive hostess escorted Mother out of the theater, hailed a taxi for her, and waved farewell. Mother sank back in the rear seat, feeling positively giddy with the personal attention and hospitality that had been hers from the very beginning to the end. The cab driver had to ask her, "Where to lady?"

"Yes, please. Oh! . . . 217 Occidental Avenue."

The driver glanced back at her twice. Mother, looking like an Oriental princess of the court, sat fanning herself with her perfumed silk handkerchief and sighing, "My, my what a grand party it was and such cultured, gentle people. Miss Mahon will be certainly glad to know I took part and helped with the picture contest." The taxicab sped through the downtown shopping district and plunged into the fish and barnacle atmosphere of the waterfront where our hotel was located.

We have often wondered if the reception committee of the gala Mickey Mouse Club party ever discovered this error. We thanked God that Mrs. Saito, the Japanese consul's wife, had not appeared. Mother might have been hustled out of the theater as an impostor and a criminal. Then we thought of something worse ... maybe Mrs. Saito had attended, but nobody had met her at the door. She would have had to pay an admission fee at the box office to get in and been forced to find a seat for herself in the audience of screaming, squirming youngsters. I wondered if an usherette had handed her a Dixie cup of ice cream and a cookie too. She probably would have resented such shabby treatment and reported it to her husband, the Japanese consul. We saw international complications arise and diplomatic relationships slip a notch between America and Japan. For days after Mother was not quite herself as she wavered between sudden bursts of laughter and mortified mutterings.

DISCUSSION

1. Why was Mrs. Itoi unable to speak English well?
2. How did Mrs. Itoi's inability to speak and understand English prove embarrassing to Kazuko? How did it get Mrs. Itoi into an unusual situation?
3. Why might attendance at a P.T.A. meeting be an excruciating experience for many Japanese mothers?
4. Why did Mrs. Itoi finally decide to go to the party? Did she have a good time? How do you know?
5. Why was Mrs. Itoi mistaken for the consul's wife?
6. Why did Mrs. Itoi feel she should be agreeable at all times?
7. What would you have done if you had been in Mrs. Itoi's place at the party? Have you ever been mistaken for someone else? What did you do?
8. Do you think Miss Powers really had forgotten all about the dress episode when Kazuko saw her next? Why do you think that? Why is it kind not to remind people of matters that are embarrassing to them?

9. What do you think might have happened if the real consul's wife had come to the party? What would you have done in that situation if you were Mrs. Itoi?

AUTHOR

Nisei (nē-sā) *Daughter,* the book from which the story you have just read was taken, is a book about the author's life. *Nisei* means someone born in America of Japanese parents.

Monica Kazuko Sone was six years old before she was told she had "Japanese blood in her veins." Even then, it meant nothing to her as she had always thought of herself as a Yankee. She lived a dual life as a child, going to both American and Japanese schools. In the American school, which she loved, she was a laughing, shrieking, happy child. In the Japanese school, which her parents insisted she attend, she was a quiet, little block of politeness. Mrs. Sone's childhood included a trip to Japan, and although the Sone family hated to say good-by to the old Japanese grandfather, she and her family were happy to return to Seattle, where they felt they belonged.

When World War II broke out, Monica and her family, along with many other Japanese-Americans, were evacuated to Camp Minidoka in Idaho. They became family No. 10,710. Life was not easy behind barbed wire, but they succeeded in accepting their fates without bitterness. When they were relocated to Indianapolis, Indiana, Mrs. Sone attended Hanover College. Later, she got her degree in Clinical Psychology at Western Reserve University in Cleveland, Ohio.

Mrs. Sone's book is a protest against people who sneer at the words *democracy* and *freedom* because they have met with unpleasantness in the course of their lives as Americans.

Her other writing consists of articles written for Japanese newspapers. She is married and has several children of her own.

CAVE of DANGER

by Bryce Walton

Matt and his best buddy, Spotty Jessup, have mapped out an area in some of the wildest land in Natacomo County, Missouri, where they dream of finding an unexplored cave.

One day Matt, always with his rucksack filled with spelunker equipment on his back, detours on his way to school to one of their unexplored areas. He discovers the long-searched-for opening to a cave and drops himself through it — just to take a quick look and to make sure he has made an authentic cave strike.

Matt dropped boldly into darkness, feeling only the excitement and awe of exploring where no other human being had ever been.

He shouted. He listened to echoes never heard before among these ancient and hidden rocks. Finally, as a pile of loose shale gave way under his boots, a shiver went down his back. His footprints would be the first, the very first.

He clung to the drop rope, gouging out a flat area safe enough to stand on. Tumbling rocks bounded into darkness and sent eerie echoes clattering.

Matt squatted beside his rucksack and dug out the flashlight. Flicking it on, he eagerly watched the beam eat into a blackness so absolute that it made the light appear like a solid column. He glanced up at the light from the drop opening. It seemed as weak and blurred now as a hazed star.

Keep an eye on that light up there, he warned himself. It has to be your guiding light if you get lost or lose your flash or your sense of direction. That light might be as important to him as the North Star is to a man sailing at night without a compass.

Rule five of the Natacomo County Cave Grotto's ten commandments blinked on and off in his mind: *You will always carry three sources of light and a waterproof container of matches.*

He hesitated a moment. He wouldn't stay down long enough or go far enough to worry about emergencies. He certainly wouldn't wander off far enough to lose sight of that drop opening. He didn't have enough caving gear, including an emergency light, to play around with.

He only wanted to figure out approximately how big this first chamber was and the number and kind of corridors leading out of it. He also wanted to make sure there were plenty of grotesque formations to attract tourists. So no need to worry about rules, he told himself. Later, when he came back with Spotty and Ernst Fuller, the Grotto's leader, to make a complete systematic exploratory survey, all the rules would be obeyed.

He had unsnapped his rucksack from the rope end. Now he hoisted it to his shoulders and angled his light around. The flash was powerful, but it failed to reach any rock formations. So the chamber was large, very large. He would soon know approximately how large, but already it had a vast hollow feel to it, like the interior of a cathedral.

He pointed the light down. Below him he saw a slide made of everything from gravel to large sharp-edged boulders. He was standing on a hill of breakdown stuff, crumbled for thousands of years by water seepage from the ceiling. He estimated the mound to be about thirty feet high, making the whole drop nearly one hundred and thirty feet! Some drop, he thought again, about twice the size of anything offered in the Moseby Wonder Caverns.

He dug in his heels and started sliding eagerly down a trough of loose shale. Overly eager, he slipped and slid some ten feet on his back, digging and pawing as helplessly as an overturned beetle, until the incline flattened out a little and he stopped. Then he proceeded more carefully. Loosened shale rattled down into the dark. As the echoes died, the dark silence seemed thicker and somehow more threatening.

Most caves are awesome, but this one was more so. The silence here was like a sound — a terrible, alien sound never heard before. That's just it, he decided; no one *has* ever heard a sound down here before. This cave is a newly found one.

After reaching a flat, red, sandy floor, he paused and angled his flashlight beam slowly about. It still failed to illuminate any formations or rocks or walls. Matt hesitated again, uneasily.

What about the drop? A very deep drop to get back out of alone. But Matt carried Prusik knots: three rope loops for going up a free-swinging or standing rope, much the way a linesman goes up a telephone pole. A sure and safe way out but so long and tedious that Matt preferred not to think about it until later.

Then he forgot about the future. He forgot about the drop. He tried to keep a straight course from the breakdown stuff to the chamber's wall. He wanted to pace off a good estimate of the distance. But large boulders looming in his path forced him to alter his direction several times.

At first, he tried to keep some sense of direction, but then he no longer cared. He only thought about going ahead, across the red, sandy floor. Dazed with wonder, he walked into a new, unexplored world. His light brought to dazzling life sights no human eye had ever before seen.

He suddenly stopped and stared, slowly letting out his breath, as his flash reflected from a great area of gypsum, glistening like millions of tiny diamonds. His hand trembled a little as he shifted his light to the left, and the glitter vanished into absolute blackness, only to reveal, farther along, more spectacular and dazzling formations.

He walked on, feeling as if he were under a strange spell, pulled into the unknown by an invisible rope.

In all his caving Matt had never seen such beautiful gypsum and travertine formations. Swinging his flashlight beam to the right, he uncovered a dense forest of great white and reddish stalactites hanging like fantastic icicles, their tips dripping water that spattered on dazzling stalagmites that thrust over twenty feet from the floor.

The awesome spectacle entirely disappeared as Matt shifted the light. Wonderland vanished instantly and completely into chilling blackness.

One thing about caves always disturbed him — the darkness.

Without some light nothing is visible. And the blackness of a cave is pure below the twilight zone. Some light exists on the earth's surface during the darkest night; human eyes cannot pick it up, but a cat's specialized eyes can. Matt knew that, down here, a cat would be totally blind, just as was every other

living thing below the twilight zone. Cave rats, salamanders, fish, and cave crickets are blind. Generations of darkness have bred sight out of them and turned them slug-white. If they cannot see, they cannot be seen, so there is no need for camouflage.

Every formation he stumbled onto topped the one before. His flash made gigantic travertine columns glow like incandescent lamps. A city of stalactites and stalagmites glistened around a suddenly revealed pool — a much bigger subterranean pool than Matt had ever seen before; its unruffled surface shone in his light like a great mirror.

By this time Matt knew the drop chamber was huge. But he still had no idea how big it was or what shape.

An hour later he still didn't know. He found stand-up corridors filled with more and more fantastic formations. He discovered crawlways, squirmways, and indications of several other caverns. He tossed rocks, yelled, then timed the echoes to get estimates of size and distance. The corridors were long and large. He ventured down one extensive corridor far enough to feel the cold sting of spray from a waterfall. A hundred feet or so beyond the waterfall, he heard the ominous rush and roar of a big underground river.

Quickly, he returned to the drop chamber and worked his way around what he thought was the other wall. Once he guessed the chamber to be roughly elliptical in shape, at least one hundred and fifty feet long and seventy-five feet wide.

A while later he changed his mind. The wall curved again, and he realized that the chamber was far larger than he had guessed. He still didn't know its dimensions or shape.

He only knew that he had made a fabulous find. He knew caves. He knew what tourists paid for. He knew that the Moseby Wonder Caverns was one of the most popular caves in southern Missouri and that it brought in thousands and thousands of dollars a year to the Moseby clan. And Matt knew that this cave was at least ten times bigger and better than the Moseby Caverns. He laughed softly. This cave would make the Moseby Caverns seem like an abandoned gopher's hole.

Then Matt suddenly knew something else, and he stopped grinning. His watch had stopped. It had stopped at 1:15, at about the time he'd fallen and slid down the hill of breakdown stuff.

He frowned at the faint radium glow of his wristwatch dial. He shook the watch; the second hand stayed dead. Must have hit it on a rock when I fell, he thought uneasily.

He shrugged. So what? Time wasn't important down here unless you planned on staying awhile, which he didn't. He couldn't have been down long, he thought, not more than a couple of hours. Right now — whenever that is — it's time to go up and out — with Prusik knots, he remembered and groaned.

He guessed he had been down for two hours. That was only an estimate, a logical guess. But a logical guess based on what? He blinked slowly and rubbed the flat of his hand across his mouth. He tried to remember where he had been, tried to remember how far he had walked, how many corridors he'd looked into, how many formations he'd stopped and stared at for how long. How long had he really stayed there, listening to the waterfall and the underground river?

Nothing became clear, and the more Matt tried to remember, the less clear this time-puzzle became. Moving in absolute darkness, relieved only by a beam of light, you never really knew where you had been or where you were going. There was never any perspective, Matt thought. He'd never thought of checking the time until just now when he discovered he had no means of measuring it.

Now he had no real feeling about how long he'd been down or where he'd been or what he'd seen. The time since entering the cave seemed vague and mixed up and shadowy and unreal. Above all, it seemed timeless.

Trying to shrug off that growing uneasiness, he walked on through a glow of aragonite crystals, or cave flowers. He started following the rock formations that he assumed were part of the drop-chamber wall. After taking a few steps, he stopped suddenly for no reason he could name.

He hesitated; then something made him jerk around and look up.

He stared up into solid blackness. He kept staring, but no glint of light appeared. The blackness remained solid and unbroken.

He squinted. He strained his eyes. But not even the faintest suggestion of light was there.

Where was the opening of the drop?

He shivered, then turned and stumbled back in the direction from which he had come. After taking three steps, he stopped and looked up and blinked slowly at the darkness. The drop-opening light *had* to be there. He walked again, stopped, and walked again, following the curve of what he assumed to be the chamber wall.

He felt the sudden tightening of his nerves as he crouched with his back against the wall and looked up into uncompromising blackness. His mouth felt dry with fear.

He couldn't know where he was without seeing the light of that drop opening. He couldn't know where he was or which way to go. I'm lost, he thought. And I've never been lost before.

He suddenly thought of his flash

and remembered the fifth of the Cave Grotto's ten commandments: *You will always carry three sources of light and a waterproof container of matches.*

Well, he had the waterproof matches. But he quickly switched off the flashlight. He told himself that he turned the light off because it might make some overhead glimmer of light less visible. No, he admitted, the real reason is I'm afraid I'm lost. And I ought to conserve my batteries.

There was only blackness. It seemed to thicken and to press against his face, eyes, mouth, and nose. He felt sweat trickle down the sides of his face. His hands gripped the flashlight so hard that he heard his knuckles crack. But he resisted the impulse to switch on the light.

Just stay cool, he told himself, and you'll figure things out.

He thought of Ernst Fuller's advice: "Never panic. Never let yourself get scared in a dark cave. You have to think your way out of tight spots. To do that, first of all you must stay calm."

And wherever Matt was, he forced himself to stand very still. He told himself to stand there, calm and cool, and figure things out.

What if I'm not in the big drop chamber at all? It was the most logical possibility — and the worst. Matt wiped sweat from his forehead with the back of his glove. He'd been sure he was following the curved chamber wall in a large elliptical path. Each time he'd ventured down branching corridors, he'd been very careful about keeping track of distance and direction and the number of steps taken; he was sure he'd always come back to his starting points.

But he still might have wandered off down some side corridor. The admission of that possibility made him shiver and hunch up in the squeezing dark. What he had thought was the chamber wall might have been a corridor wall. The long curve he'd followed might have been that of a huge corridor leading off slowly from the chamber. If so, how far along that corridor might he have come to get to where he was now? A more petrifying question was, Had he angled off down some branch corridor from the bigger one, then maybe into another corridor — and how far?

He stopped himself. Passageways and walls and corridors could cross and recross and turn into others. If he'd really wandered into such a maze, then it was stupid trying to figure it out. It's only a speculation anyway, he reminded himself, and I might still be in the main drop chamber or close to it.

He decided that the best procedure was to retrace his course. No matter how much it meandered, or where, the trail should be visible. At least he ought to be able to find bits and pieces of it. He had to use his light. Switching it on, he aimed the beam over the red, sandy floor. When he got down on his knees, he made out the faint markings of his boots. He inched back along the wall. The markings disappeared occasionally, but he soon picked them up again and kept moving, slowly, in fits and starts, sometimes probing with his flash and crawling in slow widening circles before finding the trail again.

He crawled on hands and knees, his face a few inches from the floor like a scenting coon dog's. When the sand turned into patches of bare rock, he found faint scratchings of his boot spikes. He soon started to breathe easier. No matter how tedious this backtracking might be, it must lead to his drop rope eventually. As he kept moving, his self-confidence began to revive.

But sometime later he lay on his stomach, rigid and tense, with one arm outstretched and the hand flat on the cold rock. He squinted and rubbed at the markings, but the trail kept fading. So he stopped struggling with himself and admitted the fearful reason why. His flashlight was going out. Now the light was a weak, sickly yellow. In a few more minutes it would be dead. It was already useless, so he turned it off.

This time, when the solid surrounding blackness squeezed in, he felt himself shrinking back and squinting his eyes as if threatened by physical attack.

After a while he forced himself to sit up. He slid back stiffly over the floor until he felt his rucksack pressing against the rock wall. He had no idea how long he had sat there. But his body remained rigid with fear. He felt his eyes open wide and strain at the dark, as if he expected to see something in it. Ridiculous, he reminded himself, you couldn't see anything without light. You might as well say that without light there is nothing to see. Before you came along, there was no sight here because there was never any light, and now —

He switched on what remained of his light. The vague, yellow, fading glow was like something dying in the dark, worse in a way than the total blackness.

He raised a gloved hand up and held it directly in front of his eyes. Nothing. He might as well not have had a hand at all. It really felt as if there might not be a hand there in the dark.

He clipped his flashlight on his belt and felt with his other hand. Yes, one gloved hand rasped against the other glove. And he felt the **pressure through his gloves, the** pressure on his flesh. He took off his gloves and felt again. Still, his bare hands didn't feel exactly real.

Be calm, he thought. Just stay cool and figure the angles.

Sitting there invisible even to himself, he tried to hold off panic and then terror, and he thought of the Grotto's commandments. One special rule ought to apply now, he thought:

If lost or lights all fail, you will stay where you are; you will wait patiently in the dark in order to avoid injury and to make easier the work of rescuers, who will always come.

That's a good rule, he thought, a very good rule. Stay where you are. Wait patiently in the dark to make easier the work of rescuers, who will always come. Yes, no doubt about it, a very good rule. But Matt felt a cold charge of terror.

No one knew about this cave. No one even knew it existed. No one but Matt Wilde. And that's me, he thought — Matt Wilde sitting here and waiting patiently until help comes, which means I can sit here and be calm and patient and wait, but no one will ever come. No one can ever come and rescue me, he thought, because no one has any idea where I am or where this cave is or even what part of the area this cave is in. Spotty Jessup has a map, but it doesn't show this cave. . . .

Matt sat there, rigid and cold, for a long time. He felt that it was a long time, although he had no idea how long. He might have sat there for a minute, a day, or a week for all he knew, and this uncertainty was more terrifying than the blackness that made time meaningless.

His nerves seemed to coil and uncoil, then concentrate in the tips of his fingers, around his mouth, along the bridge of his nose. He began to hear the blood thump in his ears. Later he realized he was shaking badly, and he tried to stop himself. But the shaking got worse.

Then he forgot about having the shakes. Something terrible began to happen to his body.

It's cracking, he thought, cracking like a clay statue. Millions of tiny parts, cells and nerves and tissue, all held together by millions of tiny wires, seemed to be falling apart.

Millions of tensions — millions of tiny wires snapping. He started touching his face and neck and chest. Frantically, in the darkness, he touched his shoulders and legs and feet and torso. But he couldn't see anything, and he kept feeling that his body was coming apart.

His left arm seemed to drift away from his shoulder. He told himself this couldn't be possible, but he was afraid to reach up and find out. His feet and ankles were separating. Impossible, he knew, but down there in the blackness between his ankles and feet, he felt a widening space.

Then he was running. Running was wrong, but he couldn't help running. Running without feet made no sense. But he was running, he thought, just to show how crazy that idea was — to show that he *did* have feet. Because how could you run without feet?

The comforting thought occurred to him that if he kept running, his body would have to stay in one piece. The little wires wouldn't all keep snapping.

He cried out. His body thumped. It careened off one rock and bounced painfully on another. His feet churned desperately in empty air; then he crashed down into jagged gypsum formations and rolled into icy water.

He pawed up blindly from the water and through tearing splinters of stone. Then violent little explosions went off in his head.

Matt lay curled up on his side in the dark, with his rucksack pulled in hard against his stomach. His body braced against chills and fever, he tried to deaden all his feelings and blank out his brain. Feeling and thought always ended up with concern about what would happen to him, and that was bad.

Just stay curled up here and hold onto yourself, buddy, he thought. Hold onto yourself and keep on pulling yourself together.

Time is my trouble, he thought despite his efforts not to think, or rather the absence of time because time's gone, disappeared. No idea or feeling about time, and that's really bad; no feeling about how long you've been wherever you are or how long it's taken to get there. A vague idea persists, but when or what or where or how long — no feeling about that. None, whatever. Bad. Very bad.

Day? What does day mean when absolute blackness never changes and nothing moves — no more days or hours or minutes, no more years or weeks or months because moving things make time and nothing moves here. The sun moves up and across the sky and down again — or seems to. And the earth moves around the sun, while rotating on its axis, and the moon moves around the earth. Seeing movement makes time. The same movement, repeating itself, that's what time is, but nothing moves here.

Stop thinking, he warned himself. Don't let those little wires start snapping again. Don't go to pieces like that and start yelling and jumping and running through the rocks like a crazy blind mole.

He curled up more tightly and hugged the rucksack and kept his eyes clenched shut. It was a little better that way, he decided. He felt as if he were hiding. It's a lot more warm and friendly in here, inside myself, he thought. It's me, and that's all there is left anywhere — just me. And if I concentrate on me and the inside of me hard enough, maybe it'll all hold together, specially my heart. Yes, it has a nice, regular, steady movement — a lovely steady rhythm like a clock. Yes, it beats regularly, my heart; and I can depend on it. It beats regularly about seventy-two times a minute. I'll count my heart-

beats. I'll keep counting, keep track of the beats — so many beats a minute — then I'll count the minutes. Soon, I'll figure out the hours, then the days ——

Now he tried not to listen — even to his own heart. It would never be a clock bringing time to the blackness and holding him together. It would only get louder and finally drive him crazy, make him jump up and run and fall and hurt himself again.

Wait, he reminded himself; just sit and wait and hold yourself together. Wait, wait, wait — wait without going crazy again. Wait and try to shut out that maddening sound of water dripping. And wait.

Matt shivered and kept his eyes clenched shut. I entered a cave alone. I didn't tell anyone outside the cave my whereabouts. So I can stay calm and wait, and wait forever, and no rescuers will ever come.

He sank down on the cold rock and rolled over onto his side and buried his face in his arms. He curled up and put his hands over his ears.

Watch yourself, Matt thought, or you'll go batty. He tried to laugh but flinched from the thought of what his own echoing laughs would sound like. . . .

He was sure he'd heard a sound, and he couldn't help imagining it was a hopeful sound. If it weren't a hopeful sound, he was sure he would go running off, yelling and hollering and falling down again. But come to think of it, what did he have to lose? His mind? Time? He gave a short barking laugh, and then he listened.

"Matttttt . . ."

He stared and he listened and he doubted, and he had to keep on, listening and staring. Blackness. No sound. Nothing.

Hands over his ears didn't shut out the sounds now. Small sounds rebound and echo in caves and are amplified a hundred times. Sounds climb over themselves. Echoes reflect more echoes. The source of the sounds is impossible to locate.

"Hey, you down there, Matttttt?"

He sat up slowly, trying to imagine where he was and how he moved in the blackness. He stared and stared, but the blackness and the silence were the same. Nothing was different. It couldn't be different. He had known that. There couldn't be light or any real human voices ever again.

But he kept staring and listening and hoping. And he knew that he always would, no matter how hopeless his situation was. He would never give up hoping for a beam of light, a hint of carbide flame or candlelight or flare.

He hugged his knees and rocked and tried to laugh. He did laugh, then shrank back from the ricochet-ing, multiplying echoes that got louder and louder until he seemed surrounded and buffeted by weird thunder. They sounded like a hundred Matts laughing, he thought. At what?

At Matt?

He stopped. After the weird echoes died laughing, the other sound came back.

Matt crouched against cold rock and shivered. He couldn't hold things off any longer. He couldn't hold himself together.

"I know you're down there, Matt. Hear me? Say something."

Matt shook his head and refused to open his eyes. But the voice re-echoed without mercy. He had no idea where the voice came from, even if it were real. But, of course, it wasn't real. It never was nor could be.

But the voice was so human and familiar, he thought, what a shame if it never can be real. And wouldn't all that echoing be hard to imagine?

Matt jumped up and yelled, his voice rising up and up until it cracked in a scream like shattering glass.

"Help meeeeeeeeeeee!"

Matt suddenly stopped yelling and stared at what seemed to be an explosion of light — a light flaring out white and blinding as it fell. It blazed up higher near Matt, behind a forest of helictites, making weird rock formations jump into brilliant focus. Grottoes of mysterious shades alternated with slabs of crystalline glitter. Matt kept staring and blinking suspiciously.

His breathing was slow and heavy, and he was afraid to move anything but his eyes. Finally, though, very slowly and gradually, his doubts began to give way. It was the light of a dropped flare.

Total darkness was a total nightmare, but a little light made a great difference — *you could see.* A vast relief welled up in him, and he wanted to yell and laugh and run. No, that would be wasting time, he decided; and now that he had time back again, he didn't want to waste any of it.

Dragging his rucksack, he stumbled weakly toward the light of the blazing flare. He kept watching it, afraid that if he looked away, it might disappear.

He stumbled on, and there was the hill of breakdown stuff. Matt stopped, stunned by the eerie sight of it. Suddenly the light was there and the steep high rockslide of glittering shale with the drop rope suspended above it, gleaming like a strand of giant cobweb. After all the blackness and the timeless terrors, here was the beautifully familiar drop chamber with all its comforting stillness, arching up like a cathedral.

It's like waking up suddenly out of a horrible nightmare, Matt thought, and turning on your light and seeing your own warm room at home. He felt like falling on his knees and giving thanks. But he wasn't home yet. He didn't want to waste time or risk anything happening. He wanted to get safely out of here, the faster the better.

Matt paused once as he staggered toward the hill of breakdown stuff and glanced back. He shivered at the sight of the deep black emptiness under the overhang of limestone. He had been back there only fifty feet when the flare fell through the drop opening.

Before the flare fell, he had sat in blackness, hopelessly lost and going mad. In a little while, he knew, he would have gone crazy and probably would have died there. Yes — he shivered again — he could have died there less than fifty feet from the drop rope.

But in case anyone wanted to know, Matt thought grimly, fifty feet in total blackness might as well be a million light-years of black space.

"Hey, Matt," Spotty's voice echoed eerily. "You OK?"

"Am I glad to see you, buddy! You may never know!" Matt yelled up to where his friend's round face bobbed at the top of the drop rope like a pale balloon.

"Matt, this sure looks like a monstrous cave!"

"Big enough," Matt said, as he reached the breakdown stuff and started scrambling up. "Believe me, buddy, it's big enough!"

DISCUSSION

1. What excuses did Matt make to himself for his failure to observe the Grotto's safety rules? When did he first begin to feel uneasy about being in the cave?
2. When did Matt finally decide that he was lost? With this realization, what advice came to his mind?
3. Why was Matt sure that no one would ever come to rescue him?
4. How did Matt's wish to earn money affect his judgment?
5. What did Matt mean when he said the cave was "Big enough"?
6. Why would the absence of light cause feelings of anxiety and fear such as Matt experienced?
7. Why is it difficult to keep track of time in complete darkness? Can you think of any physical signs that might aid you somewhat in keeping track of time? If so, what are they?
8. Do you think Matt was a coward? What makes you think that? Do you think extreme isolation can actually cause a person to become severely emotionally upset? Why do you think so?
9. If you had been lost in the cave as Matt was, what would you have done differently?

AUTHOR

Bryce Walton is well qualified to write about exploring and studying caves. As a boy growing up in Blythedale, Missouri, he had many opportunities for cave exploration, a hobby he still pursues.

Mr. Walton, who has been a gold miner, a railroad section hand, a sailor, a migrant farmer, and a college teacher, now devotes his time to writing. He has written more than a thousand short stories for detective and mystery magazines and many scripts for the Alfred Hitchcock television series. In 1961, one of his stories won the Alfred Hitchcock Best Story of the Year Award.

Cave of Danger, from which the selection you have just read was taken, is Mr. Walton's third book for young people. His most recent books are *Harpoon Gunner* and *Hurricane Reef.*

water

picture

by May Swenson

In the pond in the park
all things are doubled:
Long buildings hang and
wriggle gently. Chimneys
are bent legs bouncing
on clouds below. A flag
wags like a fishhook
down there in the sky.

The arched stone bridge
is an eye, with underlid
in the water. In its lens
dip crinkled heads with hats
that don't fall off. Dogs go by,
barking on their backs.
A baby, taken to feed the
ducks, dangles upside-down,
a pink balloon for a buoy.

Treetops deploy a haze of
cherry bloom for roots,
where birds coast belly-up
in the glass bowl of a hill;
from its bottom a bunch
of peanut-munching children
is suspended by their
sneakers, waveringly.

A swan, with twin necks
forming the figure three,
steers between two dimpled
towers doubled. Fondly
hissing, she kisses herself,
and all the scene is troubled:
water-windows splinter,
tree limbs tangle, the bridge
folds like a fan.

TWO YEARS
IN THE WOODS

by Betty Schechter

Henry David Thoreau, born in Concord, Massachusetts, in 1817, spent every waking moment of his boyhood roaming the fertile fields and wooded hills near his home. This love for the outdoors and the conviction that man should simplify his life and still have time for the serious business of living led Thoreau, at twenty-eight, to embark on the venture that follows.

In the spring of 1845, Henry Thoreau borrowed an ax; and, in the woods on the edge of Walden Pond, about a mile from the outskirts of Concord, he started to build himself a house. Alone in the quiet splendor of the tall trees he cut down young white pines for timber, dug a cellar in the side of a hill, and made a chimney from stones he'd carried up from the pond in his arms. It wasn't much of a house when he'd finished, but it was just what he wanted. It measured nineteen feet by fifteen feet, had a door at one end and a fireplace at the other, an attic, a closet, and a large window at each side. Proud of his handiwork, he wrote in his journal, "I intend to build me a house which will surpass any on the main street in Concord in grandeur and luxury, as soon as it pleases me as much and will cost me no more than my present one."

Next, he planted two and a half acres of beans, potatoes, corn, peas, and turnips. He had to buy a few of the building materials for his house, and he had to hire a man and a team of horses to break the ground for his vegetable gardens; but he earned most of the money he laid out by doing stretches of surveying, carpentry, and day labor. Eight months after he started living in the woods, he listed his total expenses for his house, food, clothing, and fuel and found that they amounted to only $25.21¾. That, he figured, was coming very close to the self-reliance he aimed at.

By building his own house and raising his own food, Thoreau felt that he'd made contact with the very stuff of which life is made. His house, though adequate for his needs, was neither so grand nor so costly that he felt anchored to it; if it should burn or if his crops should fail, he would lose practically nothing in terms of money and time spent. Happily he concluded that living in this way he would have to work at manual labor for six weeks of the year and could spend the other forty-six in unhurried pursuit of his happiness. At Walden Pond, Henry Thoreau had shelter, food, good health, and, best of all, his cherished leisure.

They were there, two old friends on the bench in front of the general store. Puffing out clouds of tobacco smoke, they watched the Concord townspeople hurrying about their errands and, enjoying the warmth of the winter sun, they talked. There was a lot they could talk about: it was early in the year 1845, and the country was in a turmoil over the slavery issue; there was talk of secession in the South; the fate of the vast Texas territory hung in the balance — but they were old men and their world had shrunk until it held only what they could see and the people they knew. They talked about Concord and its citizens and, especially, about the town's "character," Henry Thoreau:

Was Henry still out there to Walden Pond? He was, and it appeared like he was going to stay there for quite a bit. Must be mighty lonesome out there so far from other folks. Henry said not. His Aunt Maria'd been out there to see him, and she'd found him right happy and snug. Sometimes his fancy friends came too, and when they did, he set out the three chairs he'd got in the pine needles in front of his cabin and acted like the woods was his parlor. Wasn't it a funny thing Henry never married? He was thinking of it once. Folks said him and his brother John loved the same girl, but she wouldn't have either of them. Her pa didn't like the Thoreaus' kind of radical ways. After that, it seemed like Henry decided he wasn't the marrying kind. . . . Not the sociable kind either. Never would join anything. Even signed off from the church. Wasn't it a queer way Henry'd picked to do? Whatever in the world could he find to do with himself out there in the woods?

Thoreau lived at Walden Pond for two years, and in his own way he was busy all the time. Part of each day he devoted to providing himself with the necessities of life: he drew drinking water from the pond, he fished for his supper, he baked his own bread and roasted tender young ears of corn in the ashes of a wood fire, and he hoed his beans; but most of the time he did what most men would call nothing and what he believed was living life to its fullest. Sitting on his doorstep or walking through the woods or stretching out at full length and gazing into the clear depths of the pond, Thoreau watched and listened to the teeming natural life around him and tried to relate what he saw and heard to the lives of men. As they came to him, he wrote his thoughts in the notebook he carried with him; and later, molded and polished, they were transcribed into his journal. From his journal he culled the collection of essays, *Walden*, which he published in 1854.

Was it, as many of the Concord townspeople thought, despair and indifference to his neighbors that sent Thoreau to live alone in the woods? Far from it. In the pages of *Walden* the reader sees Thoreau as he really was — content, joyous, and so concerned with his fellow men that he wanted, above all, to communicate the wonderful answers to life's questions that he had found.

"I went to the woods," Thoreau wrote, "because I wished to live

deliberately, to front the essential facts of life, and to see if I could not learn what it had to teach, and not, when I came to die, discover that I had not lived. . . . I wanted to live deep and suck out all the marrow of life. . . ."

The marrow of life for Thoreau was a sunny morning, sitting in his doorway from sunrise till noon,

> . . . rapt in a revery, amidst the pines and hickories and sumachs in undisturbed solitude and stillness, while the birds sang around or flitted noiseless through the house. . . .

or, as he walked in his shirtsleeves by the stony edge of the pond,

> . . . a delicious evening when the whole body is one sense and imbibes delight through every pore. I go and come with a strange liberty in Nature, as part of herself. . . . The bullfrogs trump to usher in the night, and the note of the whip-poor-will is borne on the rippling wind from over the water. Sympathy with the fluttering alder and poplar leaves almost takes my breath away.

or, winter afternoons when

> . . . I frequently tramped eight or ten miles through the deepest snow to keep an appointment with a beech tree or a yellow birch or an old acquaintance among the pines.

There in the woods Thoreau found the truths he'd been seeking; there was the proof that life need not be made up only of hurry, worry, and sweat. In the *Walden* essays he compared his life to that of his neighbors, hoping that if only men could see the folly of their ways they would lift their eyes from the furrows they plowed and the rows of tiny figures they entered in their ledger-books.

Walden brought Thoreau a small measure of fame during his later life, and, after his death, it established him as one of America's foremost writers and philosophers. Henry Thoreau, Concord's "time-waster," stands revealed in the pages of his essays as a man who, having studied the small portion of the earth he inhabits, is world-wise. Discussing such homely topics as "The Bean-Field," "Sounds," "The Pond in Winter," he is economist, naturalist, critic, optimist, philosopher, and poet. Under his pen the sights and sounds that he knew came alive, carrying with them an insight into the meaning of men's lives. Concise, witty, direct, and vigorous, Thoreau's prose style mirrors the man and brings his Concord, his beloved piece of the world, vibrant and fresh, down across the years.

DISCUSSION

1. What did the author mean when he said Thoreau did not feel anchored to his home in the woods?
2. Why do you think the two old friends who sat in front of the general store could not understand how an intelligent and a well-educated man, such as Thoreau was, could be happy "out there in the woods"?
3. What were some of the truths Thoreau had been seeking in the woods?
4. How did he hope to help his fellow man by comparing his life with that of his neighbors?
5. After his death Thoreau was established as one of America's foremost writers and philosophers. Why do you think people feel this way about him?
6. Do you agree with Thoreau that a person's leisure is his most cherished possession? Why or why not? Do you think of leisure in the same terms as Thoreau? If not, what does leisure mean to you?
7. Do you think it would be advantageous if everyone had the opportunity to live as Thoreau did? Why or why not?
8. Have you known anyone who has lived in a way similar to the way Thoreau did? If so, tell about it.

AUTHOR

Betty Schechter, the author of "Two Years in the Woods," grew up in New York City. After graduating from Smith College, she worked for three years in the United States Information Office.

"Two Years in the Woods" is an excerpt from Mrs. Schechter's first book, *The Peaceable Revolution.* In 1963, this book about nonviolent resistance was an American Library Association Notable Book and the winner of both the Child Study Association Award and the Thomas Alva Edison Foundation Award.

Mrs. Schechter lives with her husband and three children in Pennsylvania. She has written one other book, *The Dreyfus Affair: A National Scandal.*

masterworks

Sam Gribley, a New York City boy, determines to live alone for a year and be completely self-sufficient by living off the land in the Catskill Mountains. His friends include Frightful, a small falcon; The Baron, a tough irascible weasel; and Jessie Coon James, a busy raccoon with thieving tendencies.

MY SIDE
of the
MOUNTAIN

by Jean George

Every day I worked to train Frightful. It was a long process. I would put her on her stump with a long leash and step back a few feet with some meat in my hand. Then I would whistle. The whistle was supposed eventually to mean food to her. So I would whistle, show her the meat, and after many false flaps, she would finally fly to my hand. I would pet her and feed her. She could fly fairly well, so now I made sure that she never ate unless she flew to my fist.

One day at breakfast I whistled for Frightful. I had no food; she wasn't even hungry, but she came to me anyway. I was thrilled. She had learned a whistle meant "come."

I looked into her steely eyes that morning and thought I saw a gentle recognition. She puffed up her feathers as she sat on my hand. I call this a "feather word." It means she is content.

One fine August day I took Frightful to the meadow. I had been training her to the lure. That is, I now tied her meat on a piece of wood covered with hide and feathers. I would throw it into the air, and she would swoop out of the sky and catch it. She was absolutely free during these maneuvers and would fly high into the air and hover over me like a leaf. I made sure she was very hungry before I turned her loose. I wanted her back.

After a few tries she never missed the lure. Such marksmanship thrilled me. Bird and lure would drop to the earth; I would run over, grab her jesses, and we would sit on the big boulder in the meadow while she ate. Those were nice evenings. The finest was the night I wrote this in my diary:

Frightful caught her first prey. She is now a trained falcon. It was only a sparrow, but we are on our way. It happened unexpectedly. Frightful was climbing into the sky, circling and waiting for the lure, when I stepped forward and scared a sparrow.

The sparrow flew across the meadow. Out of the sky came a black streak — I've never seen anything drop so fast. With a great backwatering of wings, Frightful broke her fall and at the same time seized the sparrow. I took it away from her and gave her the lure. That sounds mean, but if she gets in the habit of eating what she catches, she will go wild.

Frightful was my ears as well as my eyes. She could hear things long before I. When she grew tense, I listened or looked. One day she was scared. She turned round and round on the log she was sitting on, looked up into the tree for a perch, lifted her wings to fly, and then stood still and listened.

Then I heard it. A police siren sounded far down the road; the sound grew louder and louder. Then the siren wound down; the police car had apparently stopped on the road at the foot of the moun-

tain. I started toward my tree but had not gotten past the walnut tree before the patrol cars started up and screamed away.

We started home, although it was not late in the afternoon. However, it was hot, and thunderheads were building up. I decided to take a swim in the spring and work on the moccasins I had cut out several days ago.

With the police car still on my mind we slipped quietly into the hemlock forest. Frightful almost sent me through the crown of the forest by digging her talons into my shoulder. I looked at her. She was staring at our home. I looked too. Then I stopped, for I could make out the form of a man stretched between the sleeping house and the store tree.

Softly, tree by tree, Frightful and I approached him. The man was asleep. I could have left and camped in the gorge, but my enormous desire to see another human being overcame my fear of being discovered.

We stood above the man. He did not move, so Frightful lost interest in my fellow being. She tried to hop to her stump and preen. I grabbed her leash, however, as I wanted to think before awakening him. Frightful flapped. I held her wings to her body as her flapping was noisy to me, apparently not so to the man. The man did not stir. It is hard to realize that the rustle of a falcon's

wings is not much of a noise to a man from the city, because by now, one beat of her wings and I would awaken from a sound sleep as if a shot had gone off. The stranger slept on. I realized how long I'd been in the mountains.

Right at that moment, as I looked at his unshaven face, his close-cropped hair, and his torn clothes, I thought of the police siren and put two and two together.

"An outlaw!" I said to myself. "Wow!" I had to think what to do with an outlaw before I awoke him.

Would he be troublesome? Would he be mean? Should I go live in the gorge until he moved on? How I wanted to hear his voice, to tell him about The Baron and Jessie C. James, to say words out loud. I really did not want to hide from him; besides, he might be hungry, I thought. Finally I spoke.

"Hi!" I said. I was delighted to see him roll over, open his eyes, and look up. He seemed startled, so I reassured him. "It's all right; they've gone. I won't tell on you." When he heard this, he sat up and seemed to relax.

"Oh," he said. Then he leaned against the tree and added, "Thanks." He evidently was think-ing this over, for he propped his head on his elbow and studied me closely.

"You're a sight for sore eyes," he said, and smiled. He had a nice smile — in fact, he looked nice and

not like an outlaw at all. His eyes were very blue, and, although tired, they did not look scared or hunted.

However, I talked quickly before he could get up and run away.

"I don't know anything about you, and I don't want to. You don't know anything about me and don't want to, but you may stay here if you like. No one is going to find you here. Would you like some supper?" It was still early, but he looked hungry.

"Do you have some?"

"Yes, venison or rabbit?"

"Well . . . venison." His eyebrows puckered in question marks. I went to work.

He arose, turned around and around, and looked at his surroundings. He whistled softly when I kindled a spark with a flint and steel. I was now quite quick at this and had a tidy fire blazing in a very few minutes. I was so used to myself doing this that it had not occurred to me that it would be interesting to a stranger.

At this moment Frightful, who had been sitting quietly on her stump, began to preen. The outlaw jumped back, then saw she was tied, and said, "And who is this ferocious-looking character?"

"That is Frightful; don't be afraid. She's quite wonderful and gentle. She would be glad to catch you a rabbit for supper if you would prefer that to venison."

"Am I dreaming?" said the man. "I go to sleep by a campfire that looked as if it had been built by a Boy Scout, and I awaken in the middle of the eighteenth century."

I crawled into the store tree to get the smoked venison and some cat-tail tubers. When I came out again, he was speechless.

"My storehouse," I explained.

"I see," he answered. From that moment on he did not talk much. He just watched me. I was so busy cooking the best meal that I could possibly get together that I didn't say much either. Later I wrote down that menu, as it was excellent:

Puffballs in deer fat with a little wild garlic; fill pot with water; put venison in; boil. Wrap tubers in leaves and stick in coals. Cut up apples and boil in can with dog-tooth violet bulbs. Raspberries to finish meal.

When the meal was ready, I served it to the man in my nicest turtle shell. I had to whittle him a fork out of the crotch of a twig, as Jessie Coon James had gone off with the others. He ate and ate and ate, and when he was done, he said, "May I call you Thoreau?"

"That will do nicely," I said. Then I paused — just to let him know that I knew a little bit about him too. I smiled and said, "I will call you Bando."

His eyebrows went up; he cocked his head, shrugged his shoulders, and answered, "That's close enough."

With this he sat and thought. I felt I had offended him, so I spoke. "I will be glad to help. I will teach you how to live off the land. It is very easy. No one need find you."

His eyebrows gathered together again. This was characteristic of Bando when he was concerned, so I was sorry I had mentioned his past. After all, outlaw or no outlaw, he was an adult. I changed the subject immediately.

"Let's get some sleep," I said.

"Where do you sleep?" he asked. All this time sitting and talking with me, and he had not seen the entrance to my tree. I was pleased. Then I beckoned, walked a few feet to the left, pushed back the deerhide door, and showed Bando my secret.

"Thoreau," he said. "You are quite wonderful." He went in. I lit the turtle candle for him. He explored, tried the bed, came out, and shook his head until I thought it would roll off.

We didn't say much more that night. I let him sleep on my bed. His feet hung off, but he was comfortable, he said. I stretched out by the fire. The ground was dry, the night warm, and I could sleep on anything now.

I got up early and had breakfast ready when Bando came stumbling out of the tree. We ate crayfish, and he really honestly seemed to like them. It takes a little time to acquire a taste for wild foods, so Bando sur-prised me by liking the menu. Of course he was hungry, and that helped.

That day we didn't talk much, just went over the mountain collecting foods. I wanted to dig up the tubers of the Solomon's seal from a big garden of them on the other side of the gorge. We fished; we swam a little; and I told him I hoped to make a raft pretty soon, so I could float into deeper water and perhaps catch bigger fish.

When Bando heard this, he took my ax and immediately began to cut young trees for this purpose. I watched him and said, "You must have lived on a farm or something."

At that moment a bird sang.

"The wood peewee," said Bando, stopping his work. He stepped into the woods, seeking it. Now I was astonished.

"How would you know about a wood peewee in your business?" I grew bold enough to ask.

"And just what do you think my business is?" he said as I followed him.

"Well, you're not a minister."

"Right!"

"And you're not a doctor or a lawyer."

"Correct."

"You're not a businessman or a sailor."

"No, I am not."

"Nor do you dig ditches."

"I do not."

"Well . . ."

"Guess."

Suddenly I wanted to know for sure. So I said it.

"You are a murderer or a thief or a racketeer, and you are hiding out."

Bando stopped looking for the peewee. He turned and stared at me. At first I was frightened. A bandit might do anything. But he wasn't mad; he was laughing. He had a good deep laugh, and it kept coming out of him. I smiled, then grinned and laughed with him.

"What's funny, Bando?" I asked.

"I like that," he finally said. "I like that a lot." The tickle deep inside him kept him chuckling. I had no more to say, so I ground my heel in the dirt while I waited for him to get over the fun and explain it all to me.

"Thoreau, my friend, I am just a college English teacher lost in the Catskills. I came out to hike around the woods, got completely lost yesterday, found your fire, and fell asleep beside it. I was hoping the scoutmaster and his troop would be back for supper and help me home."

"Oh, no." Then I laughed. "You see, Bando, before I found you, I heard police cars screaming up the road. Occasionally you read about bandits that hide out in the forest, and I was just so sure that you were someone they were looking for."

We gave up the peewee and went back to the raft-making, talking very fast now and laughing a lot. He was fun. Then something sad occurred to me.

"Well, if you're not a bandit, you will have to go home very soon, and there is no point in teaching you how to live on fish and bark and plants."

"I can stay a little while," he said. "This is summer vacation. I must admit I had not planned to eat crayfish on my vacation, but I am rather getting to like it. Maybe I can stay until your school opens. That's after Labor Day, isn't it?"

I was very still, thinking how to answer that. Bando sensed this. Then he turned to me with a big grin and said, "You really mean you are going to try to winter it out here?"

"I think I can."

"Well!" He sat down, rubbed his forehead in his hands, and looked at me. "Thoreau, I have led a varied life — dishwasher, sax player, teacher. To me it has been an interesting life. Just now it seems very dull." He sat awhile with his head down, then looked up at the mountains and the rocks and the trees. I heard him sigh.

"Let's go fish. We can finish this another day."

That is how I came to know Bando. We became very good friends in the week or ten days that he stayed with me, and he helped me a lot. We spent several days gathering white oak acorns and groundnuts, harvesting the blueberry crop, and smoking fish.

We flew Frightful every day just for the pleasure of lying on our

backs in the meadow and watching her mastery of the sky. It was a pleasant time, warm, with occasional thunder showers, some of which we stayed out in. We talked about books. He did know a lot of books and could quote exciting things from them.

One day Bando went to town and came back with five pounds of sugar.

"I want to make blueberry jam," he announced. "All those excellent berries and no jam."

He worked two days at this. He knew how to make jam. He'd watched his pa make it in Mississippi, but we got stuck on what to put it in.

I wrote this:

August 29

The raft is almost done. Bando has promised to stay until we can sail out into the deep fishing holes.

Bando and I found some clay along the stream bank. It was as slick as ice. Bando thought it would make good pottery. He shaped some jars and lids. "They look good, not Wedgwood,"[1] he said, "but containers." We dried them on the rock in the meadow, and later Bando made a clay oven and baked them in it. He thinks they might hold the blueberry jam he has been making.

Bando got the fire hot by blow-

---

[1] **Wedgwood** (wĕj'wŏŏd'), a fine type of china.

ing on it with a homemade bellows that he fashioned from one of my skins that he tied together like a balloon. A reed is the nozzle.

August 30

It was a terribly hot day for Bando to be firing clay jars, but he stuck with it. They look jam-worthy, as he says, and he filled three of them tonight. The jam is good; the pots remind me of crude flower pots without the hole in the bottom. Some of the lids don't fit. Bando says he will go home and read more about pottery-making so that he can do a better job next time.

We like the jam. We eat it on hard acorn pancakes.

Later. Bando met The Baron today for the very first time. I don't know where The Baron has been this past week, but suddenly he appeared on the rock and nearly jumped down Bando's shirt collar. Bando said he liked The Baron best when he was in his hole.

September 3

Bando taught me how to make willow whistles today. He and I went to the stream and cut two whistles about eight inches long. He slipped the bark on them. That means he pulled the wood out of the bark, leaving a tube. He made a mouthpiece at one end, cut a hole beneath it, and used the wood to slide up and down like a trombone.

We played music until the moon came up. Bando could even play jazz on the willow whistles. They are wonderful instruments, sounding much like the wind in the top of the hemlocks.

There were no more notes for many days. Bando had left me saying: "Good-by, I'll see you at Christmas." I was so lonely that I kept sewing on my moccasins to keep myself busy. I sewed every free minute for four days, and when they were finished, I began a glove to protect my hand from Frightful's sharp talons.

One day when I was thinking very hard about being alone, Frightful gave her gentle call of love and contentment. I looked up.

"Bird," I said, "I had almost forgotten how we used to talk." She made tiny movements with her beak and fluffed her feathers. This was a language I had forgotten since Bando came. It meant she was glad to see me and hear me, that she was well fed and content. I picked her up and squeaked into her neck feathers. She moved her beak, turned her bright head, and bit my nose very gently.

Jessie Coon James came down from the trees for the first time in ten days. He finished my fish dinner. Then, just before dusk, The Baron came up on his boulder and scratched and cleaned and played with a fern leaf.

I had the feeling we were all back together again.

DISCUSSION

1. What did Sam mean by saying that Frightful was his ears as well as his eyes?
2. Why did Sam think Bando must be a murderer or a thief? Why did Sam want him to stay, even though he thought him to be an outlaw? Why was Sam sad when he found out that Bando wasn't an outlaw?
3. What were some things that Bando made or helped to make for Sam?
4. What two things did Bando say that showed he planned to return?
5. Why did Bando think he had waked up to find himself in the middle of the eighteenth century? Why did he use the name Thoreau for Sam?
6. Did Sam make a wise decision when he let Bando stay with him? Why do you think that?
7. Why do you think Bando began to feel that his former life had been a dull one?
8. Why did Sam feel lonely after Bando left? What helped him to overcome that feeling?
9. What was clever about the way that Sam trained Frightful? Have you ever trained an animal? If so, be ready to tell how you did it.
10. How did Sam and Frightful communicate? How do humans communicate without words? How have you been able to communicate with a pet or an animal?
11. If you had been in Sam's place, would you have been willing to let a stranger stay with you? Why or why not?
12. Sam intended to live in the woods during the winter. In what ways would this be much harder to do?
13. Would you like to try living as Sam did? Why or why not?

AUTHOR

Jean George, author of this excerpt from the book of the same name, *My Side of the Mountain,* decided when she was six years old to be an illustrator, a writer, a dancer, and a mother when she grew up. She decided also to take up swimming and iceskating as hobbies. However, shortly after she graduated from Pennsylvania State College, she found it necessary to concentrate on two careers, writing and illustrating, and to treat her other interests as hobbies.

As a child growing up in Washington, D.C., Jean George and her twin brothers were often taken by their parents into the forests along the Potomac River to camp, canoe, and fish. It was there that she learned many things about trees, flowers, birds, animals, and insects. Mrs. George has put the memories of her childhood love of nature into the books she has written and illustrated.

Her husband, John, who grew up in Milwaukee, Wisconsin, had lived the same type of life as she. So when they met and married, they shared many of the same interests. Together they have written and she has illustrated several animal biographies for young people, including *Vison, the Mink; Vulpes, the Red Fox;* and *Buto, the Great Horned Owl;* and they plan to do others.

My Side of the Mountain, which Mrs. George also illustrated, was a Newbery Medal Honor Book. In 1969, Paramount Studios made it into a movie with Tommy Eccles playing the part of Sam Gribley. Another of Mrs. George's books, *Julie of the Wolves,* was awarded the Newbery Award in 1973.

The Georges have three children, two boys and a girl, who keep Mrs. George busy. However, she says there is still time for being an illustrator, a writer, a dancer, and a politician.

FROM THE BOOKSHELF

THE SUMMER OF THE SWANS, *by Betsy C. Byars*

Fourteen-year-old Sara leaves her own small miseries behind as she searches the dense woods and rough fields for her lost, helpless, brain-damaged, younger brother.

THE MIN-MIN, *by Mavis Thorpe Clark*

This is an exciting story about a present-day Australian girl and her brother who run away to find help in solving their personal problems.

SCIENCE, ART, AND VISUAL ILLUSIONS, *by Robert Froman*

The illustrations in this book give you an opportunity to test your own visual perception.

THE MOON IN THE CLOUD, *by Rosemary Harris*

This book is a very funny, fanciful version of how the animals and people were assembled for Noah's Ark.

HAVE SPACE SUIT—WILL TRAVEL, *by Robert A. Heinlein*

A teen-ager wins a space suit and travels in outer space.

TO BE A SLAVE, *by Julius Lester*

Through the words of men and women who were once slaves, this book tells what it was like to be a slave in America.

THE KING'S FIFTH, *by Scott O'Dell*

In the 1600's, young Esteban, a map maker, sets out with six others to find the golden cities of Cibola, a legendary land in our Southwest. This story of their adventures shows the evil effects of greed for gold.

EYES IN THE FISHBOWL, *by Zilpha Keatley Snyder*

In this mystery-adventure story the life of teen-aged Dion is changed when he becomes fascinated by the weird happenings at a fashionable downtown department store.

Applause

Contents

Applause

A PROPER BURIAL

by Vera and Bill Cleaver

Roy Luther is a poor tenant farmer in Appalachia. He and his children live and work on land owned by Kiser Pease, their mean and stingy landlord. Now that Roy Luther is too ill to work the fields, his children practice wildcrafting — the harvesting of wild herbs and roots, which are used in making various medicines. These they sell to Mr. Connell, owner of the local general store.

Four years ago Roy Luther's wife died after a long illness. Now the family consists of five-year-old Ima Dean; Romey, a boy of ten; Devola, eighteen — beautiful, gentle, and "cloudy headed"; and Mary Call, the fourteen-year-old girl who narrates this story.

I am worried about Roy Luther dying and how I am to get him decently and honorably buried, but more than that I am worried about the other responsibilities he has charged me with, the other promises he has wrung from me.

Number one: I am always to take pride in having the name of Luther and instill this pride in the others too. Number two: I am to strive with everything in me to keep our family together and not ever take charity from anybody even if our tongues hang out parched down to our knees, because charity is seldom of real service to those upon whom it is bestowed; and those who receive it are always looked upon with suspicion, every need and want scrutinized. Number three: I am to keep Devola with me always. I am to be good and kind and loving to her and see to it that the others are too. I am not to let her marry Kiser Pease. If ever it looks to me like this is about to happen, then I am to go to town, find the nearest judge, tell him about how Devola is, and get him to stop it.

On my word of highest honor I have promised Roy Luther all these things. Just how I am to bring them about I don't know, nor does he. Never a strong man or one able to think things out, he spends now most of his waking hours in his porch chair. The valley is there before him, big and rich and abundant, but he doesn't see it any more. Whatever it is that started the sickness in him has taken all the caring out of him. Three or four times a day I ask him if he doesn't want me to doctor him and he always says yes, and I fetch the bottle of turpentine and smear a good amount of the stuff around on the base of his throat. . . . It is a futile action, and we both know it; but when it's finished, Roy Luther leans back and closes his eyes and says he feels better.

He's let things beat him, Roy Luther has — the land, Kiser Pease, the poverty. Now he's old and sick and ready to die; and when he does, this is what we'll inherit — his defeat and all that goes with it.

Sometimes when I look at him, I am stirred to an unholy anger. I think, "God help me, Roy Luther, I don't want you dead, and that's the truth. But since it's going to happen anyhow, I wish it could hurry up and be over with, for it's pulling us all to pieces; and I need to get on with things and try to fix them around so that life will be easier for those of us who are left."

And I get scared, and I think, "But how am I going to do this? Who will show me how, and who will help me?"

And then I get madder, and I say to myself, "Aw, quit your bellyaching. There's a way; all you have to do is find it."

.   .   .

It is so hard for me to write this next because it's about Roy Luther's leaving us.

I don't know how it happened or at what hour. I only know that when I went in to him first thing one morning, he had gone. There was a congealed redness in his wide-open, unseeing eyes, and he was already cold and a little stiff.

With a corner of his sheet I pressed his eyes closed and turned him to the wall and arranged the covering over him so that it would look like he was merely sleeping and then went out and told the others that they were not to go into his room that day, not for anything.

Devola did not question this, nor did Ima Dean. They ate their eggs and hoecake and asked were we going to wildcraft that day. I said no, and they got out two buckets and said well then, they'd just go berrying and went out the back way and swung off down the valley in the brightening morning-gloam.

Left behind, Romey pestered me about Roy Luther, saying why couldn't anybody go in to see him and why did I have his door closed and wasn't I even going to give him his bath and why were we wasting the whole day — there wasn't a thing wrong with it — and what was wrong with my face so clenched — that all of a sudden it looked like it was about a hundred years old — and was I just going to sit around staring at the wall all morning?

I looked at him, and I thought, "Oh, Lord, You sure made a mistake when You put me together. You didn't give me enough strength to carry out all I'm supposed to do. I can't do this by myself. You can see that."

I said, "Romey, Roy Luther is dead."

The sun, striking through the windows, fell across his face and it twisted; and his eyes ceased their questing and became so still, and he said, "Oh. Oh, Mary Call."

"No carrying on now," I said. "That's one of the things I promised him — that there wouldn't be any carrying on. So if you feel like doing any, don't let me see you at it, you hear me, Romey?"

Pale within his suddenly glistening face, his lips moved. "Yes, Mary Call. I hear you."

"Tonight he'll have to be buried. There's a place waiting for him up on Old Joshua. Roy Luther laid it out and dug it himself months ago. We're not to call the undertaker or the preacher. We're to do this by ourselves and keep it to ourselves. You understand me, Romey?"

His eyes, so thrust with pain and stricken, went to the wall beyond my head. "The others," he whispered. "Aren't we even going to tell the others?"

I said, "Not just now. Maybe later on in the day."

"It wouldn't be right to keep it from them," he said, and slid from his chair and went outside and stood motionless in the sun for a long minute and then took off, running out across the fields.

Ah, I felt sorry for him then, this little brother, having to take half of this cold, terrible thing and do his mourning alone and in silence.

Throughout all that day we moved, he and I, in a frozen, unreal style, pretending to the others to relish the berry cobbler on the noon table, more education from the root and herb book, and the plans for the money we were going to make.

After noon dinner Romey built a fire under the iron pot in the back yard, and Devola and I washed clothes. Ima Dean said that with the money we were going to make

from our roots and herbs maybe we could buy a washing machine, one like in the Sears catalogue, and maybe an electric lamp for the sitting room. She said she didn't like the oil lamps we used, that they smoked.

Romey said, "Aw, don't fuss so much, Ima Dean. Electricity costs too much; that's why we don't use it more."

They quarreled and I had to stop them.

Devola used the soapy water left over from the clothes to wash the kitchen floor and the back porch and sang while she was doing it. Twice she thought to ask me if I had bathed Roy Luther and attended to his other needs, and I said yes.

One by one the hours stroked by. It turned late afternoon, and Romey, half sick with dread for what lay ahead but still holding remarkably steady, got me to one side and asked me why we were keeping it from the others.

I told him because when something is finished it's easier to look back on.

He said when were we going to tell them and I said tomorrow, but after that nobody else — not anybody else was to be told — not Kiser Pease or Mr. or Mrs. Connell or anybody — because if it was found out, the county people would come and take us to rear. Possibly they'd send us to an orphanage, and we wouldn't be a family any more.

For supper Devola cooked cranberry beans with ham hock and made baking powder biscuits and opened a can of peaches. I took a tray into Roy Luther's room and forced myself to eat what was on it. I sat beside him and tried to think words of prayer, but none would come. The body under the sheet seemed smaller — looked like it had shrunk more just since that morning — and I wondered how much it would weigh and thought about how we would have to tie it to the wagon with a rope unless Romey could be persuaded to walk alongside and hold it steady with his hand. From some early lesson in mortality I thought of Roy Luther saying that there would never be any understanding of death, that it was beyond people's notions and ideas and meant to be that way.

Forgotten was the threatened visit from Mr. and Mrs. Connell. They came just as the last supper dish was being wiped, Mrs. Connell stepping from their car like some spindly bird, pausing to examine the daisy beds and the patches of wild, green fern clumped along the walkway; but her interest was not with them at all but with us, sniffing away at our privacy and our freedom. Mr. Connell followed her up the steps and proffered their offering — two loaves of homemade oatmeal bread.

I invited them into our sitting room, and Mrs. Connell drew her skirts before she lowered herself into the rocker.

"Roy Luther is asleep," I said. "And I hope you don't mind if I don't waken him. Since his fall he sleeps poorly at night."

Mr. Connell said, "Eh, law, let the man have his rest. We shouldn't have come. I told Mrs. Connell that we shouldn't, but she wanted the ride."

Devola came in and crossed over to me and leaned down and whispered to me should she offer them tea or something?

Mrs. Connell smoothed her gingham arms and smiled at all of us and said, "Oh, dear no. We couldn't take a thing, thank you. We can't stay but just a minute more. You have a crack in your ceiling, Mary Call."

I said, "Yes'm, it just came. Roy Luther's been intending to fix it, but he's just been so busy. He'll get around to it in a couple of days."

Mrs. Connell rocked and ironed her skirt with her hands. "I must say that I commend your father, Mary Call. Keeping you children together the way he has and never asking for a bit of outside help." Fussing with her skirt, straightening it, she looked across the room to Romey and Ima Dean. "But pride goeth before a fall. There might come a time when he'll be glad to ask for some help."

Mr. Connell said, "Olive, for heaven's sake."

Mrs. Connell stood. She tucked her hands inside her loose sleeves. "Well, we'd better be going. You're sure Roy Luther's asleep, Mary Call? If he's even just half awake, I'd like to see him just for a minute. Just a word of encouragement sometimes helps enormously, you know."

Out of the corner of my eye I saw Romey move to lay a hand on Ima Dean's hair.

I said, "Yes, he's sound asleep, and I daren't try to waken him."

Mr. Connell said, "We'll be getting on, then." And he stood and ushered Mrs. Connell out before him. They went past Roy Luther's closed door and out to their car and got in it and drove off.

Night had fallen. It was time to bury Roy Luther.

The peaks of the mountains were enveloped in shaggy drifts of undulating, translucent fog.

I blamed it on the mountain air, how it hurt to breathe, as Romey and I, pushing and pulling the creaking toy wagon on the top of which Romey had constructed a makeshift bed to contain the trussed, shrouded figure, strained upward toward Roy Luther's final resting place on Old Joshua. The shovel we'd tied alongside him clanked a little with each turn and jolt.

At one point a raven, black and lustrous, came flapping out from a bush and flew alongside us, his hoarse *tok, tok* weird and hollow.

"Go away, bird," whispered Romey, and it flew off.

We went around a fallen tree, and I looked back at Trial Valley, misted white from rim to rim, lonely as a moonscape. "Lord," I thought. "Oh, dearest Lord. Please don't let me give out now. It's only up a little ways further. I want to do this decent, Lord. It has to be decent so that afterward I can say to the others that it was, and they'll have that much to remember at least."

From out of an empty space the raven came winging back again and lighted on top of the body on the wagon and again made his sharp, metallic cry. I shooed him with my hand, and he soared upward into the somber air and disappeared.

The wagon creaked, and there was the sound of our breathing. The bracken beneath our feet was dew-wet and slick. We were drowned in the dampness and the smudgy darkness.

Romey was crying but trying not to let on to me that he was. We passed under a dripping tree, and a small cloud of fog streamed past us. We went over a knobby, exposed root, and the wagon bumped against it, and the figure on the wagon shifted. We felt it do that and stopped. I looked back at Romey, and though his face was blurred, I saw his pain and fear.

"It isn't anything to be afraid of,"

I said. "It's all in your mind. Come on now, it isn't much further."

Hunched and desolate, Romey said, "You're awful, Mary Call. *This* is awful. It shouldn't be done this way. He should have a proper burial."

"Romey, this is going to be a proper burial. Just as soon as we get him up there, I'll see to it that it's proper. Come on, let's go."

"No. I'm not going any further. It's awful."

"It isn't awful, Romey. It's as good as any other kind of burial. Maybe it's even better. It's the way he wanted it. It's what I promised."

"I don't care about that. It's awful. You're awful. You think you know everything. You're stingy. We've got the money; there's almost sixty-five dollars in the money can now. Let's take him back and tomorrow go after the undertaker and give Roy Luther a proper funeral."

"No, Romey. This is the way he wanted it, and this is the way it's going to be. Come on now; it isn't much further. Let's get on with it."

Romey sank to his knees beside the wagon. He put his head down on the rim of it. "No. I can't do it. I don't care what happens, I can't. I don't care if the county people come and get me. Let 'em. If they did, I wouldn't have to look at you any more. You old, stingy gut, you."

"Be careful now, Romey. You're making me mad."

"Good. That's what I want you to do. Get mad. I want you to get mad. I hate you."

"Romey —"

"Oh, shut up!" he cried. "And stop staring at me. Haven't you got any place else to look?"

"Romey, come on now, Romey. I can't do this by myself. I would if I could but I can't. You've got to help me, that's all. So come on now and do it."

For a long interval he didn't move or speak. The wind above us shivered the tree branches, and again the raven came back and flew around us but this time didn't alight.

Standing there on the gloomy trailway, waiting for Romey to recover, I wondered how I could be so calm — how I could just stand there in the gray darkness with the cold handle of the wagon in my hand and the cold tree moisture dripping down on me and the dead body of my father there before me and not be afraid of how grisly it all was.

It's because I'm tough, I thought. I'm so tough that if a bear came out of the side of the mountain over there, I could knock him cold without even breathing hard. And that's all, and if anybody's got a better idea how I should handle this and all the other things left to me, just let them come on and tell me about it; but I don't hear anybody saying anything.

Back in the bushes the raven said, "Tok. Tok." And Romey stood up and passed one hand over his face and said, "I'll get even with everybody someday; you just watch and see if I don't. We'll go on and bury him here now, but someday we'll be back to get him. Someday we'll come back here and get him and take him to the best and biggest cemetery in the whole world, and we'll give him the best and biggest funeral anybody ever had. Better even than the one Napoleon Bonaparte had."

I remarked, "Romey, Napoleon Bonaparte didn't have a big, flashy funeral. He had a simple one. He was buried in a valley next to a stream he loved beside some willow trees."

"You're so smart," muttered Romey, and leaned and straightened Roy Luther's body. He put his hands down on the rim of the wagon, one on each side of the white knob that was Roy Luther's head, and said, "Well, pull if you're going to!"

Pushing and pulling, we moved upward again over bare rock and across great patches of moss and lichen and around trees and through clawing brush; and after some little while of this we came to the stand of black spruce where, within, Roy Luther had himself prepared his burial site — a hole in the earth four or five feet deep, covered with stout, broad planks left over from some carpentering job on Kiser Pease's place.

We drew the wagon up close to the edge of the grave, and I said to Romey we should sit and compose ourselves before we commenced, but he wouldn't be still even for one second. He was in a fever to be done with the task. He started trying to remove the planks, but they were too heavy, and I had to help him. When they were all laid to one side, we looked down and saw that the hole itself was lined with yet more of them, and in a stout voice Romey said, "It was a lot of work. It must've taken him a long time to dig down through all this rock. He must've known it was coming a long time before it did, Mary Call."

"Yes," I said.

"You bawling?"

"No."

"I didn't think you were. There's nothing to bawl about, is there?"

"No."

"All this dirt and rock piled up around. He left it here for us to pile on top, didn't he? So the animals wouldn't get to him."

"Yes, I think so."

"So that's what we'll do."

"Yes."

"So should we get on with it?"

"No, wait a minute. I want us to say some good things now ... the good things in our hearts that we remember about our father."

With his fair head bent reverently and his hands folded priestly,

Romey stood beside the wagon, beside the body of our father, and in a lilt he said, "He was gaysome sometimes before he took sick, and when the notion struck him, he could be as tough as whitleather. He loved us all fair, though he never said so. He never whipped us, and I was proud to have him for my daddy, and now I hope he'll stay peaceful here."

"He will," I said. "He will."

Romey lifted his head and looked across at me. "Your turn to say something now."

Beyond Romey's slight figure I saw this tree, alone and different from the rest, its branches all streamed back in one direction from the winds that had battered it year on year. It was quiet now because there was no wind; but I could imagine what it looked like in a storm, bending and twisting in the gusts and the rain, resisting with all of its grit the forces that would uproot and destroy it. It looked old and tough, and the sight of it made me feel old and tough; I felt like the tree and I were related. I couldn't think of anything more to say good about Roy Luther than had already been said, so I told Romey this; and then together we knelt and said the Lord's Prayer; and then, with some clumsiness, we loosened Roy Luther from his bindings and slid him into his grave. He went in neat.

With the shovel we then covered the grave with the planks and the loose earth and rocks, and I said, "The Lord is your shepherd now, Roy Luther. Be happy with Him and don't worry about us."

Romey said, "Amen."

Going back down the mountain, Romey said he believed that we had given Roy Luther a proper burial.

DISCUSSION

1. Why did Mary Call tell only Romey that Roy Luther was dead? Having told Romey, why did she feel sorry for him?
2. Romey was horrified at the way his father was to be buried. What did he suggest they do? Why did Mary Call refuse to follow his suggestions?
3. What did Mary Call see that reminded her of herself? Why did it do so?
4. Why do you think Roy Luther prepared his own burial site and did not want a traditional funeral?

5. Mary Call stated that she was tough. Do you think she was really as tough as she thought she was? Why or why not? Would she have shielded Ima and Devola from Roy Luther's death until after the burial if she was so tough? Why do you think that?

6. Who do you think was the more sensitive person, Mary Call or Romey? Why do you think so?

7. What attribute did Mary Call show by saying, "There's a way; all you have to do is find it," when she referred to making life easier for the family? Do you agree there's always a solution to any problem that might arise? Why do you think that?

8. Do you think Mr. and Mrs. Connell came for a strictly social visit? If not, why do you think they came? How did Mr. and Mrs. Connell differ in character?

9. Should Mary Call have buried Roy Luther without telling anyone except Romey? Why or why not?

10. Do you agree with Romey that Roy Luther had a proper burial? Why do you think that?

AUTHORS

When Vera and Bill Cleaver moved to North Carolina, they discovered that there were whole families in the Appalachian region who supported themselves by wildcrafting. Curiosity led the Cleavers to stop and ask questions of the people they saw digging roots and gathering berries. This, in turn, led them to new friendships and eventually to the exciting idea that became the book *Where the Lilies Bloom,* from which the selection you have just read was taken.

The Cleavers are a husband-and-wife writing team. Together they have written many short stories that have appeared in magazines in the United States and Europe. Other books written by the Cleavers are *Ellen Grae, Lady Ellen Grae, Grover, The Mimosa Tree,* and *The Mock Revolt.*

The Messenger to Maftam

Harold Courlander
and
George Herzog

Among the Soninke people, many days on foot north of the Gulf of Guinea, there lived a man by the name of Mamadi. He was poor, and lived in a small and unpretentious house. Yet Mamadi was much respected everywhere because it was said that he never told a falsehood, no matter how small.

One day Bahene, chief of the Soninke, after having heard a long conversation about Mamadi, said in an irritated way:

"Who is this man Mamadi who is so full of virtue and cleverness that he never makes a false statement?"

"He lives in the small village of Ogo," his councilors told him. "He is known far and wide, because he never says a thing that isn't so."

"I believe this character is an exaggeration," the chief said. "There is no such man, either in the desert or the plains. Have him brought here for me to see."

So the messengers brought Mamadi to the chief, and Bahene said to him:

"Mamadi, is it true that you have never lied?"

"Yes, it is true," Mamadi said.

"It is hard to believe," Bahene said. "There is no one alive who hasn't at some time or other said something that wasn't strictly so. Yet, the people say it is true. But tell me, are you certain that you won't ever tell an untruth?"

"Yes, I am quite certain," Mamadi answered.

"How can one be so sure of such a thing?" Bahene asked. "Isn't it presumptuous to say in advance what one will do, without even considering the circumstances?"

"The circumstances are quite unimportant," Mamadi said, "for I am unable to say what is false."

From THE COW-TAIL SWITCH AND OTHER WEST AFRICAN STORIES *by Harold Courlander and George Herzog. Copyright, 1947, by Holt, Rinehart and Winston, Inc. Reprinted by permission of Holt, Rinehart and Winston, Inc.*

"Well, you seem to be a virtuous man," Bahene said. "If your tongue is as faithful to your principles as you say, then I'm wrong in thinking there is no man who doesn't lie. But if you do lie, then you will commit an act more offensive than when an ordinary person lies, because the ordinary person makes no such virtue of his tongue. So take care, Mamadi, for the day you do tell a lie will be a bad one for you. If the Soninke people ever catch you in a falsehood, I'll have you beaten with ropes!"

When Mamadi had gone back to his village, Bahene said to his councilors:

"That village man is putting on airs! He must have some virtue, since his reputation is widespread. But it requires more than virtue to tell no falsehoods, it takes cleverness as well. Mamadi's certainty that he can't tell a lie is arrogant. He needs a lesson!"

Early one morning, several days later, Bahene sent for Mamadi again. The village man arrived before Bahene's house to find him and his men standing with their weapons in their hands.

"Mamadi, I need you to do a service for me. Please go to my other house in the village of Maftam to deliver a message to my wife. Tell her that we have gone hunting for antelope, and that we shall arrive at Maftam today at noon. We shall be very hungry and shall want plenty to eat. Wait there, and you will eat with us."

Bahene and his hunters started out as though to hunt, while Mamadi took the trail to Maftam, hurrying so that he would get the message there in time for the chief's wife to prepare food. But as soon as Mamadi was out of sight, Bahene turned around and went back to his house. He put down his weapons, and said to the men in his hunting party:

"Well, I have changed my mind! We won't go hunting after all. Nor will we go to Maftam today. This country fellow Mamadi who carries the message to my wife believes that he can't tell an untruth. We'll see. He will tell my wife that we are hunting and that we are going to bring an antelope. He will tell her that we shall arrive at noon, and that we will be very hungry. But none of these things will happen. When we finally get there we shall have a great laugh, for the poor villager's wisdom isn't as great as his virtue. And then Mamadi shall be beaten for his arrogance."

Mamadi hurried to Maftam. It was three hours away on foot. When he arrived he went to Bahene's wife and said to her:

"I am carrying an urgent message from Bahene."

"What is it?" she asked him.

"Of that I am not sure," Mamadi said.

"How can you carry a message of which you aren't sure?"
Bahene's wife was getting angry.

"What are you supposed to tell me?"

"It is likely, rather, or so it seemed, perhaps, possibly, or, on the other
hand more or less certainly, probably less than more, or more than less,
that Bahene went hunting."

"It's not very clear," Bahene's wife said. "Did he or didn't he?"

"It's the way I said," Mamadi went on. "When I saw him and the
hunters they were clearly going hunting. I could tell by the way they stood
around with their weapons in their hands. Yet of course people sometimes stand around like that when they have just returned from the hunt.
It's not likely that they just returned from the hunt, though, because there
wasn't any meat, but of course they could have hunted and not found
any game, so I suppose they were going hunting instead of coming back,
more or less, to be sure, somewhat, none the less, however, or at least
that was the general impression that was to be gained from the conversation, which was fairly explicit, in a way . . ."

"Try not to get excited," Bahene's wife said. "I don't yet understand
whether he is going hunting or not. But what other news is there?"

"Well, it would be wise to be prepared to cook an antelope, of some
sort, just about, in case they catch one, although certainly that is Bahene's
general intention, possibly, most likely, more or less, that is, in the event
they have gone hunting."

"Of all the people among the Soninke villages, Bahene had to pick
you!" she said in disgust. "What else is there to know, almost?"

"Oh, yes, there won't be much time, it would seem, and Bahene's
hunting party will assuredly, in all likelihood, be somewhat, or exceed-
ingly, or conceivably hardly at all, hungry, when they arrive here exactly
or approximately at noon, if they do, although it is most probable, and
there is no grave doubt that they won't, even though some question arises
as to the certainty, of which there could be some doubt, within bounds,
probably . . ."

"Wait! Stop a moment!" Bahene's wife cried out. "So far I haven't
learned a thing! Is there something more precise you can tell me?"

"Something more?" Mamadi continued. "Oh, yes. I am to wait for him here until he arrives, if that is possible, or even likely, or otherwise . . ."

"Stop your babbling!" Bahene's wife said. "Is he coming or isn't he? And when will he be here?"

"Well, now, as I said before, more or less clearly than I might have, somewhat, or not altogether, it appears, seemingly, though not conclusively, or even assuredly, that Bahene might, at least ought to, sooner or later . . ."

"Never mind!" Bahene's wife interrupted. "Tell me no more! The more you say the less I know!"

Then Mamadi lay down upon a mat to await the chief's arrival. Noon came and went, but Bahene and his hunters didn't appear. Night came, then morning, and finally the chief arrived in Maftam with his following. They all laughed as they saw their messenger waiting for them in the court.

"Well, our meal is perhaps a little spoiled, but no matter," Bahene said, "for we have proved that even a most virtuous man may allow his tongue to speak a lie, and that this man's arrogance is more noteworthy than his virtues."

"How is that?" Bahene's wife asked.

"Why, he told you that we had gone hunting, when we hadn't, and that we would be here yesterday noon, when we weren't, and that we would bring an antelope, which we didn't. So now he is to be beaten as a lesson to him."

"No," the chief's wife said, "he said that you would do this or you wouldn't, that it was likely or unlikely, or certain or uncertain. He delivered the message, but he gave it with so many qualifications and exceptions that I really didn't get any sense out of him at all."

Bahene was crestfallen. It was he, not Mamadi, who was shamed in public. So he had presents given to Mamadi, and said to him:

"I was wrong, Mamadi, and you are, in truth, a virtuous and wise man. I know now what all the other Soninke people already knew, that you will never tell a lie."

"That is quite true," Mamadi replied. "I never never shall, presumably, it is certain, probably . . ."

DISCUSSION

1. How did Bahene test Mamadi's statement that he could never tell a falsehood? How did Bahene's plan backfire?
2. What did Bahene do when he realized it was he, not Mamadi, who was shamed in public?
3. What two attributes did Bahene say were required in order not to tell a falsehood? How did these attributes apply to Mamadi?
4. Should a person say in advance what he will do without even considering the circumstances? Why or why not?
5. Was Bahene just in trying to trick Mamadi? Give a reason for your answer.
6. If Mamadi had delivered the correct message to Bahene's wife, would he have really told an untruth? Why or why not? Is being evasive in delivering a message as bad as being untruthful? Why or why not?
7. Mamadi used a kind of double talk. Have you ever used double talk? If so, why did you use it?

AUTHORS

Harold Courlander grew up in Detroit, surrounded by people of many different nationalities. This, he feels, was the beginning of his interest in other nationalities and cultures. After college and during World War II his travels took him to India, Africa, Haiti, Cuba, the Middle East, and Europe, where he was exposed to much folklore. Mr. Courlander is well known as a novelist and student of folklore, and in addition to folktale collections for children, he has published two books on the life and arts of the Haitian people and a novel about a dictator in the West Indies.

The Cow-Tail Switch and Other West African Tales, the book from which "The Messenger from Maftam" was taken, is the only book Harold Courlander and George Herzog have written jointly. Mr. Herzog, a Hungarian by birth, studied at the University of Berlin and came to the United States in 1925. He earned his doctorate at Columbia University, did research work at Yale University and the University of Chicago, and has made many field trips to remote places. He is a specialist in primitive music and languages.

Winter's Tale

I come of a long line of honest workers,
Down-to-earth, thrifty, with a scorn for leisure;
And I've no sympathy to waste on shirkers,
Or those who pass the time in idle pleasure.
Vagrants and profligates deserve their fate —
So why should I be troubled to remember
One shivering vagabond who, last November,
Came begging food and shelter at my gate?

He'd spent the summer fiddling and romancing
While decent folk laid in the winter store —
My house is snug and warm, the cupboard's full;
But evenings, somehow, seem so long and dull.
I wonder what they're like: music, and dancing. . . .
I wish I hadn't turned him from my door.

SARA HENDERSON HAY

290

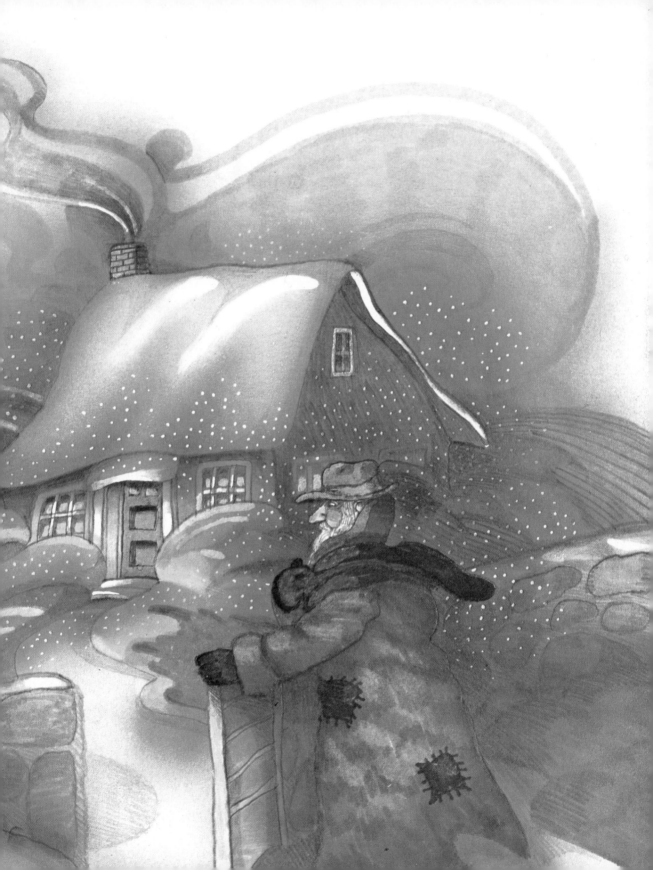

THE GREAT HOAX

by Robert Silverberg

On August 25, 1835, the readers of the New York *Sun* were given a very startling story indeed. At long last news of Sir John Herschel's scientific expedition to South Africa had reached the United States — and the *Sun* had a scoop on the story.

Herschel was one of the world's greatest astronomers. His father, Sir William Herschel, had been the leading astronomer of the eighteenth century; among his many achievements had been the discovery of the planet Uranus. William Herschel's only son, John, had no new planets to his credit, but he had carried out an important survey of the stars of the Northern Hemisphere. In 1833, he set out for Capetown, South Africa, to study the stars of the Southern Hemisphere. He and his family arrived on January 15, 1834, for a stay of several years. By March 4, Herschel was at work in his observatory at the Cape, and all the world waited for news of some remarkable astronomical discovery.

A year and a half later the world was still waiting. Herschel, painstakingly making his observations, had sent no news home from South Africa. Then, in August of 1835, the New York *Sun* broke the long silence. On a Tuesday afternoon the *Sun* hit the streets with an account of Herschel's findings.

Herschel, it seemed, had trained a powerful new telescope on the moon — and had found life there! Trees and vegetation, oceans and beaches, bison and goats, cranes and pelicans — all this, and much more, could be seen on the face of earth's satellite! New York was agog with the astounding revelation.

The *Sun* showed great restraint in featuring the story. It made the front page, to be sure, over in the right-hand column. Instead of a bold, attention-getting headline there was the inconspicuous title:

GREAT ASTRONOMICAL DISCOVERIES
Lately Made by
Sir John Herschel, L.L.D., F.R.S.
At the Cape of Good Hope

The *Sun* said that its articles were reprinted from "the supplement to the *Edinburgh Journal of Science,*" published in Scotland. Seven articles in all ran in the *Sun;* and before the series had ended, the young newspaper's circulation had boomed all the way up to 19,360 — making it the biggest-selling paper in the world.

The first installment said nothing about living creatures on the moon. It began in a wordy, old-fashioned way, speaking of "recent discoveries in astronomy which will build an imperishable monument to the age in which we live and confer upon the present generation of the human race a proud distinction through all future time." The rest of the first article told of John Herschel's observatory at the Cape, speaking with authentic-sounding, scientific detail about his various telescopes.

The remarkable new discoveries, it was stated, had been made with a revolutionary type of telescope. The best available telescope, according to Sir John, would allow him to view the moon as though from a distance of forty miles. That was not good enough. However, Herschel had devised a new telescope on boldly different optical principles. It cast an image on a screen, and a microscope could be used to magnify that image.

The trouble with this pretty theory is that it would not work; when such an image is magnified, it quickly becomes so faint that nothing at all can be seen. But the author of the article had a glib way of skipping over such difficulties or of burying them under a barrage of scientific-sounding words. Thus, the *Sun's* readers learned, Herschel had found a method of "transfusing artificial light," thereby brightening the image. A "hydro-oxygen microscope" was used to show details.

The big telescope itself had a light-collecting lens twenty-four feet in diameter. (By way of comparison the biggest telescope in use today, at California's Mount Palomar Observatory, has a two-hundred-inch mirror, that is, seventeen feet in diameter.) According to the *Sun* the casting of the giant lens began on January 3, 1833, but after eight days of cooling, it was found that the lens was flawed. The job had to be done over. The second lens was cast on January 27, and when examined early in February was found to be all but perfect. (It took years to cast and polish the mirror at the Mount Palomar Observatory.)

"The weight of this prodigious lens," the article said, "was 14,826 lbs., or nearly seven tons after being polished; and its estimated magnifying power [was] 42,000 times. It was therefore presumed to be capable of representing objects in our lunar satellite of little more than eighteen inches in diameter, provided its focal image of them could be rendered distinct by the transfusion of artificial light."

Herschel supposedly had sailed for Capetown with his great lens on September 4, 1833. (Actually he left London on November 13.) The newspaper told how two teams of eighteen oxen each had hauled the lens to a high plateau, thirty-five miles northeast of Capetown, where Sir John set up his telescope. The observatory itself was described in the most minute detail; the author of the article studded his paragraphs with resounding and impressive terms and phrases like "angle of incidence," "focal distance," "theodolite," and so forth.

The patient reader, his curiosity aroused by this lengthy scientific preamble, at last got the first hint of what Herschel had seen. On January 10, 1834, Herschel had trained his vast telescope on the moon, the article declared. The microscope, when applied to the image from the telescope, revealed rocks of a vivid greenish-brown and then clusters of a dark red flower, "precisely similar to the . . . rose-poppy of our cornfields." The delighted astronomer next gazed upon a lunar forest; the trees were evergreens, some resembling English yews, others "as fine a forest of firs, unequivocal firs, as I have ever seen cherished in the bosom of my native mountains."

New wonders followed: an ocean, bordered by "a beach of brilliant white sand," with high waves and deep-blue water. Then a strange district where "a lofty chain of obelisk-shaped, or slender pyramids, standing in irregular groups, each composed of thirty or forty spires," could be seen. A twist of the fine adjustment revealed that the obelisks were "monstrous amethysts of a diluted claret color, glowing in the intensest light of the sun!"

Then came a barren desert of chalk and flint. Next, there swam into view a wild forest of oaklike and laurel-like trees and at last the first lunar animal life to be seen — shaggy creatures much like bison. Soon Herschel spied a beast "of a bluish-lead color, about the size of a goat, with a head and beard like him, and a *single horn*," and then pelicans, cranes, and other water birds wading for fish in a large river.

By this time the readers of the *Sun* found it torment to wait for the next daily installment. The unicorn had provided a stunning climax for the second article; by the third day newsboys were selling enormous quantities of the paper — as fast as they could get them to the streets.

There was much to gasp over on the third day. Palm trees with crimson flowers, bears with horns, reindeer and elk and moose, and a beaver-like animal that lacked a tail and walked on two feet — all this and more greeted the *Sun*'s readers. An island fifty-five miles long in a great sea offered geological miracles: "Its hills were pinnacled with tall quartz crystals of so rich a yellow and orange hue that we at first supposed them to be pointed flames of fire." A miniature zebra, long-tailed birds like golden and blue pheasants, even lowly shellfish on the shores, all were caught by Sir John's keen telescopic eye.

The *Sun* had more revelations in the succeeding installments: cliffs with outcroppings of pure gold, a sheeplike animal with "an amazingly long neck" and "two long spiral horns, white as polished ivory," a romantic and beautiful wooded valley; and in the fourth article the paper actually announced the existence of men of the moon!

It was while peering at the wild valley that the astronomers "were thrilled with astonishment to perceive four successive flocks of large-winged creatures, wholly unlike any kind of bird, descend with a slow, even motion from the cliffs on the western side and alight upon the plain." When they landed, they folded their wings and walked like human beings in a manner "both erect and dignified."

The newspaper declared that "they averaged four feet in height, were covered, except on the face, with glossy copper-colored hair and had large wings composed of a thin membrane, without hair, lying snugly upon their backs from the top of the shoulders to the calves of the legs. The face, which was of a yellowish-flesh color, was a slight improvement upon that of the large orangoutang, being more open and intelligent. . . . In general symmetry of body and limbs they were infinitely superior to the orangoutang. . . . The hair on the head was a darker color than that of the body, closely curled but apparently not woolly, and arranged in two curious semicircles over the temples of the forehead. Their feet could only be seen as they were alternately lifted in walking; but from what we could see of them in so transient a view, they appeared thin and very protuberant at the heel. . . ."

The moon men with the batlike wings seemed to be engaged in conversation. Herschel saw them gesturing with hands and arms, as though talking. Before long, his telescope found the moon men swimming in a large lake, spreading their wings and shaking them duck-fashion to rid them of water when they emerged. At length, the "man-bats," as Herschel supposedly dubbed them, flew off into the darkness and were lost to view.

Further telescopic exploration located a temple in a lovely setting, rimmed by hills "either of snow-white marble or semitransparent

crystal, we could not distinguish which." The temple itself was three-sided, "built of polished sapphire, or of some resplendent blue stone, which, like it, displayed myriad points of golden light twinkling in the sunbeams."

Later, other temples of equal beauty were discovered. No one, though, seemed to visit them except flocks of wild doves. The author of the *Sun*'s article asked, "Had the devotees of these temples gone the way of all living, or were the latter merely historical monuments?" He hoped that one day an answer would be forthcoming as further lunar study progressed.

Near one of the temples more moon men were sighted "of a larger stature than the former specimens." The penetrating eye of the telescope revealed them as they ate a large yellow fruit like a gourd, ripping away the rind with their fingers and gobbling the meat avidly. Then, too, they could be seen sucking the juice of a smaller red fruit. "They seemed eminently happy and even polite, for we saw, in many instances, individuals sitting nearest these piles of fruit select the largest and brightest specimens and throw them archwise across the circle to some opposite friend. . . ."

It seemed that the moon men never engaged in any activity but "collecting various fruits in the woods, eating, flying, bathing, and loitering about on the summits of precipices." In the kindly, fertile environment of the moon, labor and industry were unnecessary. Nor was there war or weapons, apparently, though fire was known.

The last of the seven articles trailed off in vague observations of other planets and then returned briefly to the moon for a last look at a new tribe of moon men "of infinitely greater personal beauty" than the others, very much like the angels of "the more imaginative schools of painters." The *Sun* concluded the series by informing the readers that forty pages of mathematical calculations, which had accompanied the original articles in the *Edinburgh Journal of Science,* would not be reprinted because of their extreme difficulty and lack of popular appeal.

The *Sun* series caused a sensation. It was an age when scientists were making wonderful new discoveries constantly and when very little was known about the moon's surface. Here were scientific-sounding articles declaring that the moon was a veritable paradise with wooded glades, streams and rivers, and handsome winged men and women. Sir John Herschel himself was the authority for this, was he not? Who could question Sir John's statements?

The other newspapers were quick to comment on the astounding revelations, and on September 1, 1835, the *Sun* proudly printed excerpts from their editorials. "Sir John has added a stock of knowledge to the present age that will immortalize his name," said the *Daily Advertiser,* an Albany paper that regarded the discovery with "unspeakable emotions of pleasure and astonishment." The New York *Times* offered the opinion that "the writer displays the most extensive and accurate knowledge of astronomy.... The accounts of the wonderful discoveries in the moon, etc., are all probable and plausible." The *New Yorker,* no relative of today's magazine of that name, hailed "a new era in astronomy and science generally."

Two Yale professors named Olmstead and Loomis hurried down from New Haven to confer with an editor of the *Sun,* Benjamin Day. They were excited by the story and wanted to see the original Edinburgh articles with those forty pages of mathematical calculations. The editor referred them to a reporter named Richard Adams Locke, who stalled them awhile, then told them that the articles were at the *Sun's* printshop. The professors set out for the printer, but Locke sent a messenger ahead of them, instructing the printer to send them somewhere else. Olmstead and Loomis were shunted from office to office all day and, finally, without getting to see the calculations, gave up and returned to Yale.

The *Journal of Commerce,* a distinguished rival newspaper, was so taken with the moon story that it wanted permission to reprint it as a separate pamphlet. A *Journal of Commerce* man paid a call on *Sun* editor Day and was also sent to see Richard Adams Locke. Locke tried to talk the man out of reprinting the articles. He gave no reason at first, simply suggesting it might do the *Journal of Commerce's* reputation no good to put out the pamphlet. Finally Locke broke down and told his fellow reporter the truth: the entire moon story was a hoax.

Herschel had never found life on the moon, neither unicorns nor bat men nor two-legged beavers. He had no twenty-four-foot telescope lens, no "hydro-oxygen microscope." The details of the story were purely imaginary. What's more, Locke revealed, the *Edinburgh Journal of Science* had gone out of business several years before, and so this series could not have been, and was not, a reprint. He, Richard Adams Locke, one of the New York *Sun's* cleverest and most able reporters, had invented the whole business.

The following day the *Journal of Commerce* printed Locke's confession and gleefully denounced the supposed Herschel discoveries for the hoax they were. The *Sun,* which had run the articles as a stunt to build circulation, saw a chance to keep the fun alive. The paper denied that Locke had ever admitted anything to the *Journal of Commerce* man. Every paper in the country, the *Sun* said, had praised the articles. But the *Journal of Commerce* was an exception "because it not only ignorantly doubted the authenticity of the discoveries but ill-naturedly said we had fabricated them for the purpose of making a noise and drawing attention to our paper."

Keeping their faces straight, the editors and reporters of the *Sun* went on insisting for another two weeks that the moon story was honest. Then, on September 16, 1835, the *Sun* finally confessed to the hoax in print. The newspaper-reading public sorrowfully came to realize that the wonderful forests and lakes of the moon did not exist.

Locke had written a brilliant science-fiction story, and the *Sun* had slyly passed it off as fact. The reporter's poetic style, his clear description, and above all his confident use of scientific language had made the hoax vividly realistic. It has been claimed that he received technical assistance from a French astronomer named Jean Nicholas Nicollet (nĭk'ə-lā'), then living in New York, or from one Dr. Dick, author of a work on means of communicating with the moon. Locke himself maintained that he had written the articles without help. His grand hoax is a good key to the state of popular scientific knowledge in the United States in the year 1835. So very little was known about the moon that it was not at all difficult for the glib and extremely plausible hoax to win thousands of believers.

As for Sir John Herschel, whose good name had been dragged into the moon story, he remained in South Africa carrying out important scientific observations until 1838. His report on the work, not published until 1847, said nothing at all about the unicorns and bat men that dazzled our believing great-great-great-grandfathers in the summer of 1835.

DISCUSSION

1. Why did the New York *Sun* stretch the story out into seven articles?
2. How did Richard Locke cover up inconsistencies in his articles?
3. What did the acceptance of the articles tell you about the average man's knowledge of science in the United States in 1835?

4. Why do you think Locke chose Sir John Herschel as the "author" of his articles?

5. Why do you suppose competitive papers didn't verify the story? How could they have done so?

6. Why did the editors of the *Sun* publish this story even though they knew it was not true? Do you think they were justified in publishing science fiction as truth? Why do you think as you do?

7. If you had lived during the time this hoax was printed, do you think you would have believed it? Why or why not? Which discoveries might you have thought plausible? Which ones not plausible?

AUTHOR

Robert Silverberg is the award-winning author of a number of scientific and technical works. His book, *Scientists and Scoundrels,* from which "The Great Hoax" was taken, is entirely devoted to hoaxes.

At the age of eighteen Mr. Silverberg sold his first science-fiction novel. Since then he has written over a hundred books and six hundred stories and articles. Mr. Silverberg and his wife, an electrical engineer, live near New York City in a large, old house that was once the home of Mayor Fiorello La Guardia. She is his technical advisor on the futuristic machines that he uses in his science fiction. Their hobbies are collecting rare books and raising cats.

Mr. Silverberg's favorites among his science-fiction books for young people are *The Gate of Worlds* and *Across a Billion Years.*

The Secret
of the Wall

by Elizabeth Borton de Treviño

On a day in September I walked down to Cantaranas (kän-tär-än'äs) Plaza and past it, along the narrow cobblestone street; and there was the great *zaguán* (sä-wän'), the entrance to the *secundaria* (sĕ-kōōn-dä'ryä), our high school. Beyond I could see the broad, white ascending steps of the university, where I would go one day.

The streets of Guanajuato (wä-nä-hwä'tō) smell of dried chilies, of jasmine and carnations in pots behind the iron-barred windows, of hot baked bread, and of burro droppings. It is my town in central Mexico, a romantic old town that has lived days of wealth and luxury because of the rich silver mines nearby and days of poverty because

of the turmoil of revolutions and social change. Heroism has been here, in these little winding alleys and broad, stone, fountain-centered plazas. Faith is here, in our many beautiful churches, soaring into the sky. Many artists have lived here and loved Guanajuato and painted it. My family has lived here since the days of my great grandfather,

and I, Carlos, always knew the legends of some of the streets, of many of the old houses, and the stories of ghosts and hauntings, some violent, some tender.

School smelled like schools everywhere, of chalk dust and disinfectant soap and boys. I found my classroom and a seat on the aisle where I could rest my leg by extending it out along my desk. Three years ago I had had polio. It left me weak in the back and in one leg; I still have to take special exercises and wear a brace for some hours every day. But Dr. Del Valle (dĕl vä′yĕ), who took care of me when I was sick, had said at last that I could walk to and from school every day and that I would be getting stronger all the time. Yet I knew that I would not be able to take part in the games or play out in the court during recess. All the boys were younger than I, but almost all were taller and broader too. The only one I knew was Serafin (sĕ-rä-fēn′), Dr. Del Valle's youngest boy. He stood half a head taller than any of the others and was handsome and strong. I thought, Serafin will surely captain one of the ball teams — soccer or basketball or baseball — and he will be president of the class.

But I was wrong. When the first recess for games came, I went to sit under the arcades and watch, and I saw the shouting boys choose up sides. The games professor passed out mitts and bats and balls. Serafin was a swift runner, but he didn't try very hard. He seemed uninterested, and when one of the other boys jostled him, he dropped out. "Coward!" they called after him, but he just shrugged his shoulders. He came over and sat down by me, looking very sullen.

"It's a silly game anyhow," he said.

"I wish I could play!" I burst out.

"Why?" he asked. "You don't get anything out of it. It's just exercise. Getting knocked about and hurt sometimes. Foolishness. I play a much better game by myself every day."

"You do? What game?"

"I may tell you someday." Then he got up and sauntered off. He walked down one of the corridors slowly, looking at his feet, and then he stooped to pick up something and put it in his pocket. I turned my eyes back to the noisy fun in the school patio. I had hopes of distinguishing myself in another way. My father is a fine chess player, and groups of the best players in our town meet at our house on Saturday evenings. During the years of my illness Papacito (pä-pä-sē'tō) had taught me how to play and had bought me a small chess set that was portable and on which the pieces could be fixed, so that a game might go on from where it had been left off days before. There were no gentlemen in Papacito's chess circle who were unwilling to sit down to a game with me, and once I had even beaten Don Mario (dōn mä'ryō), the postman, who often came. He was the champion of Guanajuato.

Limping home after that first day in class, I tried to place Serafin in my chess game. A knight? Perhaps. Not a bishop or a tower. And, of course, not a pawn. He was too independent for that.

Tía Lola (tē'ä lō'lä) had made my favorite *polvorones*[1] for supper to celebrate my first day back to school. Tía Lola is Papacito's sister, who came to live with us after my mother's death.

As the days went by, I became more interested in all my classes. I often took my chessboard to school and, while the others were at games, Professor Morado (mō-rä'dō) sometimes played with me. The boys were pleasant, but careless with me; they thought me a cripple because I had to wear my brace some days. Only one sought me out, Serafin.

He began walking home with me afternoons, sometimes chatting, sometimes morosely making no comment on anything I said. He often leaned down to pick up a button or a bit of cord or a pin.

"That's my game," he said to me suddenly one day. "Finders Keepers!"

---

[1] **polvorones** (pōl-vō-rō'něs), a type of bread, similar to shortcake.

"How silly! You can't often find anything worthwhile."

"Oh, but you're wrong! I often do! I must have one hundred pesos' worth of stuff piled up at home that I found this way. Besides, just now we were only wandering along. But sometimes I pick out people and follow them. You'd be surprised how often they put down a package and forget it or leave their umbrella or even drop money!"

"But ... but ..." I stuttered, "if you see them drop something, you ought to give it back!"

"No," he answered stubbornly. "Finders Keepers. That's the game."

"But what do your parents think about this? Tía Lola would never let me keep anything I found if it were valuable. Or my father either. I'd have to find out whom it belonged to and give it back or give it to the poor."

"Ah, my father and mother don't even know about my game, and I shan't tell them," he responded. "Papá is always out, all hours of the day or night on his calls, and Mamacita (mä-mä-sē′tä) is usually in bed with a headache. They don't care what I do."

I was troubled about all this, but I did not talk it over with my father or Tía Lola for a very selfish reason: I had no other friend, and I did not want to be deprived of Serafin, unsatisfactory and worrisome though he was. I knew he was cowardly, secretive, and selfish, but he was a companion. So I kept silent, though I never did go to his house. He sometimes came to mine but only to talk or play with my dog in the patio.

I was not very lonely. I often went to Cantaranas fountain and took my chessboard. I could work out problems in chess there and watch the people passing by.

I was doing this about five o'clock of a November day when dusk was beginning to let down veils of darkness over the town. I had just closed my chessboard and was about to start home when a workman came toward me from one of the streets that led down into town. From his plaster-covered shoes and the sacking that he still wore over his shoulders and his dusty shirt and trousers, I could tell he was probably working on one of the new buildings that were going up near the entrance of the city.

He was about nineteen, I thought. He smiled at me shyly. "I have seen you going to high school early in the morning," he said. He paused and shuffled his feet. "And I have seen you sitting here in the afternoons, studying."

"That's right."

"My name is Martin Gonzales (gōn-zä′lĕs)," he said suddenly, after a long pause. "I am going to ask you to do me a favor."

"Gladly, if I can." I thought he might ask for a peso.

"I want you to write a letter for me."

"But I don't have any paper or an envelope."

"Bring them tomorrow and write a letter please. I will pay you the fee."

The next day I waited for Martin and wrote his letter for him. It was a note to a girl in another town. He was ashamed for her to know that he could not write. He put the letter away, carefully inside his dirty shirt, and turned his bright eyes toward my chessboard. I asked if he knew the game, but he shook his head. Idly I explained the moves and the names of the pieces.

Then began a curious friendship. Martin passed by the fountain every afternoon, sometimes bringing with him another big, shy workman who wanted a letter written. I began to develop a small but regular business, and I looked forward to that hour in Cantaranas Plaza. It comforted me to think I was doing something useful, and I began to plan on teaching them to read a little when vacations came.

Serafin was scornful and did not often drop by anymore. "How stupid!" he said. "Writing silly letters for oafs."

"Martin is no oaf! I am teaching him chess, and he will be a good player!"

"I don't believe it!"

"Stay and watch then! Here he comes now."

Martin came hurrying along. I presented them, and Serafin had the grace to take Martin's calloused hand after it had been dusted against his trousers and deferentially offered.

I had the pieces set up on my little board. Martin drew the white, so he had first move. He made an opening gambit I had never before seen used. I did not know the defense, and he soundly beat me. Serafin's eyes were starting from his head, for like most of us boys in Guanajuato he knew something of the game.

"¡Caray![2] You stopped me in my tracks, Martin!" I cried. "Who showed you that gambit?"

"I made it up," he told me, pleased. "I thought about the chessboard all day as I was working. I could see it in front of my eyes, every piece, so I played a game with myself, in my imagination; and it seemed to me that the opening I used just now was a good one."

Martin arrived on Saturday evening in clean, freshly-ironed, cotton work clothes. Like all our country people he has perfect manners, and, of course, so has my father and so have his friends. They made Martin welcome, and my father sat down to play his first game with him. To my amazement he defeated my father in the first game, and the second one was a real struggle, finally

---

[2] **¡Caray!** (kä-rī'): Confound it!

306

ending in a stalemate. My father was perfectly delighted, and the others crowded round to congratulate Martin.

"Young man, you are a chess genius, I think!" cried Don Mario, the postman. "You must join us every Saturday! Keep our game keen!"

After he had left, my father and his friends talked excitedly about Martin. They had in mind to train and polish him and enter him in the spring state championship chess games.

The next day there was a piece in the paper about a treasure having been found by workmen when tearing down an old house in Celaya (sě-lä′yä). Under the flagstones of the patio they came upon a strongbox filled with silver coins. My father read the item aloud.

"My friend Luisa, in Guadalajara (wä-dä-lä-hä′rä), had a friend who found a buried treasure in the kitchen of the house they bought," contributed Tía Lola.

"Well, it happens often and it is reasonable," explained Papacito. "Mexico has gone through violent times, and insurgent and revolutionary armies have swept in and out of so many towns that the people often buried or hid their valuables so as not to have to surrender them. And then, of course, sometimes they couldn't get back to retrieve them. Or sometimes they died, and nobody ever knew what had happened to their money."

I was thinking this over as I walked to school, and in the first recess Serafin sought me out, full of excitement.

"Did you read about the treasure in Celaya?" he asked me, breathless. "Let's go treasure hunting here! There must be quantities of old houses where people have buried money!"

"Well, yes. My father said there was every likelihood. But how? Which houses? And how would you start? Nobody would even let you begin!"

"Why couldn't Martin tell us where? He works with a wrecking crew, knocking down old houses, doesn't he? He could sneak us into one some night!"

"Tía Lola wouldn't let me go."

"Don't tell her!" counseled Serafin impatiently.

"Well . . ."

It was the deceit that unnerved me. But the call of adventure was strong, and, I'll confess it, I longed to go treasure hunting. I resolved to speak to Martin.

I had my chance when he stopped by Cantaranas Plaza after work. I was waiting for him.

"We began to tear down the old house of the Lost Grandfather today," he told me. "The workmen are not happy about it. They say it is haunted."

"Yes? Tell me about it?"

"The Lost Grandfather groans and howls there on windy nights;

people have heard him. He was an old gentleman who simply disappeared during the last revolution."

"Strange. Aren't you afraid to work there, Martin?"

"I? No. I am only a simple, uneducated fellow. But I do not believe in ghosts," he told me scornfully.

Serafin was eager to go out that very night, but he decided that he had better reconnoiter first. But the next day at recess he told me in whispers that the situation was perfect. There was a watchman, but he was very old and deaf and did not know anything about the ghost.

"His daughter brings him his supper at about nine o'clock, and he eats it, and then he goes to sleep on some sacks in the back. To try him out, I even pounded on the gate and struck the rocks of the patio with a small steel bar I have. The old fool did not hear a sound. We will go tonight!"

I was scared but terribly eager to go just the same. Little prickles of excitement ran up and down my spine all day.

Just at dusk Serafin came by for me. He had a long, paper-wrapped parcel under his arm. "An iron bar with a pointed tip," he said, "and a candle."

As we left, I had a bad time with Tuerto (tōō-ĕr'tō), my little white dog with a black spot around one eye. Tuerto whined and begged to come with us, and he got out twice and had to be brought back in and

scolded before he would not try to follow me. I believe he smelled my excitement.

As we came near the haunted house, we saw the watchman's daughter just arriving.

"Good! She's early!" hissed Serafin. She left the big *zaguán* slightly ajar as she went in, and, pulled and pushed by Serafin, I followed. We were inside!

At last the watchman's daughter left, calling *adios,* and the old man made the sign of the cross behind her as the *zaguán* clanged to. Then he shuffled off to somewhere in the back.

"Come in now," said Serafin. "He eats and rests way back there, where they have begun taking out the rear walls. I want to try inside, around the fireplace. That's where lots of treasures have been buried."

We went cautiously into the big central hall of the house. It was quite dark and very mysterious. A little light drifted in from the street, but the shadows were deep; and there were strange noises, little scurryings and rattlings. Our eyes grew used to the dark. Soon we made out the fireplace. From it stretched out two walls, at the far ends of which there were doors into other rooms.

"Let's sound those walls," suggested Serafin. "You go along there and I'll go here. See if they sound hollow to you. Like this." And he went along, giving a smart rap on the plaster. I dutifully did as I was told, almost forgetting the watchman, but the walls sounded the same along their length to me.

"We might as well open up anyhow and see how solid they are," whispered Serafin, and he went at a place in the wall not far from the chimney. I was terrified. It seemed to me that the clanging and banging would bring not only the watchman but even people from the street in upon us. However, Serafin labored away to no avail.

"I'll try over here," he panted, and again he dug at the wall, but there seemed to be nothing but firmly set bricks inside.

"Here. You try." He gave me his improvised pick, and I went at a place on the other side of the fireplace. At first the plaster gave way easily. Then I came upon the same hard bricks. But as I struck and pried at them, one of them crumbled away, and another, and I put my hand in. There was an opening!

Serafin almost shouted in his joy. "I'll open it up more, and then you get inside and see what's there!" He worked away very fast and soon had a hole in the hollow wall through which I could just squeeze my shoulders.

"Get in!" he urged, and pushed me.

"It's terribly dark," I said. "Give me the candle."

He passed it in to me and I lighted it. I stood inside the wall in a very narrow passage. The air was still and dead, and the candle flickered along the wall.

And then suddenly there was a deep, mournful groan. I started and dropped the candle. As I struck against the wall, plaster and bricks rained down, and I found myself cut off. I tried to scratch and scrabble my way out, but in the dark I had no way of knowing whether I would be able to get free again.

"Serafin!" I called with all my might, but there was no answer. Only, at my shout, more plaster and bricks fell.

I was scared to death. I stood there and cried until I realized that I would have to be sensible and think.

I cannot pretend that I was able to do this immediately. I suffered from a confusion of feelings. I thought I might be buried alive; I feared our being caught in this house, where we had no permission to be; I was frightened of the dark and of the sounds. But eventually I was able to control myself.

I was not scared by the groan. I did not believe in ghosts, and I knew there must be some natural explanation. I felt sure Serafin would go at once and bring help. And after a bit I realized I would not smother, for there was a thin breath of air from somewhere in the wall that moved along my cheek.

It came to me, at last, that I might find some opening in the wall, and cautiously I started exploring. Luckily, I had some matches in my pocket, and though I scrabbled around trying to find the candle, I could not. So I lit a match, and in that light I went along, feeling the sides of the hollow wall close against me until the match burned down to my fingers, and I was in darkness again. In this way I passed around a bend in the wall, where it curved out around the fireplace, I thought, and emerged into the wall beyond, which was also hollow. But there, as I lit a third match, I saw, suddenly illuminated, a skeleton fully dressed in the clothes of the last century and sitting on a low bench. It was wedged between the walls, and on its knees was a box. It was a terrible figure, but even in that first moment of shock and revulsion I felt pity. What had been a man must have had himself walled in here, with his treasure ... and no one had ever come back to free him. Was it the Lost Grandfather?

I said a prayer for the soul of that pitiful skeleton man and then tried to maneuver myself around in the wall and feel my way back whence I had come. I decided to save my matches; and when I felt the fallen rubble, I lay down very gingerly to wait for rescue, saying my prayers all the while.

I may have dozed from fear and hunger and cold, for I awoke, startled, to hear a dog yelping. It was my Tuerto! And as I came to myself and realized where I was, I heard scratching and striking along the wall. I hurried back in case some more bricks should tumble down, but before long there was an opening; the rubble was being pulled away, and there was Martin, looking in, with his face all pale and drawn.

"Thank God! He's all right!" he called.

And I heard Tía Lola and my father echo, "Thank God!"

He pulled me out, and Tuerto leaped upon me and almost smothered me with doggy kisses. Then I was enclosed in my aunt's arms, and I felt my father's hand on my hair.

I can't remember much more of what happened until they got me home and to bed, and Tía Lola gave me a drink of hot lemonade.

Serafin had abandoned me. They did not know he had even been with me until I told them.

Martin had happened to come back to our house that evening to tell my father that he could not play chess on Saturday; and as Tía Lola opened the zaguán to him, Tuerto had shot out and into the street.

Tía Lola had been crying. She was worried, for it was after eight, and I had not come home. Martin said to her, "Look, the little dog is trailing him! I'll follow and bring back Carlos."

My loyal Tuerto led Martin straight into the haunted house and to the wall. Martin had called my name, but I had been asleep and did not hear. Anyhow, he rushed back to bring my father and Tía Lola and also a pick. And so they had found me.

In bed, safe and warm, I remembered the poor skeleton. "There is a dead man in the walls," I told them, "holding a box of treasure on his lap. Please go back and get it, Martin!"

"Shall I?" Martin looked at my father.

"We'll go," said my father, and they left me to Tía Lola.

I tried to stay awake until they came back, but excitement and fright had taken their toll, and I fell deeply asleep. I did not know until the next morning that Martin and I had a fortune between us. The skeleton was extracted from the wall and given a decent burial, and my father looked up in the old records of the city and of taxpayers on the old houses to find out his probable identity. Then he had searched for relatives, but there seemed to be none. So, after my father paid the taxes on the treasure, it remained for us. Finders Keepers.

It was not so very much after all. The box had held silver coins and some jewels, but these were not of much intrinsic value anymore. Still, something like 20,000 pesos remained to be divided between Martin and me.

"What will you do with your part?" I asked Martin, a few days later.

"I shall take care of my mother and my little brothers, and I shall go to school," he cried.

But in the Saturday evening chess circle my father and his friends decided among them that they would teach Martin to read and write and coach him until he could pass examinations and then go on to evening classes. Meanwhile, he was going to be their champion in chess tournaments, and he could make some money giving exhibition games.

"What will you do with your part of the treasure?" Don Mario asked me. They were all eating *enchiladas*³ and drinking coffee after their game. Before I could answer, there was a clamor at our

---

³ enchiladas (ĕn-chē-lä′däs), a hot, spicy Mexican food.

zaguán. And the big knocker sounded several times. Tía Lola led in Dr. Del Valle and Serafin.

Dr. Del Valle gave Serafin a push into the center of the room. "Begin," he ordered his son.

"I am sorry," stammered Serafin.

Dr. Del Valle was trembling with emotion. "I never thought I would see the day when I would feel so ashamed of my son," he told my father. "He has just now confessed to me that he induced Carlos to go with him to that house, to break into the walls and look for treasure, and that when the wall caved in, he ran home and left Carlos there, perhaps to die!"

Serafin stood with drooping head, and two tears slid down his cheeks. "I am sorry," he whispered again.

"We knew," said my father. "We realized that Serafin must have been paralyzed with fear. That is why I did not speak of it to you. He is forgiven. Isn't he, Carlos?"

"Of course," I answered at once.

For what else could I say? I knew what it was to be scared senseless, almost to panic. I couldn't hate Serafin, even though Tía Lola did. I was even, in a way, sorry for him, for I knew that he would never be anything in the Great Chess Game but a simple pawn, like me. Martin would end as a knight.

"I suppose by rights," I said to Serafin, not being above heaping some coals of fire on his head, "at least part of the treasure should be yours. You started looking in the wall where it was found."

He glanced hopefully at me as I went on. "So I trust you will agree with me about what to do with it. I want to give it for a classroom in one of the new schools being built down by the highway. We could name that room." He was disappointed, I could see. But he was trapped. Or, as Tía Lola said later, he made a virtue of necessity.

"Whatever you say, Carlos," he answered meekly.

"Why don't we name it for the Lost Grandfather?" I cried.

And so it will be. My father turned over the money to the Education Department, and a plaque will be affixed to one of the rooms saying, "This room was built with funds left by the Lost Grandfather." The president of Mexico is coming to inaugurate the school, and several others and Serafin and I and all our relatives and Martin and the whole class at school and Professor Morado will be there. All Guanajuato will be in gala dress. The day will be a great *fiesta*.

Olé, poor Lost Grandfather. Your treasure will be of good use, at last.

DISCUSSION

1. What physical handicap did Carlos have?
2. What happened that caused Carlos and Serafin to begin thinking about finding buried treasure? How did Serafin intend to use Martin?
3. Tell in your own words how Carlos felt when he was trapped in the wall.
4. What bearing did Carlos's physical handicap have on the story?
5. Serafin was Carlos's only friend at school. Do you think Serafin met the criteria for being a friend? Why or why not?
6. What indications are there in the story that Carlos had a warm, happy home life and Serafin did not? How do you think their home lives affected their attitudes and behavior?
7. Several days passed before Serafin related his part in the treasure hunt. What do you think made him finally confess to his father?
8. What did Tía Lola mean when she said Serafin "made a virtue of necessity"?

9. What is your reaction to the principle of the game Finders Keepers?

10. How did a casual meeting between Carlos and Martin turn into a warm friendship? Do you think their friendship will be more lasting than that of Carlos and Serafin? Why or why not?

11. Most people are disappointed when they are defeated in a game. Why was Carlos's father delighted when Martin beat him at chess? Does this make you admire Carlos's father? Why or why not?

12. Do you think Serafin will become a better person because of the events that happened to him? Why or why not? If your answer is yes, in what ways will he improve?

AUTHOR

After the publication of her first poem at the age of eight, Elizabeth Borton de Treviño, author of "The Secret of the Wall," considered herself a writer. Encouraged by her parents and her teachers in high school and at Stanford University, she continued to write for many years before her first book, *Little Aztec Cousin*, was published in 1934.

After graduating from college, Mrs. de Treviño studied violin at the Boston Conservatory of Music and worked as a music reviewer and reporter for a Boston newspaper, the *Boston Herald*. The newspaper sent her to Mexico to do a series of interviews. There she met Luis Treviño Gomez, who was assigned as her guide. When they were married a year later, she added *de Treviño*, meaning "wife of Treviño," to her name. The de Treviños have two children and live in Cuernavaca, a suburb of Mexico City.

Mrs. de Treviño has written several books for young people, including *I, Juan de Pareja,* the Newbery Medal winner in 1966. She is interested in art, plays the violin in several chamber music groups, and lectures in Mexico and the United States.

TURNER
and
NATURE

by Fred Gettings

Joseph Mollard William Turner was perhaps the greatest of English painters and is considered one of the world's great painters of light and atmosphere. He was born near Covent Garden in London on April 23rd, 1775. At an early age, when he was about thirteen, he began to earn his living by drawing and painting scenes of churches and towns, as well as local beauty spots. He became quite popular as a painter in this way and was elected to the British Royal Academy.

Gradually, however, his style changed, and people who had praised him before could no longer understand what he was trying to paint. He had, in fact, begun to paint light and movement in a new and startling way. Friends and critics who were not accustomed to his new way of looking at nature thought that he had gone mad, and he was accused of making "pictures of nothing." His accusers said of him what some people say of many artists today — that he was not looking closely at nature, that he was not finishing his pictures properly, and that he was painting in blots and streaks!

But Turner took no notice of what people said and continued to paint. His subject was nature and light, and these two things he studied intently. Light itself almost shines from his pictures, and it is hard to believe that Turner's public could not understand what he was painting. They were quite wrong when they thought that he was not looking closely at nature, for sometimes he went to extremes just to study some effect of light.

In 1842, he painted a picture of a snowstorm at sea, which is surely

Top: SNOWSTORM *by Turner, The Tate Gallery, London.*
Bottom: RAIN, STEAM AND SPEED *by Turner, The National Gallery, London.*

one of the most remarkable pictures of a storm that was ever painted. You can feel the surge of the ocean waves and almost hear the shrill scream of the wind — yet people still said that it wasn't naturalistic! Such a picture could only have been done after a close study of the sea during a storm. Turner had, in fact, gone aboard a ship to watch the sea in bad weather when a very fierce storm arose. Far from being frightened, Turner was fascinated by what he saw, but as he remained on deck, there was a danger of his being swept overboard. He, therefore, ordered the sailors to lash him to the mast so that he could watch the sea in safety. He stayed there in the terrible gale, according to his own account, for over four hours. Surely such a magnificent picture was worth all that effort!

The following story that is told about Turner gives some idea of how he "filled his mind with materials drawn from a close study of nature." A young woman who was traveling in a train in 1844 was astonished to see the man opposite her suddenly take off his top hat and lean out of the window. He remained there for some minutes, in spite of the fact that it was raining very hard and the train was going at full speed. The man was Turner, and the result of this close study of nature is "Rain, Steam and Speed."

Turner's understanding and ability to paint light was far ahead of his time. He was, in fact, called "the father of the impressionists" by one critic, though he died in 1851, long before impressionism was thought of. He was so far ahead of his time that he was scarcely understood by his friends, and for a time he refused to exhibit or show his great paintings, fearing people would think he was mad.

SKILL LESSON 5

IDENTIFYING STORY ELEMENTS

One quality that all human beings seem to have in common is the ability to enjoy a good story. Historians have discovered that the people of ancient times appreciated hearing an exciting story long before writing was invented. Storytellers were important for the entertainment they provided. Later, with the invention of writing and the printing press, anyone who could read could enjoy a good story whenever he chose to do so.

Every story, whether it be in print, on television, or on the movie screen, has four elements in common. We call these story elements PLOT, CHARACTER, SETTING, and THEME.

The *plot* of a story is the series of events or actions that take place in the story. An effective way of holding a reader's attention in a story is by keeping him in suspense as the plot unfolds. Very early in a good story some problem is set, and as you read on, you keep wondering just how that problem will be solved.

Notice in the story "Carlos Charles" how the authors capture your attention immediately. Carlos and Vicente have experienced a plane crash and appear to be in great danger. Carlos decides to go for help. Carlos's decision to seek assistance and the incidents that follow constitute the plot of the story. Through the events of the story — Carlos's difficulty in getting through the swamp, his sighting of the fishing boat, the problem of sharks, his rescue by the fishing boat, and the rescue of Vicente — the plot develops suspense through the very last sentence.

In "Five-Yard Fuller" the author opens the story with attention-getting conversation. Five-Yard says, "Mister, excuse me for bustin' in, but you look like you're the boss of this football team. I'm looking for a job." From that moment the plot begins to unfold. The first event is Coach Ding's walking away from Five-Yard and trying to ignore him. What events occur from that point on to make up the plot of the story?

The *character* or *characters* around whom a story revolves are another important element in a story. The characters in a story must be presented in such a way that the reader can picture them clearly. Their actions and reactions within the framework of the plot must be believable and logical.

Sometimes a character in a story has special qualities that make that person stand out. In "Navaho Rain" Bright Morning's strength of character actually causes certain events to happen. Her intense love for her people and the desire to return to her natural environment give her strength and determination.

Usually the main character is the most interesting one. There are stories, however, that have very interesting minor characters who contribute much to the stories. In "A Day for Antonio" the main character is one with whose feelings and emotions you can identify. However, Mr. Sandoval, who plays a lesser role, has certain qualities that distinguish him as a wise individual. He is also responsible for certain events in the story.

Many writers develop situations that help you learn more about the major character. Each of these situations provides more information about that character and helps you identify with him in his struggle to solve a problem. His actions and decisions give hints about the nature of his personality.

To understand a character well, you should try hard to identify with that person. This identification, however, should fit the conditions of the story. As you read, visualize the major character in your mind's eye, notice his actions, and evaluate whether his decisions are wise, thoughtless, illogical, or too emotional. For example, remember how Carlos decides to go for help after the plane crash. He could have remained with Vicente and hoped for a plane to spot them. Carlos chooses to brave the muddy jungle and seek aid from fishing boats near the coast. Johnson, another passenger on the plane, has drowned in the mud, but Carlos decides to ignore this warning and to travel about a half mile in search of rescue.

Was this a wise decision on Carlos's part? Would you have made a similar decision? Did you experience Carlos's fear and agony as he plods through the muddy jungle? Visualizing Carlos with your imagination helps you to understand the character clearly and enables you to identify with him and his actions.

Perhaps one of the most interesting characters you have read about thus far is Antonio Ramírez in "A Day for Antonio." One reason for his being such an interesting character is that you could feel his emotions. Could you feel his shyness, his fear, his sadness, his pride? What are the situations in the story that cause those emotions to arise?

Another important story element is *setting*. Every story must occur in a particular place and at a particular time. The story "The Great Storm" is set in a lighthouse station off the coast of Maine and takes place over a period of weeks in January and February of 1856. Find the passages in the story that indicate the time and place.

A vastly different setting from that of "The Great Storm" is the city setting of the story "The Street Kids." The flavor of the city can be seen in passages like this one:

> When June days grew steamy, even the best of street games could become a drag. This was when everybody thought of water. For decades the Hudson had been too polluted to swim in. There were always the hydrants if the cops felt lenient and if the older guys didn't have a stickball game going in the road.

Yet, in the midst of construction fences, public pools, and tall buildings is Mr. Serendipity's garden. It is this unique and unexpected setting within the city that is the heart of the story. How does the garden play an important role in the plot of the story?

Another example of the importance of setting in a story can be found in "The Dolphin Girl." The craggy coastline of ancient Greece in a wartime atmosphere provides a fitting setting for a story filled with conflict and action.

Theme is another important story element. The theme is the basic idea or the message that a writer wants to share with you. The theme underlies all of the action in the story, is contained within the plot, and is revealed to us as we begin to understand how the plot and characterizations are interrelated.

If you were asked to select one quality that is outstanding in the character of Carlos in "Carlos Charles" and in the character of Abbie in "The Great Storm," you would probably choose courage or bravery. Identifying courage as a major character trait in Carlos and Abbie helps you define the theme. A message contained in the story "Carlos Charles" is that a decision to face great danger is sometimes necessary in order to help a fellow human being. A somewhat similar theme is evident in "The Great Storm." Abbie braves the dangers of the storm and overcomes her own fears in order to preserve the safety of men at sea as well as that of her own family.

Not all themes are developed in a serious mood. "Beat the Queen" gives a message through a humorous technique. Pat O'Sullivan Pinkerton has to overcome some serious physical problems. Although Pat does not think his problems are funny, the author develops the theme in a humorous way. What message do you draw from Pat's actions? What situations in the story led you to your conclusion?

When you consider the elements of a story, it is important to see the relation of one element to another. Rarely does a single element make a story. "Navaho Rain," for example, interweaves plot, characters, and setting. The character Abbie in "The Great Storm" takes on added importance because of the setting. Through the character and setting comes the message of importance of believing in yourself and your ability to overcome danger and fear.

Although we tend to treat each element separately, we should always consider the interaction of the four story elements. The story "A Proper Burial" is a good example of the relationship of the four elements. The setting in a poverty area helps to bring out the strength of the characters, especially Mary Call. The theme of respect or love is developed through the courage of the characters in overcoming the problems of everyday living. Each event in the story helps to develop the plot to its final conclusion.

Discussion

Help your class answer the following questions:
1. What are the four elements common to all good stories?
2. What is meant by the plot of a story?
3. What events develop the plot in "Five-Yard Fuller"?
4. How should an author present the characters in a story?
5. What is meant by the setting of a story?
6. What is meant by the theme of a story?
7. How can the elements in a story relate to one another?

On your own

On a sheet of paper write the number of each question that follows and then your answer to it. If necessary, refer to the story named in the question.
1. *Who is the major character in "The Slave Who Bought His Freedom"? Who are the minor characters?*
2. *What is the setting for "Cat and the Underworld"?*
3. *What is the setting for "My Side of the Mountain"?*
4. *What is the plot of the story "Security Check"?*
5. *What is the theme of the story "Cave of Danger"?*

Checking your work

If you are asked to do so, read aloud one or more of your answers. Listen while other students read their answers and compare your answers with theirs. If you made a mistake in any of your answers, find out why it is a mistake.

WINTER TREES

I think that I shall never ski
Again against so stout a tree.

A tree whose rugged bark is pressed
In bas-relief upon my chest.

A tree that with bacchantic air
Wears ski poles in its tangled hair.

. . .

I've learned my lesson: Fools like me
Should never try to shave a tree.

CONRAD DIEKMANN

"Winter Trees" by Conrad Diekmann. Reprinted by permission from Sports Illustrated, January 5, 1959. Copyright © 1959 Time, Inc.

SKI TOURING

by Jean George

It is six A.M. of a winter Sunday in Putney, Vermont, a crossroads town of clapboard houses, a steepled church, a school, and a country store. The frosted mountains loom darkly. There is a foot of new snow, but lights go on in the houses as families arise and start to pack lunches. Minutes later the lights go off, doors open, and laughter fills the crimson dawn. Toddlers, kids, parents, and even grandparents snap their feet into narrow touring skis and glide off through the fields, bodies bent toward ski tips, arms swinging. They move toward the houses on the mountainside, where more join the parade as the sun rises and twinkles on icy peaks. Children prance on their skis, call to each other, and disappear into the silent forest, their voices muted by the powdery snow that covers trees and trail. Adults glide leisurely behind, setting their pace to the very young.

By noon many of these families rendezvous on the sheltered side of a hill, where the view is a glistening panorama of valleys and tiers of white mountains. The tea buckets are filled with snow and set to melt and boil on a small fire. Homemade bread, cheeses, smoked ham, raisins, and nuts are served for lunch, along with the kids' favorite peanut-butter-and-honey sandwiches.

Many an afternoon brings the more athletically-minded youngsters down from the mountains to the meadow in front of the Putney School for races and instruction. An Olympic cross-country skier is there demonstrating his famous "kick" — the push on one ski that sends the other skimming. As this year's squad goes through an afternoon workout, the meadow and roads are decorated like a Christmas tree with brightly colored parkas and sweaters hung on tree limbs and fence posts

by sweaty contestants. The day is over when the last red coat has been claimed, and the school grounds are returned to black and white. A few skiers, who have dallied after dark, strap lights to their heads, attach them to batteries in their pockets, and wind down the roadway like fireflies in the night.

A visitor to Putney may ask: "Is this a new craze?" The answer is that there is nothing *new* about ski touring. It has had its advocates for centuries. Putney is but one center of its fast-growing popularity in the United States. From Washington, D.C., to California, wherever there are a few inches of snow, ski tourers are out on the plains, in the forests, on frozen lakes, roadways, and golf courses; thousands of ski tourists are sailing on seas of snow.

From an inauspicious beginning several years ago ski touring has caught the nation's fancy, and today there are 100,000 enthusiasts registered with various clubs. Nobody knows how many have taken up the sport on their own. One indication is the George Washington's Birthday Race in Vermont, patterned after Sweden's *Vasaloppet* (vä-sä'lŏ-pĕt), or free-for-all overland race. Nine years ago forty registered for the Vermont event; last year more than four hundred signed up.

In simplest terms ski touring may be described as a way of taking a pleasant summer hike in the middle of winter. It can be enjoyed by anyone, young or old, in that beautiful season when many people think they must stay indoors. It can get you out for the little pleasures of the day — visiting a friend, exploring, or simply gliding off into the park or woods for some exercise and fresh air.

The cross-country touring ski is lightweight, about four pounds. The bindings hold only the tips of the shoes to the skis, leaving the heels free to lift during a gliding stride. Snowshoes are for winter walkers, too, but they require deep snow and are awkward by comparison. The touring ski needs but a few inches of snowfall to skim lightly along.

Unlike the alpine, or downhill skier, the ski tourer does not need cleared slopes, chairlifts, or steep mountainsides. In fact, he avoids all of these, seeking gentle contours — a hill in Connecticut, an orchard in Oregon, a flat roadway in Kansas, a narrow garden trail in Washington, D.C. There are none of the injuries that go with downhill skiing — no broken bones, no muscles cramped from long, tense downhill runs. On

the contrary ski touring has been adjudged one of the best forms of exercise. According to a study by Dr. Nils Eie of the Ulleval Hospital, Oslo, it forces the skier to carry his upper body load correctly on his spine.

Many of the strongest advocates of ski touring today are the downhill skiers of yesterday. Dr. Eric Barradale of Brattleboro, Vermont, one of the first serious ski tourers in America, switched over twelve years ago while he was waiting to get on a ski lift. He recalls inching along in a line of hundreds, thinking of his days at Dartmouth College when he stepped out the door, put on his old wooden skis, and got all the way across town in less time than it was taking him to reach a chair to the top of a mountain. That afternoon, he hung up his alpine skis, took down his old wooden boards, and stepped out his back door again. He has not been back to a ski lift since.

Ski touring actually began in prehistory, probably with Stone Age man in Arctic Norway. Wooden skis of that vintage have been found in postglacial bogs, and there is a 4,000-year-old rock carving depicting skiers dashing after game. The Vikings (with the addition of a pole or

brake) attended wintertime weddings, funerals, and clan gatherings on skis. Today whole cities in Norway fall silent on weekends as their people pour out into the Scandinavian countryside. Babies ride in backpacks, and children fall in behind their parents. There are those of many seasons in the crowd too: Eighty-four-year-old Peter Ostye of Oslo, Norway, skis about 500 miles a year and is still going strong.

The Scandinavians were also the missionaries who began carrying the ski-touring gospel around the world. In 1856, the legendary Norwegian, "Snowshoe" Thompson, a U.S. postal agent on the Western frontier, first skied over the Sierra Nevada, camping at night in the snow, moving by day on skis, and bringing the mail to snowbound miners. He bombed into mountain towns to the accompaniment of barking dogs and shouting men, distributed the mail, then helped the locals make skis and end their dreary winter isolation.

Ski touring began to boom in the United States in the mid 1960's, and now ski resorts everywhere are catering to touring enthusiasts.

The missionary zeal still makes converts. Last winter, for instance, the Putney School team descended one Sunday morning on the campus of Columbia University in the heart of Manhattan Island and showed city-bound students how to ski around their campus on a light blanket of snow, skimming gracefully between benches and statues. The team next dumbfounded the citizens of Hartford, Connecticut, when they romped into town and blazed a track on the plaza in front of the state capitol building. From there they drove to Waltham, Massachusetts, ninety-three miles away, where they showed onlookers how to turn town parks, highway shoulders, and playgrounds into useful winter recreational areas.

But there are also those who make the most of close quarters. Sixty-eight-year-old Edwin Gray of Putney gets in shape for races by charging around his and his neighbors' backyards on his cross-country skis. And Manhattanite Morton Lund has been known to ski across the Brooklyn Bridge!

My first steps across an open meadow in a nearby state park were clumsy. I kept sliding backward; then I bent my knees, shuffled, and gained ground. By the time I reached the woods, the knack was coming. Within minutes I was noticing some of the marvels of wintertime that I had been missing all these years. I found the trail of a fox, and written in the snow nearby were the adventures of a white-footed deer mouse during the night — a dive in the snow, a skid on the ice. Birds were moving in their winter formations — nuthatches, chickadees, and downy woodpeckers, cooperating in finding food sources and warning of enemies. In a patch of sunny snow several springtails, primitive insects, vaulted into the air. The wild show was intimate, and its stage was awesome.

As I climbed uphill with surprising ease, I passed deer tracks I did not dare follow, for deer "yard up" in winter. If disturbed, they can break a leg or become bogged down in the deep snow and starve to death.

Snow plopped from tree limbs, revealing the fat buds that were waiting for spring, and icy streams gleamed turquoise-blue. Later, as I sailed up to my car, I was astonished to discover that I had skied the trail in half the time it took me to hike it in summer.

When the next storm blew up, the snow was no longer a house confiner. A new road was mine: down the steps, out across the garden, and, following the natural contours of the land, over the top of the snow to town.

That evening my daughter brought some old wooden skis of her grandfather's down from the attic, and we went out onto the moonlit snow. The earth was silver and blue; she was sailing at my side, and the magic of ski touring was suddenly ours. Like a snowflake it is a world made of sparkles and angles — and so beautifully simple you almost miss it.

DISCUSSION

1. What are some of the pleasures the author has derived from ski touring?
2. When snow is not available, what sport would be similar to ski touring? Why?
3. What are some of the hazards of downhill skiing?
4. What are the advantages and disadvantages of ski touring as opposed to downhill skiing?
5. For what main reason was ski touring first used? What is its most popular use today?
6. What advantages, other than the ones the author mentioned, can you think of for ski touring?
7. Do you prefer or think you would prefer ski touring or downhill skiing? Why?

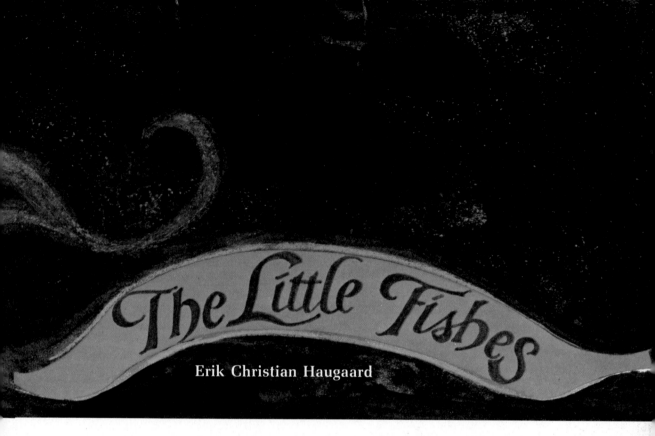

The Little Fishes

Erik Christian Haugaard

In European cities during World War II lived "the little fishes" — hungry, homeless children, begging food and money to survive.

Guido, a twelve-year-old war orphan, is living in the confusion and misery of wartime Naples like many other "little fishes." After a heavy bombing raid eleven-year-old Anna and her small brother, Mario, come in desperation to Guido. Their aunt has been killed in an air raid and their home completely destroyed. For a while Anna and Mario live in Guido's home, a cave outside the city that he shares with an old carpenter. By paying the carpenter a few lire each month, Guido is able to call a section of the cave his own — a small but important luxury for anyone living in a time when so many are homeless. Then one day the carpenter sells his equipment to another man and departs. Guido, Anna, and Mario are ordered to leave the cave, for the new tenant needs the space for his own family. If the police discover that the children have neither a home nor relatives, they will be sent to one of the many orphanages notorious for both hardship and brutality. Before the authorities become suspicious of them, Guido decides that he, Anna, and Mario must leave Naples at once.

When a human being is mortally wounded, he dies quickly; and even while he is dying, death takes possession of him and says: "He is mine."

A city does not die, for life even among the ruins will continue to deny its doom. Children whose parents have been dead but a week will play; grownups will make new homes in the cellars of destroyed buildings. Even the rats with their hard little eyes have, somewhere among the rubble, naked little babes that they return to.

Still the smell of death is there; but the inhabitants do not recognize it, for they have grown used to it, as farmers grow accustomed to the heavy, sweet smell of the orange blossoms. If you came as a stranger to the city, things would fill you with horror, things that the people living there do not even notice. You might even say, "This city is dying," and flee from it with fear; but your fear would not have sprung from the ruins, not even from the smell of death that comes from beneath them, but from your memory, which was still filled with the life of peace, of another world, of the dew of morning. You would be as a horse who was led to a muddy hole to drink, a horse who that very dawn had drunk from a pure spring. The horse would turn away; yet I have seen animals in Calabria (kə-lā′brē-ə) during the hot month of August swallow the moist earth that weeks before had ceased to be a pool. Such animals were the citizens of Naples in the beginning of the summer of 1943.

"You will have to wash him and yourself too. You are both dirty."

Pleadingly, Anna looked up at me; then she took Mario by the hand and led him to the center of the cave, where I had placed a bucket of water. The water I had gotten from the public faucet on the square. It was the only place in the whole district where one could get water. During the day there were long lines of women and children with pails and pitchers waiting their turns. I had been there that morning before the sun rose; and although I did not have to wait, I was not the only one who had come so early.

"Take his clothes off," I ordered. "You can't wash him like that."

Anna, who had been wetting her hands in the bucket and then rubbing Mario's face and arms gently as if she were merely trying to moisten them, let her hands fall to her sides.

"I am sorry," I said, as Anna started to rush to the far corner of the cave. "I am sorry," I repeated, and she turned to listen. "You see, I don't want anyone to notice us. I want everyone to think that we are just on an errand for our parents."

Mario stood still while I took off his clothes. I knew where there was a forgotten pile of wood shavings that the carpenter had not taken with him to use as fuel for his wife's cooking. With a handful of these I began to scrub Mario. His eyes filled with tears and he sniveled.

"When we go, you must try not to cry or else everyone will notice us. You must follow your sister and me . . . and try not to cry." The little one nodded his head and met my glance. His eyes were still moist but his expression was very serious. I smiled and he tried to smile back.

To dry himself, Mario sat down just outside the cave on a rock. It was a rock that had fallen from the cliff during the last air raid. Mario crossed his arms in front of him, each hand resting palm up on his thighs. "He is so thin and weak," I thought. "That is why tears are his only response to everything."

Anna was carrying the bucket to the corner of the cave. "Your ears and your neck," I called after her.

"I cannot get clean with dirty water," she replied.

"Bring me the bucket," I said, "but wash your feet in it first."

The wind came from the sea and smelled salty and fresh. When I arrived at the square — although it was only an hour after the sun had risen — there was already a long line of women. As I waited my turn, I looked about the piazza; here I had played and talked with the other children. Suddenly I became frightened of leaving Naples. I remembered how I had lost my cave and I grew angry. It was true that I had planned to go away from my cave because I had decided I ought to leave the city; but it had never occurred to me that it could be taken away from me. I had believed it to be my home; therefore, I had thought of giving it up; but if I could be ordered to leave from one day to the next, then it had never been mine.

Little Mario was still sitting near the entrance to the cave when I returned, still looking as earnest as before. Anna was standing inside in her dirty cotton petticoat. Her dress lay on the carpenter's bench. I could not tell what the material was, but it was brown and torn. I had never seen her wearing any other dress. "At home . . . at your aunt's, didn't you have any other clothes?" Anna shook her head and picked up the bucket. "Finish washing; then dress the little one," I said. I walked to the mattress and sat down on it; I was so annoyed that I told myself that the carpenter had been right: I should have left alone.

Near my mattress I kept my shoes, my extra shirt, and an old pair of pants. Inside the mattress was a small cigarette box of metal;

in this I kept the ten *lire* that the count had given me; I had saved it to use when I left the city. I slid my hand in and took out the box, which I shoved into the one of my pockets that had no hole. My extra shirt I folded into a kerchief that I had found one day among the ruins. The old pair of pants I decided to leave behind; they were not worth carrying. I also owned a comb, though several of its teeth were missing, and a knife with a sharp point.

Anna and Mario were both dressed again. The little boy had a pair of worn shoes on, but Anna was barefooted. I wetted my hair and combed it. Mario's hair was still moist from having been washed. I tried to comb it, but there were many snarls, for it had not been combed in a very long time. Mario grimaced and tears appeared in his eyes, but he did not cry out. I gave the comb to Anna. When she was finished combing her hair, she apologized, for two more of the teeth were missing. Once more I attempted to comb Mario's hair, and this time I did get it smooth.

"Come," I called.

I let Anna and Mario go out before me. The thought that I had had about regretting that I was not going alone came back to me and filled me with disgust for myself.

It was now eight o'clock in the morning, and at the piazza there were dozens of women and children waiting for water. Among them was a girl the same age as Anna. I knew her. Her name was Maria, but it was not the girl I was noticing as much as the dress she was wearing. It was not new, for although Maria had parents, they were poor; yet compared to Anna's it seemed almost new.

I approached Maria boldly. "I want to buy your dress."

She was surprised; for though we would often sell things that we found and a boy had once sold his shirt for a bread, we seldom traded in our own clothes — maybe because none of us had any to spare. "I'll give you two *lire* for it," I said.

"I'll think it over while I wait to get the water," she replied.

She was almost at the end of the line. I was eager to get as far outside the city as possible that day. "It will take too long," I argued. "Come now and we'll talk about it."

"I can't sell it anyway.... My mother wouldn't let me. What do you want it for?"

"It is for her." I flung out my arm towards Anna, who was standing at the curb. "She has her only dress on." Anna must have guessed what I had said, for she looked embarrassed. "We are going away. Her aunt was killed. I am afraid we will be picked up."

Maria smiled pityingly toward Anna, and I said quickly, "Three *lire* and her dress!"

"I wouldn't want her dress. It is torn and dirty."

I looked at Maria. She was clean and her hair was combed.

"I have another dress at home," she said after a long pause. "You can buy that one for her. But I must get the water first."

"Is it as nice as the one you have on?" I asked, for now I wanted Anna to have that dress and no other.

"It is better than hers and clean."

I heard the contempt in her voice, and I said, "You didn't wash your dress, your mother did.... I will give you five *lire* for the dress you have on." The girl shook her head and picked up her pitcher. There were still several women ahead of her.

I tried to convince myself that it could not matter so much how we were dressed; but each time I glanced at Anna, the argument seemed futile, for I wanted her to have a clean dress that was not torn. "*Va bene* (vä bā′nā) ... All right," I said. "But hurry up," I added foolishly.

Time passed slowly as we watched the women fill their buckets and pitchers and carry them away on their heads. Before the war a woman would always place a handkerchief or a clean rag on top of her head to protect her hair from what she carried, but now the cloth was usually missing. It was not only because even a small

bit of material had value, but the women did not seem to care so much about their hair any more. Finally, it was Maria's turn; she filled up her pitcher and gestured for us to follow her.

The house that she lived in had not been damaged by any of the bombings. It was a better house than most, and the door looked almost new.

"Wait here for me," she said. "I will be right back. I don't want my mother to know."

"On which floor do you live?" I asked.

"The third," she replied, and disappeared into the house.

We sat watching that building for so long that Anna suggested that Maria was playing a joke on us. I had just decided to go away when we saw her coming out of the door. As she closed it behind her, we heard a woman's voice calling her.

"Here it is." Maria held out the dress that she had carried crumpled in a bundle under her arm. Although it was much better than the one Anna was wearing, the dress was well worn and was not nearly as pretty as the one Maria had on. It was a very plain dress and the belt was missing.

"Two *lire*," I said.

"Three," the girl insisted, and pretended that she was about to refold the dress.

I responded by shrugging my shoulders to show my disinterest in paying so much. "How do I know that it even fits?" I said nonchalantly. But then I saw Anna's face, which had an expression that was a sad and curious mixture of defiance, shame, and desire. "She wants the dress," I thought. "You'll have to find a place for her to try it on," I said to Maria.

"Come," Maria ordered, and led Anna into the house. Later Anna told me that she had been up in Maria's home and that her mother was there, so Maria must have lied to us when she had said that her mother would not let her sell the dress.

When they returned to the street, Anna was smiling broadly; the dress, if anything, was a little too big for her. Nervously, Anna's hands moved about her waist as she tried to adjust the dress better.

"All right," I agreed, and gave Maria the three *lire,* which she slipped into her left shoe.

"Where are you going?"

The girl's question caught me by surprise. "North," I answered, but I might just as well have said south, or maybe not, for Naples was filled with people coming from the south, where the misery was said to be greater than ours. Besides, the south was where my aunt and uncle lived, and there, too, was the churchyard where my mother was buried. "To Cassino (käs-sē′nō)!" I blurted.

I knew that there was a city north of Naples by that name and that there was a monastery there.

"What is it like?"

I glanced at Anna questioningly. We were still in the outskirts of Naples, and the sun had already set.

"The place that we are going to, Cassino."

Along the street on which we were walking, the houses were low; each was surrounded by a high wall, behind which was a garden. Between many of the houses there were empty spaces.

"Cassino is a city," I replied without turning to look at her, for I did not want to admit that I did not even know whether it was a large or small city.

"I am tired." Little Mario was behind us. He looked very tired. His bare feet were covered with dust. I had taken his shoes away from him because I thought it was a waste for him to be wearing them now when it was so warm.

"Soon we will find a place to sleep," I said cheerfully, for I knew from experience that Mario would cringe at a frown, as if he had been promised a beating, while a smile could sometimes make him smile back. Already I was finding out the curse of being a leader — that though filled with doubt yourself, you cannot allow it to show in your face or the tone of your voice. Ahead of us the road divided and there was a signpost. I was hoping

that it would say Cassino and tell us how far away that city was.

One sign read: Aversa (ä-věr′sä); the other: Caserta (käz-ěr′tä). In which direction was Cassino? The road to Caserta appeared less used, as if it would lead more quickly into the country. The name seemed familiar; maybe one of the children we knew came from there. "We shall go via Caserta," I said to Anna. I almost laughed, for I realized that the reason I had chosen this road was that the names sounded alike — Cassino, Caserta.

Soon we were in the country. There was pastureland. I was looking anxiously for a place for us to sleep, for it was growing dark. It was warm, and we could have slept anywhere in the fields; but I suspected that Mario would be frightened of lying out in the open without walls around the darkness. At last, in one of the fields, I saw a small stone shed. We would only have to climb over a low fence to get to it. There were vines growing in the fields, so there would be no animals there.

I listened, half expecting a dog to bark as we approached the hut. In the cities dogs are afraid of human beings, even children, for city dogs are used to being kicked and having stones thrown at them; but the dogs of the country are different; they belong to the soil, to the farm, and will defend it against intruders.

No dogs barked. We entered the hovel; it had not been used for a long time. There was no door and part of the roof had fallen in. Some grapevines that had been cut off at the last pruning were stacked against a wall. I told Anna to select the thinner ones while I cleared a corner of the hut for us to make our beds.

Even the finer of the vines were too hard to sleep upon, so Anna and I plucked some of the tall grass that grew around the hut to cover them. On top I spread out Anna's old dress and my shirt for Mario to sleep on.

"I'm hungry," Mario said. Before leaving the city, I had bought a big bread; now I cut off three heavy slices of it. I gave the end piece, which was the smallest, to Mario because he was the youngest.

We had nothing to drink, nor could I recall having passed any wells near the vineyard; but not far beyond the hut was another field, and separating it from this one was a row of trees. I could not see for it was too dark, but I knew that farmers often planted fruit trees at the edges of their property. Still eating my bread, I made my way to the trees. They were mostly fig — a fruit that is not ripe until August. Luckily, there was a single plum tree among them. The plums were small and hard, and I did not pick very many, for unripe fruit could have given us stomachaches that would have made walking practically impossible.

"Here." I gave four plums each to Mario and Anna. They were sweeter than I had expected them to be; and I thought how fortunate the people in the country were, for here there was always fruit, even in the winter, for that is the season of the oranges. Suddenly I felt proud. "You have brought two children out of Naples, Guido," I thought. "You have fed them and found a place for them to sleep. We shall be all right, Guido."

I could hear little Mario and Anna sleeping, but I could not sleep myself. I was tired but I could not relax. My legs felt as though the blood were tickling them. I got up quietly and walked outside. There was almost a full moon, and the stars were very pale in the sky. In the distance I heard the bark of a dog; such a sound makes one feel lonelier.

"Luna ... Moon," I said the word out loud, but in a whisper, for it is a magic word, as are the words you use in a prayer. "Madre di Dio (mä′drā dē dē′ō) ... Mother of God." These are sacred words, but they are also magic ones, and you say them slowly, softly. Even "bread" can be a magic word when you are hungry. Why are there magic words, words you only whisper? Why are they different from the words you shout in anger? A bat flew above my head, and I recalled that there had been many bats on my uncle's farm; but I had never seen one except at night when it is like a shadow flying above you. "Bat," that is an ugly word, for most people do not like bats. "Casa mia (kä′zä mē′ä) ... my house," that is soft and sweet. I smiled into the night because I was having such strange thoughts, and I wondered if everyone had thoughts like that. Did grownups?

Would we be in Caserta tomorrow? What would that town be like? Like Messina (měs-sē′nä)? No, it must be smaller and it is not near the sea. Would it be a village like St. Marco, where I had walked with my mother? I reminded myself that St. Marco was in the mountains and so small that there was no road sign pointing the way to it. As if moved by a gentle wind, my thoughts drifted to my mother, and I thought no more about the city of Caserta. In my mind I saw the stone fence on which my mother and I had sat. I remembered the lizards that I used to watch while she talked. Had I been strong ... duro (doo′rō) ... as she had wished me to be? Had I been kind? I saw her face as it had been when she had been well; and I understood for the first time that although she had been very gentle, she, too, had been duro, like iron.

I must have fallen asleep, for Anna's voice startled me. She was calling my name and she sounded frightened. I was sitting in the shadows of the grapevines, and she could not see me. "Anna," I called.

She was standing just outside the entrance to our small hut, and her face was filled with moonlight. "Guido," she whispered back. She said my name over and over again as she came towards me. "Oh, Guido." She sank down on her knees beside me. "I thought you had gone! I thought you had gone!"

I stroked her hair, and for a long time we said nothing to each other. I was watching the clouds pass in front of the moon when I heard her whisper, "I will remember to wash." Then she sat up. "You see, my aunt was sick for so long, and we had only one room; they wouldn't let us use the kitchen. Now there is no house and they are all dead."

"It does not matter," I said, and did not ask who *they* were. At that moment I felt that nothing that had happened to us in Naples mattered. But it was the moon and the soft night wind that gave me these thoughts, for everything that happens to you matters. Everything leaves a little scar — both the good and the bad — and when you grow up, then the scars are the story of your life.

DISCUSSION

1. Why does the author say that "a city does not die"?
2. How desperate were the citizens of Naples in the beginning of the summer of 1943, and why were they so desperate?
3. What were Guido's feelings about taking Anna and Mario with him?
4. How much money did Guido spend for a new dress for Anna? Why did he feel that buying a new dress was important?
5. Do you think Maria was being deceitful by saying her mother would not let her sell her dress? Why do you think she said this?
6. Why did Anna promise Guido that she would remember to wash?
7. How can "scars" be "the story of your life"? What "scars" did the children have already?

8. Should Guido have had mixed feelings about taking the children with him? Why or why not? What would you have done if you had been in Guido's place?

9. Was it important for Guido to spend part of his savings so that Anna could have a new dress? Why or why not?

10. What would you do if you were left alone in the world and had to rely on your own resources? How would this change if others were relying on you — if you had to assume responsibility for them?

11. Do you have words that you think of as being magic words? What are some of them? Why do they seem like magic words to you?

AUTHOR

Erik Christian Haugaard, who was born in Copenhagen, Denmark, has been a farm laborer, a sheepherder, a carpenter, a vagabond, a poet, and the author of many excellent books for young people as well as books of drama and poetry for adults.

The selection you have just read, taken from his book of the same name, won the Boston Globe—Horn Book Award and a Book World Children's Spring Book Festival Award in 1967 and the Jane Addams Book Award in 1968. Some other outstanding books by Mr. Haugaard are *A Slave's Tale, Orphans of the Wind,* and *The Rider and His Horse.*

Mr. Haugaard came to the United States when he was in his teens and attended Black Mountain College in North Carolina. He was an air gunner in the Royal Canadian Air Force in World War II and received a War Service Medal from Christian X of Denmark. Mr. Haugaard has returned to Denmark, where he now lives with his wife, Myrna Seld, who is also a writer, and their two children, Mikka Anja and Mark.

JOHN PAPPAS TRIES OUT FOR THE METS

by Robert Lipsyte

John Pappas appeared on the second day of spring training. He was thin and pale, and he looked about seventeen years old. He said he was twenty-one and that he had come to St. Petersburg, Florida, to be a pitcher for the New York Mets. Nobody knew what to do with him.

In any other major-league clubhouse that spring, the equipment manager or the assistant trainer or maybe even the bat boy would have heaved John Pappas out the door. But this was the second day of the Mets' very first spring, and no one was sure enough of his own job to make a decision about someone else. So Pappas just stood quietly in the hushed, green-carpeted clubhouse, his sneakers under one arm, his glove under the other.

Out on the field a collection of strangers with hopes was trying to sort itself into a team. Rabbit-quick rookies made impossible leaping catches — always when the coaches weren't looking — and the older players, some of whom had once been stars with other teams, tried to sweat themselves down into shape for the long season ahead. The borderline players worked hardest of all, running extra laps around the outfield, taking long turns in the batting cage, and chattering, "Atta-boy, baby, show him the hummer, good hand, chuck it in there," because Casey Stengel, manager of the Mets, had a reputation for favoring players with spirit and hustle. The borderline players knew that if they didn't make it with this brand-new team, they would probably slide right out of the major leagues.

Pappas stood for a long time in the clubhouse, politely but firmly telling anyone who asked that he had no intention of budging until someone from the Mets gave him a tryout. Finally, a tall, sad-faced man came out of a side office and looked into Pappas's steady, brown eyes. He introduced himself as John Murphy, an official of the new club.

"Where are you from?" asked Murphy.

"New York City," said Pappas.

"When was the last time you threw a ball?"

"Last Sunday, in New York," said Pappas.

Murphy's eyes narrowed, and he smiled a triumphant little smile. "It snowed in New York last Sunday."

Pappas nodded. "Yes, sir. But not underneath the Triborough Bridge."

Murphy's eyes widened. He motioned Pappas to a wooden bench in front of the lockers and sat down beside him. The young man said he had bought four regulation National League baseballs and pitched them at a painted square on a concrete wall under the bridge. After he was satisfied, he ran for several miles in a nearby park. Then he packed for spring training.

He had arrived in St. Petersburg at three o'clock that morning, he said, after his first airplane trip. It was also the first time he had ever been more than a hundred miles from his parents' home in Queens.

Murphy listened and nodded and pulled at his long, sad face. Then he stood up. "We're not holding tryouts here, John." He pointed through the open clubhouse door to the practice ball fields. "There would be a million guys out there if we were."

"I don't see a million guys out there," said Pappas seriously and softly. When Murphy shot him a hard glance to see if he was being smart, Pappas looked down at his black pointy shoes.

Murphy sighed. "You play high-school ball?"

"My high school didn't have a team, Mr. Murphy, but I played Police Athletic League ball. I don't remember which precinct."

"Did anyone ever say you were professional material?"

"No, sir."

"Do your parents know you came down here for a tryout, John?"

"No one knows, Mr. Murphy."

Murphy's voice became gentle. "Do you go to school?"

"I was going to City College at night, but I stopped going to classes. And I quit my job. I was working in a furniture store. I told my mother I was coming down for a vacation, and then I'd look for another job."

Almost wearily, Murphy said, "This is not a tryout camp."

Pappas took a deep breath. "Mr. Murphy, I don't have much experience, and I'm willing to spend a few years in the minors. But I think I can pitch, and I want to find out now. I want to succeed in the world, and I can do it if I set my mind to it."

"Of course you can," said Murphy, "but there are many ways to succeed in the world besides major-league baseball."

"I'm going to stay here until someone looks at me pitch," said Pappas, running a bony hand through his black pompadour. "If they tell me I'm no good, I'll just finish my vacation and go home and set my mind to something else."

Murphy stared at Pappas for a long time. "Okay, John," he said. "You get a catcher and a place to throw, and I'll come look at you."

They shook hands, and Pappas, smiling now, bounded out of the clubhouse. "Thanks, thanks a lot," he called back over his shoulder.

Murphy watched him go, then shook his head at us and walked back into his office. Another newspaperman turned to me and said, "That's a flaky kid for you. I don't know why Murphy wastes his time."

"What do you mean flaky?" I said. "He might really have it; he might be a star. And who says Murphy could tell from one tryout?"

"Johnny Murphy was once a great relief pitcher for the Yankees," said the other newspaperman, "and I think you're a flaky kid too."

The weather was erratic in St. Petersburg that week, sometimes cool, almost always windy. John Pappas ran in the mornings near his motel and found youngsters to catch his pitching. Three days after he first showed up, a local newspaper arranged for Pappas to use a nearby high-school ball field, and Murphy promised to drive out to watch him pitch. Murphy said he would even bring a professional catcher.

The morning of his tryout Pappas went to the Mets spring-training camp at Miller Huggins Field and found a seat in the sun on the grandstand. A little less pale now, but still thin and tense, he sat in a crowd of elderly tourists and pensioners and watched the Mets work out. I sat with him for a little while. He pointed at four young Met pitchers who were taking turns throwing for batting practice.

"That could be me," he said.

At 3:38 P.M. on February 23, 1962, John Pappas had his chance. While a dozen newspapermen and photographers watched, he strode onto a scruffy pitching mound and put everything in his slight body behind the baseballs he threw at Bill Whalen, a young catcher from the Mets' camp. Pappas threw for eighteen minutes in silence. He was wild, and he wasn't very fast.

At 3:56 P.M. Murphy walked out to the mound and put his arm around Pappas's thin shoulders. "All you have is guts, son," he said.

They shook hands. Murphy thanked Pappas for giving the Mets a chance to look him over. Very kindly, he told Pappas to forget about professional baseball. Maybe if he were only fifteen years old it might make sense to keep at it, but at twenty-one he had too far to go and too much to learn.

Pappas thanked Murphy for giving him a tryout. He said he was satisfied and now he was going back to New York.

"I always would have wondered," said Pappas, "but now I know. I just wasn't good enough. Now I'll look for something else, some other way of being somebody."

The ball field slowly emptied, and soon there was just Pappas and two or three of the younger newspapermen who had secretly hoped that this thin, sallow, round-shouldered, young clerk would turn out to have an arm like a bullwhip, a live fastball that hummed, and a curve that danced in the sun. I think we were more disappointed than he was, and we were talking mostly for ourselves on the ride back to town, telling Pappas that there were other ways to succeed in the world besides major-league baseball and that he was way ahead of the game; after all, how many men actually get a chance to try out, to find out once and for all? Pappas nodded and agreed and smiled and thanked us for our encouragement.

It was dusk when we reached his motel. The last time I saw John Pappas, he was framed in the car window, and he said: "You know, I'm sorry they didn't give me a chance to hit. I'm not a bad hitter. And I play the outfield too."

DISCUSSION

1. What was there about the Mets in the spring of 1962 that made it possible for an unknown to receive a tryout?
2. What were the newspapermen's feelings about John Pappas before the tryout? After the tryout?
3. Was Pappas physically strong? Why or why not?
4. This is a true story. Name some things that make it almost unbelievable.
5. What was Murphy's advice to Pappas after the tryout? Was it good advice? Why or why not?
6. From what is told in the story, describe Pappas's character.
7. Would you have the nerve and determination to do what Pappas did? Why or why not?
8. Does this story remind you of the story about Five-Yard Fuller? How were the stories the same? How were they different? How were John Pappas and Five-Yard Fuller alike? How were they different?

AUTHOR

Robert Lipsyte, a well-known sports writer for *The New York Times*, is the author of *Assignment: Sports,* from which the story about John Pappas was taken.

Mr. Lipsyte, a graduate of Columbia College and the Columbia Graduate School of Journalism, is a three-time winner of the E. P. Dutton Best Sports Story of the Year Award. In 1966, he received Columbia University's Mike Berger Award for Distinguished Reporting.

SEQUOYAH

by Nancy Caldwell Sorel

While living in the Cherokee territory of Tennessee, young Sequoyah
(sĭ-kwoi'ə) and his companions would
argue as to whether the mysterious
power of "the talking leaf" was a gift
from the Great Spirit to the white man
or the white man's own discovery.

Sequoyah's companions had seen
white men with books and had seen
them write messages on paper. They
were convinced that this form of communication was just another of those
blessings that the Great Spirit had
seen fit to bestow upon the white man
but not upon the red. But Sequoyah
strenuously maintained the opposite:
that the Great Spirit had had nothing
to do with it and that the white man
had himself invented "the talking
leaf." It was an argument that remained fixed in his mind and continued to haunt him with its possibilities.

Sequoyah was born about 1770,
most probably the son of a white
trader named Nathaniel Gist. Nobody dwelt much on these matters of
little significance. The important facts
were that his mother was a member
of the family of the Emperor Moytoy
and the legendary warrior-king Ocono-
stota (â'găn-û-stâ'tă); that Sequoyah
was born in the Indian village of Tas-
kigi, later Tuskegee (tŭs-kē'gē), just
five miles from the sacred town of
Echota; and that he was a Cherokee.
He became a craftsman in silverwork,
an accomplished storyteller, and a
happy participant in the Green Corn
Dances, footraces, and ball games.
And, along with his entire tribe, he
was illiterate.

Sequoyah's life might have continued without incident if an accident
had not left Sequoyah partially crippled. As a result he had more leisure
and more opportunity to ponder the
idea that the red man also might come
to possess the secret of "the talking

leaf." He began to wander off into the woods and spend hours there alone, avoiding everyone, playing like a child with pieces of wood or making odd little marks with one stone on another. His wife and friends offered no encouragement or even sympathy, for they were convinced that he was either going mad or in communication with the spirits. Months became years, and the lack of sympathy became ridicule and contempt. But Sequoyah was obsessed with his dream.

At first Sequoyah tried to give every word a separate character, but eventually he realized the futility of such an approach and settled on assigning a character to each sound. When his friends and neighbors talked, he no longer heard what they said but listened to the sounds, trying to separate them and trying to identify any new sound that he might theretofore have missed. What he eventually achieved was not so much an alphabet as a syllabary — eighty-six characters representing all the sounds of spoken Cherokee — which, when combined, produced a written language of remarkable simplicity and effectiveness. It had taken twelve years.

There are many stories of how Sequoyah presented his "alphabet" to his doubting people and overcame their reluctance to try it. According to one legend, there was actually a great demonstration before the chiefs, during which his little daughter read aloud what the chiefs had privately told him to write on a paper and thus

in a single moment amazed and convinced everyone. According to another story, the alphabet was carried piecemeal from that part of the tribe still in Tennessee to the other part now in Arkansas. So beautifully simple and precise was Sequoyah's alphabet that it could be learned in a very few days. Moreover, whoever learned, taught; until suddenly a most remarkable thing had happened. Within a matter of months a population that had been almost entirely illiterate suddenly became almost entirely literate! And the lame little man who had been ridiculed by his people was now respected, revered, and regarded as a superhuman and a great benefactor.

In 1828, Sequoyah was named one of a delegation of Arkansas Cherokees that went to Washington to attempt to settle with the federal government all the unfulfilled promises of all the previous treaties. Sequoyah's fame preceded him; he was the subject of much attention in the capital. Charles Bird King asked him to sit for a portrait, and many newspapermen requested interviews. Jeremiah Evarts[1] asked him why and how he had invented the alphabet and later wrote this account of Sequoyah's answer:

He had observed that many things were found out by men and known in the world but that this knowledge escaped and was lost for want of some

---
[1] **Jeremiah Evarts** (ĕv'ərts): American lawyer, philanthropist, and writer.

way to preserve it. He had also observed white people write things on paper, and he had seen books, and he knew that what was written down remained and was not forgotten. He had attempted, therefore, to fix certain marks for sounds and thought that if he could make certain things fast on paper, it would be like catching a wild animal and taming it.

The result of the Washington visit was that the Cherokees agreed to yet another treaty by which they exchanged their lands in Arkansas for new and more extensive ones in what is now Oklahoma. Most of the Cherokees were still clinging desperately to their ancestral territories in Tennessee and Alabama, but the Arkansas band, to which Sequoyah now belonged, once again uprooted itself and moved westward to Oklahoma. Sequoyah, now in his sixties, built himself a new cabin with his own hands, tended his little farm, and at intervals traveled up through the woods to the salt springs. There he would live for days or weeks at a time, filling his kettles, tending his fires, scooping out the salt, and pausing in his work to talk to anyone who — out of curiosity to see and speak with the now-famous Cherokee philosopher — sought him out there.

But the Great Spirit did not allow Sequoyah to end his life in the tranquillity of the forest around Lee's Creek. The federal government, which had for so long coveted the Cherokees' ancestral land in Tennessee and Alabama, contracted a treaty of removal; and well-armed soldiers drove some seventeen thousand Cherokees from their homes. The long trek westward began, months of suffering ensued, and some four thousand Cherokees died before the great mass of them began to arrive in the Oklahoma territory in the spring of 1839. Problems arose immediately. The new arrivals greatly outnumbered the already established inhabitants; there were profound conflicts over the land, over the make-up of the local government, over everything. Sequoyah, foreseeing an irreparable breach, brought his influence to bear on the side of reason and necessity. At a meeting of the tribe an act of union was adopted, and the Cherokees of Alabama, Tennessee, Arkansas, and Oklahoma united to become the Cherokee Nation.

But even then Sequoyah could not rest. According to tradition, a band of Cherokees had migrated west of the Mississippi at just about the time that Sequoyah was born. Where were they now, these lost Cherokees who did not know of his alphabet or of the new nation? Sequoyah, now aged, set off with a party of nine horsemen and headed south. Legend has it that before he died, somewhere deep in Mexico, he did find the lost Cherokees. Not long afterward that genus of California redwoods that included the largest trees in the world was named "sequoia" after the "mad" little man who spent hours in the woods making odd little markings.

DISCUSSION

1. What did the Cherokees call a message written on paper? How did they think the white man received the gift of written communication? What was Sequoyah's belief?
2. What happened to Sequoyah to give him more leisure time? What did having this extra time lead to?
3. How long did it take for Sequoyah to devise his syllabary? For what reasons did Sequoyah say he had devised it?
4. What other man have you read about in this book who built his house with his own hands and spent much time in the woods? How were the two men alike? How were they different?
5. Would you have persisted as Sequoyah did if your wife and friends offered you no encouragement and thought you mad? Why or why not?
6. Do you think it is appropriate for the great redwood tree to be named after Sequoyah? Why or why not?

AUTHOR

Nancy Caldwell Sorel, author of "Sequoyah," has been a news writer, an editor, and a teacher of English. Her husband, Edward, who illustrated the book *Word People,* from which the selection you have just read was taken, has illustrated several children's books. His caricatures have appeared on the covers of such magazines as *Time* and *Atlantic Monthly,* and he is the creator of "Sorel's News Service," a syndicated cartoon feature.

Mrs. Sorel, her husband, their four children, and a big Newfoundland dog live in New York State.

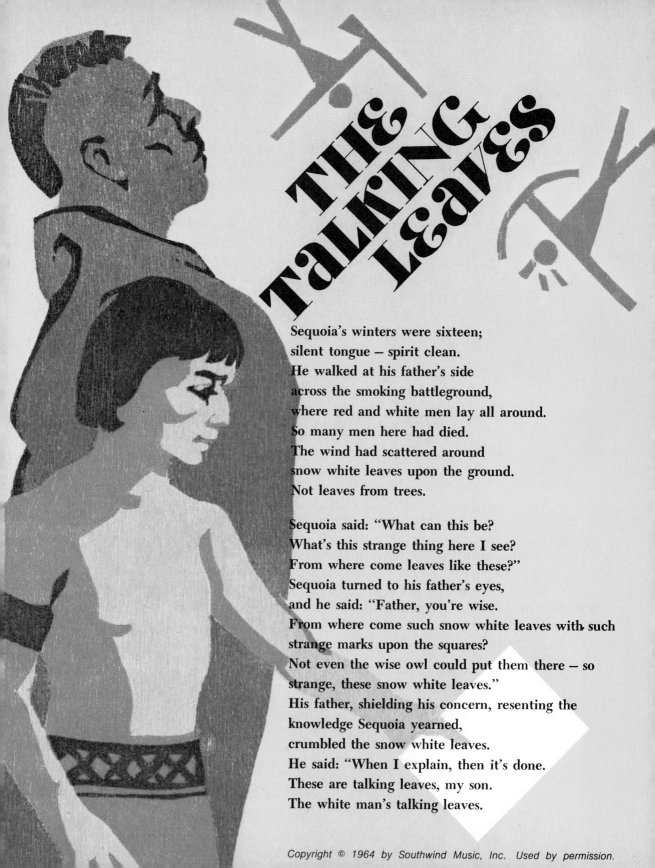

THE TALKING LEAVES

Sequoia's winters were sixteen;
silent tongue — spirit clean.
He walked at his father's side
across the smoking battleground,
where red and white men lay all around.
So many men here had died.
The wind had scattered around
snow white leaves upon the ground.
Not leaves from trees.

Sequoia said: "What can this be?
What's this strange thing here I see?
From where come leaves like these?"
Sequoia turned to his father's eyes,
and he said: "Father, you're wise.
From where come such snow white leaves with such
strange marks upon the squares?
Not even the wise owl could put them there — so
strange, these snow white leaves."
His father, shielding his concern, resenting the
knowledge Sequoia yearned,
crumbled the snow white leaves.
He said: "When I explain, then it's done.
These are talking leaves, my son.
The white man's talking leaves.

Copyright © 1964 by Southwind Music, Inc. Used by permission.

"The white man takes a berry of black and red, and
an eagle's feather from the eaglet's bed.
And he makes bird track marks.
And the marks on the leaves, they say, carry
messages to his brother far away.
And his brother knows what's in his heart.
They see these marks and they understand the truth
in the heart of the far-off man.
The enemies can't hear them."
Said Sequoia's father: "Son, they weave bad
medicine on these talking leaves.
Leave such things to them."

Then Sequoia, walking lightly, followed his father
quietly. But so amazed was he.
If the white man talks on leaves, why not
the Cherokee?
Banished from his father's gaze, Sequoia went
from place to place.
But he could not forget.

Year after year, he worked on and on.
Till finally he cut into stone the Cherokee alphabet.
Sequoia's hair, by now, was white. His eyes began
to lose their light.
But he taught all who would believe that the
Indian's thoughts could be written down.
And he left us these talking leaves.

JOHNNY CASH

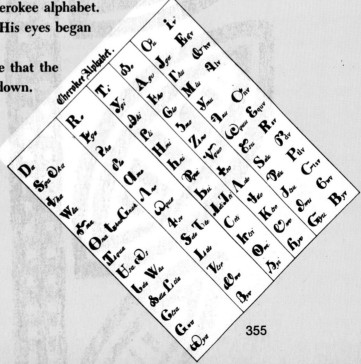

355

CHRISTMAS
ON WOLF CREEK

Adrienne Richard

Billy Catlett, whose nickname is Pistol, is growing up during the big depression in the 1930's in the small town of Great Plains, Montana. In the summer of his fourteenth year he helped his family financially by taking a summer job at Sam Tolliver's ranch, "riding the range" with the cowboys for whom he developed admiration and affection, particularly Tom Driscoll. But when fall came, Pistol had to say good-by to ranch life and return to school. Now it is early December; with two blizzards having already hit, it promises to be one of the worst winters Montana has ever known.

I had delivered the afternoon prescriptions for Acton's Drugstore, where I had picked up an after-school job, and was hurrying up the street before it grew dark. The store windows glittered with Christmas lights, and the snow was shoveled into huge windrows at the outer edge of the sidewalk. I was thinking about stopping for a hamburger before going home to dinner when I saw Sam coming toward me on the street.

Just seeing him made me feel good; and watching him I thought, if I ever had to be fifty, I wanted to look like Sam. He carried himself erect and springy, and he looked heavier than he was, buttoned into his soiled sheepskin coat. His hat brim had more of a roll on the right side than the left, because that was the way he ran his free hand along it when he lifted his hat to wipe his forehead on his sleeve or maybe just ease the sweatband.

When he saw me, his rough face didn't change expression. It just warmed up, and he held out his hand and greeted me and called me Pistol; and I felt as good as if I had suddenly, by accident, dropped into the right hole; and then he asked me what I was doing with school out and if I wanted to come out to the ranch for a few days and help Tom drive a herd over to Wolf Creek, where he had been able to stock feed for them. The herd was already quartered at Tom's place, so the drive would only be about ten miles, not a big day's work. Red was in the Wolf Creek camp, looking after another herd, and Tom and I would drive the rest over there.

Sam knew there wasn't much question whether I wanted to or not, just would my parents let me go, and I could leave a message for him at the Marshall House when I found out. I raced home to find my mother, who said it was all right as long as I was home by Christmas and dressed warmly. I hauled my saddle and heavy leather chaps to the front porch and stowed my extra shirts and pants and mitten liners and overshoes, which fitted over my high-heeled boots, into a duffel bag with my razor, which I didn't need yet; and I was ready, prancing, when the next morning Sam appeared in his Model A coupe.

The road was covered with snow. The loose layers had blown off, leaving bare the tracks that had been beaten into the frozen surface. The day was gray and still and cold, and the trip passed swiftly enough as we discussed, man to man, the seriousness of range conditions and what the future might hold.

The herd was quartered at Tom's place, halfway between Sam's main ranch and Wolf Creek, and we went there to prepare for the drive. Tom had a modest spread and ran his cattle with Sam's and worked for Sam. The little house was dominated by a radio with a gigantic horn.

"This place is a pigpen, Driscoll. You need to get a woman in here somehow," Sam said, and Tom rubbed his hair, laughing. It struck me funny, too, to think of Tom with a woman, a wife, maybe kids. To me he was perfect and complete when he was on his horse working cattle on the open range.

Early the next morning we got ready for the drive. I put on my long underwear, wool pants, Levis, and chaps and a work shirt and a wool shirt and a coat and a Scotch cap that had a flap from ear to ear and boots and rubber-soled felt overshoes and my big mittens with two linings. Tom wore the same number of layers, and it didn't feel particularly cold.

"There's a friend of yours out here," Tom said.

It was Sundance! His sorrel coat was as thick as a well-fed cat's, now that it was winter, and his intelligent eyes were watching me with interest.

"Just go easy. Nobody's been on him since you left."

I went easy, and Sundance responded. It felt good just to ride him.

Tom let the herd out of the corral. There was an old lead cow, and she immediately struck out, taking first place from the others. As soon as we drove them onto the prairie, the whole herd strung out behind her. The little calves fell behind and the cows went ahead, sometimes bunched behind the lead cow but mostly plodding in single file. They were strung out for almost a quarter of a mile, with Tom and me riding at a walk behind them. The old lead cow seemed to know where she was going because she hit the trail with little guidance. Once in a while Tom lit out around the herd to turn her one way or the other, but not often.

The first hour passed, but the sky grew no lighter. The sun did not come out. The ceiling hung low and gray and heavy. The old snow crackled under the hooves of horses and cattle. Windless, smoking cold breath eddied around our mouths and the heads of the stock. The little calves were silent.

About ten o'clock it began. The snow fell at first in small, dry flakes, straight down. I watched it gather on the curly, red-brown backs of the calves before me. It was beautiful. The whole world around us, locked in gray and cold, was complete and perfect for me. I was riding my maverick with the man who had broken it for me, the man I admired more than anyone else, driving cattle across the open slopes of my homeland; and I had no room nor need for any other world. When the snow stirred on the brown backs, when the flakes thickened and the wind rose, I still found not a flaw in my perfect realm.

The wind was sharp, driving the snow before it in long white strings. It came across the long slopes and frozen snow-crusted ridges with nothing to stop it. There was no growth in this region but lines of bare cottonwoods meandering along creek bottoms. The pine hills lay south, and north were only more snow-locked slopes and prairies and frozen gumbo hills.

Soon we couldn't see the lead cow. The snow heaped on the curly rumps ahead of me. I swung my rope, partly to keep my arms warm, and flicked a rump to keep it moving. What would stop us from getting lost, I wondered. We might wander forever and freeze to death, and I looked at Tom; but if any such thoughts came to him, he never breathed it or looked it. If we were lost, he would know what to do. He would find a creek bottom, make a lean-to of saddles, build a fire, and butcher a calf. I halfway hoped it would happen.

"Hold up, Pistol." Tom was swinging off his horse. I looked around, wondering, until I saw the little red-brown carcass stretched out in the snow. The curly flank rose and fell, rose and fell, and his soft eyes were half shut. Tom lifted him onto his feet and held him a moment. Knocking off the snow and ice and giving him a slap, he sent him ahead.

We followed. A few yards farther on, another calf lay in the snow. I jumped down and picked him up, brushing off the snow and ice and letting him go with a slap. Another ten feet farther, a third had sprawled in a drift, stretched out upright like a merry-go-round pony. Tom got down again, and this time he didn't remount. He wrapped the reins around the saddle horn and walked ahead. As soon as I saw him wrapping the reins, I swung down, too, and dallied mine around the horn, and side by side we hiked on. The horses followed, their heads slung low and the snow instantly gathering on the saddles and along the manes where our bodies had given protection.

The old lead cow didn't stop. Somewhere a quarter or a half mile ahead, out of our sight, utterly alone in the stinging blizzard, she was breaking the trail to Wolf Creek. She led the way laterally up a long rise with the cows plodding in her hoofsteps and the little calves blindly following and with Tom and me behind. She passed over the ridge and struck a drift. The entire procession slowed noticeably, but it didn't stop. She breasted the drift as it grew deeper and deeper until it broke around her shoulders. She never halted. The cows followed through the white defile she trampled for them.

Noon came and went and along with it my fourteen-year-old hunger pains. We had no lunch, no candy bars, no canteen of coffee, nothing. I wondered how much of the ten miles we had covered. The herd moved more and more slowly. The far side of every ridge was deep in drifts. More and more calves floundered and stopped, and we were continually lifting one out of a drift and setting him going in the beaten track. Tom laid the smallest across his empty saddle. It lay there, half dead, its flanks slowly and just perceptibly heaving under the snow, which gathered swiftly over it.

The light began to fail. The gray deepened shade by shade, but the wind continued to whine past my ears, laden with snow. Every so often Tom held up his mitten and watched the snow collect on the back. "If the wind stays behind us, Pistol," he told me, "we are all right." Then he disappeared into the slot ahead. I picked up a calf lying in the trail and another sunk in a drift. I suddenly felt my aloneness and perishability against the vast, inhuman storm. I knew how easy it was to panic and rush headlong into the drifts, breasting them

like great breakers until I could go no farther and snuggle, exhausted as the small calf, into the folds of snow. When Tom appeared, he looked better than ever, and he said, "That old lead cow, she's quite a girl." We fell in side by side again between the last calf and the horses, and half walking, half blown, we went down the trail.

Up the rising slope, down through the drifts, along a creek bottom to the rising ground of the next ridge, we plodded. It was now night — four, six, eight o'clock, I didn't know. I virtually didn't manipulate my arms and legs. They moved through the great distance of fatigue like independent mechanisms set in motion long ago. I was aware, little by little, that I moved more slowly, and my brain gradually came to focus on the idea that the wind had dropped. I lifted my head from the trail before me. It had stopped snowing, and the darkness was black, indeed, all around us.

Tom said, "There it is."

We had come to the ridge of a long slope, and across the abyss of drifts and darkness shone one small crossed square of yellow light, the shack at Wolf Creek.

There was nothing left in me for a wild, cowboy yell, but my spirits came up for a moment above the weariness. The old lead cow broke the drifts for one last time, heading downhill toward the cow camp. It lay somewhat protected under a crescent of cliff. The shack, sheds, corrals, and pens were spread out in the lee of the cliff, and the snow was not deep around them. Tom strode ahead and opened the gate for the herd to plod through. The moment they did so, the little calves bellowed and the mothering up began.

In the commotion of mooing and little calf bawls, the shack door opened; a long slice of yellow light fell across the snow, and Red joined us. With a little conversation like "Howdy," "What took you so long?" "A bit snowy underfoot," Red and Tom set to work. Tom led his horse into the shed and unsaddled, and I followed him. I could hardly loosen the cinch and drag the weight of the saddle across Sundance's back. Tom measured oats for his horse, so afterwards I did for Sundance. Then Tom strode to the trough and swinging an ax broke the ice. I tottered after him and heaved the chunks out of the water, but he wouldn't let me drop them right there. I had to fling them as far as I could so that the cows wouldn't stumble on them. While we were opening the trough, Red hitched a team to a wagon, and Tom swung sacks of cottonseed cake and bales of hay into the wagon bed. I staggered after him and tried to do it too. Then Tom climbed into the wagon and I followed; and with Red driving, we circled the pen, breaking open the sacks of cotton-seed cake and snipping baling wire and emptying sacks and bales into the wagon's wake. I didn't dare stand at the edge because my legs were giving out. After an endless time the job was done, the team un-hitched, and the three of us headed for the shack.

No human shelter will ever look as good to me as the cowboy shack on Wolf Creek that night. That one-room cabin with the plank floor and plank wainscoting with beaverboard walls and ceiling, a window or two and the door, was lit with a gas lantern and heated to the point of suffocation by a small, iron, wood-burning, spit-and-argue stove and a big black wood-burning cookstove. There were plank shelves for dishes and canned food, bins by the door for potatoes and onions, pegs on the wall for clothes, a table and chairs, and one large, sagging, feather-ticked double bed.

When we stepped through the door, Tom and Red began to peel. They took off their Scotch caps and coats and overshoes and high-heeled boots and Levis and shirts and wool pants until they were down to their oatmeal — button-seated, baggy-bottomed, saggy-kneed long-john underwear — and there they stopped. So I shed layer after layer until I looked just like them, only smaller.

Red had hauled inside a great haunch of beef, frozen to the mar-row, and flung it on the table. As soon as he was down to his long

johns, he tackled it with a huge butcher knife and a meat saw and sliced a steak as thick as my forearm. Telling me to peel those spuds and stoke the fire, Red stood at the cookstove, showing us noth-ing but his button-seated rear view, and prepared a dinner no gourmet chef will ever equal and no diner appreciate more. He fried thick slabs of home-cured bacon in a huge skillet and then heaped the potatoes I had sliced into an inch of bacon grease and cut the bacon chunks into them. He opened a great can of tomatoes and dumped them into a pan and pulled bread apart and stirred it in. He freshened the coffeepot by throwing in more grounds and pouring in more water and moving the pot to a hotter place on the stove's black surface; and then he flipped that steak into the largest skillet of all, heated smoking hot. I put a stack of bread and the bowl of home-churned butter and the canned milk and a bowl of jam on the table. When Red had every-thing ready, he sliced the steak onto worn tin plates and heaped the edges with fried potatoes and stewed tomatoes. We pulled up our chairs and fell into it, hunched over it with a slice of buttered bread in one hand, smoking coffee beside our plates, saying practically noth-ing, just eating and eating and eat-ing until it was all gone.

Afterwards, Tom and Red pushed back their chairs. Tom slapped his chest where his pocket should have been, looking for his cigarette makings, and his eyes met mine in a certain way so that I got up and brought his tobacco sack and washed the dishes without a word. While I washed, I listened to their laconic, understated, deadpan cowboy talk. I wanted terribly hard not to laugh out loud and be just as straight-faced as they were; but shortly I was doubled up over the dishpan, laughing so hard my stomach muscles, already weary, knotted in unbearable cramps.

I wondered where I was going to sleep since there was only one bed. Maybe Red had a bedroll somewhere. I was more than ready when Tom said, "Okay, Pistol, you get in the middle, so's you don't get lost." Still in my long underwear I crawled into the center of the ancient double bed. The coil springs groaned and creaked as Tom, over six feet and two hundred pounds, took one side, and Red, a little shorter and scrawnier, took the other. "Now, Pistol," Red said, "don't you do no thrashin'...." And I didn't notice anything until I heard a scratching.

When I opened my eyes, I found the cabin flooded with blinding sun, and I saw Tom in his long johns standing at the window, scraping away the frost with his pocket-knife. Red swung out of bed and leaned over his shoulder.

"It fell some," Red said.

"You read it and tell me," said Tom, stepping aside.

"I read sixty-three below."

"That's what I read."

I read the thermometer myself. There was no mistake. The mercury had fallen to sixty-three below.

We stoked the fires and dressed in the numerous layers, pulling scarves around our mouths and noses until only the eyes showed, and went out. The routine care was the same as the first night. We moved very slowly to avoid deep breathing. The air was like a knife blade in my lungs, and my nostrils seemed to stick together after each inhalation.

When we finished, Red prepared another monumental meal. This time he scraped away a layer of lard in a crock and extracted pork sausage patties; and he fried them along with another heaping skillet of potatoes and stacks of wheat cakes, Mapleine syrup, and fresh coffee.

At breakfast Tom said that we wouldn't be going back that day. We'd just have to wait for the cold to break. I didn't care if it ever did.

The days went by, and the cow camp remained locked in deep cold. We fed and watered the stock several times each day. Tom checked each animal daily and doctored those that needed it. Red made us boots of newspaper that fitted inside the overshoes, and we wore these instead of leather boots for warmth. We put on tin pants, lined with canvas trousers, when we went out, and we moved slowly and never stayed long. When they weren't worn, the tin pants still looked inhabited, hanging in a row against the wall. In between trips I listened to Red and Tom making cowboy talk, hilarious tales of past roundups and drives and trips to town and mutual acquaintances, that broke me up over the dishpan or the cards or the checkerboard. The airtight shack grew strong with wood fires and leather and horse clothes and men in long underwear. My spirits sank on the morning I awoke in my niche in the feather bed to find the weather noticeably warmer.

Tom and I rode side by side on the trail home. It was the same one the old lead cow had broken. We trotted most of the way in the brilliant sun and arrived at Tom's place just after noon. Sam's Model A was sitting in the yard. I asked Sam what day it was, and it was past New Year's. Christmas was over. I had been gone two weeks with no word to anyone and been in a frozen cow camp eighty miles from home, which was in the middle of nowhere; anyway, I had had the time of my life.

Sam took me into town that afternoon and let me off in front of our ample old house. My mother was hurt that I hadn't been there for Christmas. My father bawled me out for wounding my mother — didn't I have any consideration for others — but later he asked me how it was out there, and I said diffidently, "A bit snowy underfoot," the way, I hoped, that Tom had said it.

DISCUSSION

1. What two requests did Pistol's mother make when Pistol asked her permission to accompany Tom? Why did Pistol have to disobey one of her requests?
2. Why was the location of the shack at Wolf Creek a good one during a snowstorm?
3. What did the temperature drop to at Wolf Creek?
4. Why did Pistol and the men have to move slowly outdoors? What did this slow motion prevent?
5. What did Pistol mean by saying that just seeing Sam made him feel good?

6. Why do you think Pistol took his razor with him if he didn't need it?
7. What was the first time in the story that you got an inkling that Red had a good sense of humor?
8. Why did Pistol not care if the cold spell ever broke?
9. What might have happened if Pistol had tried to fulfill both of his mother's requests?
10. What did Pistol think Tom would do if they got lost in the storm? What problems might arise if they were forced to do this?
11. Would you "halfway hope" to get lost in a snowstorm as Pistol did? Why or why not?
12. Why do you think Sam said they would be all right if the wind stayed behind them? How would they be hindered if the wind blew directly in their faces?
13. Even though Pistol missed Christmas at home, he felt he had had the time of his life. Have you ever had Thanksgiving or Christmas away from home? Tell how you felt about it if you are asked to do so.

AUTHOR

Adrienne Richard grew up in Illinois and Arizona. She is a graduate of the University of Chicago and has studied at the University of Iowa and Boston College. Perhaps having three sons of her own motivated Mrs. Richard to write about the adventures of Billy Catlett in *Pistol,* the book from which "Christmas on Wolf Creek" was taken. *Pistol* won a Notable Children's Book Award in 1969 and was listed on the Horn Book Honor List in 1970.

In addition to *Pistol,* Mrs. Richard has written feature stories for newspapers, reviews of children's books for *The New York Times,* and the script for an educational film, *Leonardo da Vinci.*

Mrs. Richard has many interests, but her greatest interest is the study of great classical civilizations. In 1969, she went to Israel as a member of Boston College's Institute of Archaeology. One of the two novels for young people she is now working on has Israel as its setting.

SKILL LESSON 6

RELATED IDEAS

In a story or an article the author often uses certain clue words to establish relationships among the ideas he is presenting. Among the most common relationships are those that have to do with TIME, or the ORDER OF EVENTS. In each of the following sentences what clue word helps you understand the order of events?

1. Bob and Sally stopped for a snack after they saw the movie.
2. The quarterback threw the pass before he was tackled.
3. While my mother and father were out, I finished my homework.

What did Bob and Sally do first — stop for a snack or see the movie? What word helped you answer that question?

What happened first in the second sentence? What word helped you decide?

In the third sentence two things were going on *at the same time.* What word tells you that?

In addition to the words *after, before,* and *while,* other words that often act as clues to the order of events include *then, already, until,* and *as.* In the following sentences what clue words help you understand the order of events? Just when did the two events told in each sentence occur?

1. My aunt gave me a book that I had already read.
2. The phone call came before we left for the airport.
3. There was complete silence as the dancers performed.
4. After I washed my hair, I called Tom.

367

5. While the hamburgers were cooking, we set the table.
6. Ron read the newspaper and then watched television.
7. The girls played badminton until the bell sounded.

Look for clue words that will help you understand the order of events in the following paragraph. Then on a sheet of paper list the events of the paragraph in the order that they happened.

I reached the bus station at eight o'clock, but the bus had already left. After I checked the departure time of the next bus, I started toward the cafeteria. Before I got there, I bought a paperback book at the newsstand. I drank coffee and read until it was time to board the bus.

Another way in which an author shows relationships among ideas is by telling why something happened or is so. This is called the CAUSE-EFFECT relationship. The following sentence is a common example of this kind of relationship:

The skiing was poor last weekend because the warm weather had melted much of the snow.

In that sentence why was the skiing poor last weekend? Which part of the sentence states the cause or reason? Which part of the sentence states the effect or result? The word *because* in that sentence serves as a clue, indicating that the sentence probably contains a cause-effect relationship.

In each of these sentences which part of the sentence states the cause? Which part states the effect? What is the clue word?

1. We were forced to turn back because the road was blocked by a fallen tree.
2. Because the taxes were so high, the people demanded an investigation of government spending.

In the examples of cause-effect relationships you have read thus far, the clue word was *because*. Other words and expressions, such as *since, therefore, consequently,* and *as a result,* may serve as clue words that signal cause-effect relationships.

Identify the cause-effect relationship and the clue word in each of the following sentences:

1. We are wearing our raincoats, since the weather has been so unpredictable lately.
2. The library was closed this week; therefore, we cannot return our books until next week.
3. The heavy rains flooded the highway; as a result, it was closed for several hours.
4. Because she had a cold, Mary was unable to go to the football game.
5. The state legislature passed a law banning billboards; consequently, all billboards must be removed within sixty days.

In written material you will frequently find clue words that signal relationships by CONTRAST, or CHANGE OF DIRECTION. One such clue word is *but.* What two ideas are being contrasted in this sentence?

The team played very well, but they lost the game.

Having read just the part of the sentence that tells how the team played, you might expect the rest of the sentence to tell by what score the team won. However, the rest of the sentence tells that the team lost. The word *but* serves as a clue and alerts you to the fact that there is going to be a contrast or change of direction in the sentence. Other clue words and expressions common to this relationship are *nevertheless, yet, although, however, even though, in spite of,* and *on the other hand.*

In the following paragraph several contrasts are being made. Decide what the contrasts are and then identify the particular clue words that helped you.

When you drive a car, you should obey all the rules of the road; however, not every driver does so. Although a yellow "caution" light is a warning to slow down, it causes some drivers to increase

their speed in order to "beat the light." There are always drivers who disregard the rules of the road; on the other hand, most drivers do adhere to the regulations. The national accident rate is high enough; yet, it would be considerably higher without the safe and sane drivers.

Another kind of relationship often found among the ideas a writer is developing is that of ADDING FURTHER INFORMATION. As with other relationships, clue words often signal the addition of further information. What additional information is added in this sentence?

Larry received a sweater for his birthday; in addition, he received a jacket and shoes.

The additional information is that Larry received a jacket and shoes for his birthday. The first part of the sentence told of his receiving a sweater. The expression *in addition* served as a clue to the fact that further information would be coming. Other clue words that often signal a relationship that adds further information include *besides, moreover,* and *furthermore.*

In each of the following sentences and groups of sentences what information is being added? What clue word helps you know that?

1. The union members received a cost-of-living wage increase. Furthermore, they received most of the fringe benefits which they had asked for.
2. Our new dishwasher has cut dishwashing time in half; besides, it gets the dishes much cleaner.
3. Linda was elected class president. Moreover, she received the vote of every one of her classmates.

In each of the following sentences or groups of sentences there is a clue word that signals a relationship among ideas. Decide what the clue word is and identify the relationship as *order of events, cause-effect, contrast,* or *adding further information.*

1. All the buildings on Avon Street will be torn down because a hospital is to be built there.

2. A number of buildings in the town of Elkton were demolished by the tornado. In addition, many trees were damaged.
3. We were disappointed that the audience was so small, but we were pleased that we made enough money to pay all expenses.
4. While the band played the national anthem, the audience stood at attention.
5. Before we got to our seats, the game had started.
6. The PTA has raised enough money for a new curtain for the auditorium stage; however, the curtain will not be ready in time for the music festival.
7. Great puffs of black smoke suddenly roared skyward from the volcano; as a result, the village had to be evacuated.
8. The court ruled that the city manager had been fired illegally. Furthermore, it ordered that he be given back pay for the time he was out of office.
9. The Rangers did not show up for the game on Saturday; therefore, they forfeited the game.
10. The train glided swiftly across the flat plains; then it slowed down on its climb up the rugged mountain.

So far you have been studying sentences and paragraphs in which there is just one type of relationship. However, in some sentences and paragraphs there may be a combination of relationships. There are two types of relationships in the following sentence. Look for clue words that will help you identify the relationships.

Before we left the house, we fed the cat because we expected to be out quite late.

The clue word *before* signals an order-of-events relationship. In what order did the first two ideas in the sentence take place? The clue word *because* signals a cause-effect relationship. Why was the cat fed? What cause brought about that effect?

Each of the following sentences and groups of sentences contains more than one relationship. Use the clue words to help you figure out what those relationships are.

1. After we watched the parade, we went to visit Jill, but she was not at home.
2. There was a four-inch base of snow on the slopes; in addition, it snowed for five hours on Monday. Nevertheless, snow-making machines were put into operation to ensure perfect skiing.
3. We worked on the science project until it was twelve thirty. As a result, we had a late lunch.
4. There are many kinds of edible mushrooms; however, it takes a real expert to distinguish edible mushrooms from poisonous mushrooms. Consequently, you should never eat mushrooms that you find in the wild.
5. Pilots flying in an easterly direction make use of the powerful jet stream because it cuts their flying time. On the other hand, they try to avoid the jet stream when they are flying in a westerly direction.
6. Because the aim of the Olympic games is to link together in sporting friendship the peoples of the world, five colorful, interlocked rings were chosen. Furthermore, their colors, blue, yellow, black, green, and red, were chosen to include at least one color from every flag of every nation in the world.
7. As the ship started to sink, an SOS radio signal was sent out. However, the call of *mayday* had already been sent by a passing airplane.
8. Football umpires use hand signals because voice communication is impossible. In addition, they use red flags made of cloth to indicate penalties.

Discussion

Help your class answer the following questions:
1. What are four types of relationships among ideas that you often find in written material?
2. What are some of the clue words that go with each relationship?
3. In the paragraph on page 368 what was the order of events?

4. What clue word helped you identify the cause-effect relationship in each of the five sentences on page 369? What was the cause and what was the effect in each sentence?
5. On pages 369–370 what contrasts did you find in the paragraph about driving a car?
6. What was the relationship and what was the clue word in each of the ten sentences on pages 370–371?
7. What relationships and what clue words did you find in the eight sentences on page 372?

On your own

Identify the relationships and the clue words in the sentences and groups of sentences below. In some of them you will find more than one relationship and more than one clue word.

1. A suspension bridge costs less to build than other kinds of bridges. However, a great disadvantage of this kind of bridge is that it sways with the wind.
2. Because it has such a keen sense of smell, the bloodhound is used to help track down criminals and locate missing persons.
3. After the Roman army defeated Carthage, it went on to conquer Macedonia, Greece, and other countries. As a result, the Romans controlled all the area bordering on the Mediterranean Sea.
4. Credit cards enable people to purchase goods without having to carry large amounts of cash. In addition, a credit-card holder can purchase something before he acquires enough cash to pay for it. But the responsibility of not getting deeply in debt remains with the credit-card holder.
5. One of the most helpful uses of radar is in weather forecasting. Radar can detect destructive storms that are 200 miles away. Furthermore, it can determine the size, speed, and even the direction in which a storm is traveling. Consequently, there is time to warn people living in the path of the storm so that they can make appropriate preparations.
6. Some people object to rock music because it is usually performed at such a high volume and intensity of sound; yet it is now so

popular that hundreds of radio stations play only rock music.

7. Quicksand is composed of a deep mass of jagged or round grains of sand. When constantly moving water passes through these grains, they become separated. Therefore, the sand loses its rigidity and will not support any considerable weight.

8. A person who finds himself sinking in quicksand should remain calm and avoid becoming panic-stricken. In addition, he should try to remain motionless, lying flat on his back with his arms outstretched. When his weight equals the weight of the sand he has displaced, he will then float on the sand.

Checking your work

If you are asked to do so, read your answers to the sentences and groups of sentences. Find out whether or not you identified all the relationships and all the clue words. If you did not, make sure you understand what the relationships are and what clue words help identify them.

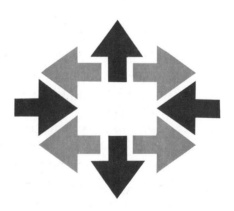

GIANTS of the Earth

by Clifford B. Hicks

On the cosmic scale of size that apparently rules this mysterious universe, man stands almost at the midpoint. He is just about as much smaller than the greatest known star that burns in the velvet heavens as he is bigger than the electron.

But on the size scale of *living* things, man is a giant walking the earth. Surprisingly, there are relatively few animals or fish that are larger than man himself.

Still, we respect anything larger than ourselves — and for a reason that echoes down through the ages. Back in the dim reaches of time any creature of superior size threatened our forefathers' existence. We are marked by that fear and are still awed and fascinated by the elephant and the whale, the ostrich and the giant squid, simply because they are *big*.

The biggest creature that ever lived is still alive today. Its size is incredible, far larger than any of the dinosaurs. In fact, the animal is so large that *no one has ever had an undistorted view of it.* But the odds are high that this remarkable creature will be hounded into oblivion within just a few short years. It is the blue whale, which weighs 150 tons or more and measures upward of one hundred feet long. It is equivalent in bulk to about thirty large elephants or three of the mightiest dinosaurs that ever lived. The heart of this remarkable animal can weigh over a thousand pounds, the liver almost a ton, and its great tongue a whopping 8,900 pounds.

Adult blue whales live in the icy waters of the Antarctic but go north to more temperate waters to mate. The cow has all the attributes of a good mother; for seven months she nurses her three-ton calf, delivering about 1,000 pounds of milk — some 130 gallons — per day. The eighteen-month period from mating to weaning precludes more than one birth every two years. This low frequency of birth is one reason the blue whale soon may vanish.

Man's greed is the other reason. In spite of international efforts to protect the blue whales, they are rapidly being exterminated by the whaling ships of several countries.

More familiar to us is the largest and heaviest of all the *land* animals — the African elephant. The greatest land animal ever *recorded* was an African bull elephant shot in Angola in 1955. It weighed twelve tons, and if you want to see it yourself, all you have to do is step into the Smithsonian Institution in Washington.

Elephants, or at least their forebears, once ruled much of the earth. Remains of the mammoth (the ancestor of the elephant) have been discovered over much of North America, Europe, and Asia.

Today's African elephant has, in effect, painted itself into an evolutionary corner because of its great size. The weight of a large elephant may range upward from five tons. Consider the problem of so much bulk: In order to support it, the elephant must have tree-sized legs.

Elephants are remarkably intelligent creatures, considered by most authorities to be easier to train than any other animal with the possible exception of the domesticated dog. An enraged elephant is one of the most dangerous creatures on earth, but a normal elephant is astonishingly gentle and patient.

Ordinarily, elephants live in herds of from five to forty animals, and the herd provides its own form of social security. If danger threatens, the adult males quickly form a protective circle around the weaker members. This is somewhat surprising, as many animals in nature are ruthless toward weak members of their own kind. Hunters tell fascinating — and confirmed — stories of how elephants help out comrades who are in trouble. If a member of a herd falls sick, the entire herd will wait for it to recover. In some cases elephants have brought food and water to a fallen comrade for weeks.

Fortunately, for its own continued existence, the elephant takes well to captivity. Although, in years to come, man may continue to destroy the elephant's land and even the elephant itself, it seems likely that these remarkable giants of the earth will continue to live in captivity for generations to come.

If you'd never heard of a giraffe, the tallest of all living creatures, you'd find it impossible to imagine one. The giraffe is just plain incomprehensible. With neck erect the giraffe may tower to a height of more than eighteen feet.

Visitors to Kenya are fascinated. Great angular derricks move slowly across the darkening bush. If you look up through a grove of flat-topped acacia trees, you may find a pair of huge eyes, soft and quizzical, looking down at you through the foliage like a towering peeping Tom.

Furthermore, the giraffe is a living scientific legend, for it figures prominently in the development of the theory of evolution. For more than one hundred years biologists have argued over *how* the giraffe got to be that way and have used their own speculations as evidence to support their theories. Lamarck,[1] for example, argued that in the dim past there was a primitive giraffe-like creature which, in order to reach the most succulent of leaves, stretched upward on its legs and lifted its neck as high as it would go. This stretching process, according to Lamarck, made the creature's neck and legs longer, and it passed these longer members on to its young.

Thus was born the theory of the *inheritance of acquired characteristics.* Actually, the theory was a lot of hogwash. This simple illustration disproves it: If you, for example, develop extremely strong muscles in one hand because of the nature of your work, your newborn child will not have such overdeveloped hand muscles.

Along came Darwin[2] and made the giraffe even more famous. According to Darwin some of the giraffe-like creatures happened to be born with slightly longer necks (whether they *wanted* them or not). These particular creatures, because they could reach more leaves, were more likely to survive. In the long run, because more long-neckers survived, they left more descendants, all of whom carried the "long-neck" and "long-leg" genes. This is the theory of *natural selection.*

Most biologists now feel that Darwin, too, was wrong about the giraffe in particular but right in the essentials of his work. In the modern view the giraffe-creature with the longest legs was most likely to survive attacks by its natural enemy, the lion. As its legs

---

[1] **Chevalier de Lamarck** (shĕv'ə-lîr' də lə-märk'): French naturalist.
[2] **Charles Robert Darwin** (där'wĭn): British naturalist.

grew longer (through natural selection), it simply *had* to develop a longer neck in order to reach all the way down to the ground to get water. One condition required the other. Only an animal with both could continue to exist.

By far the largest of all the 8,600 bird species that inhabit the earth is the ostrich. The ostrich is one of nature's apparent practical jokes, a creature of extreme contrasts: nature's ugliest duckling with her most gorgeous plumage; a creature of low intelligence that can be tamed and ridden; a bird with remarkably keen vision (it sees in full color, incidentally), yet with such poor hearing that it often grazes with gazelles in order to take advantage of those graceful creatures' keen ears; a bird that runs like the wind along its grassland runway, wings outstretched in a laboring effort to get airborne, though it can't fly even as far as a barnyard chicken.

Largest of all the fishes is the whale shark, first discovered off Cape Town in 1828. Specimens have been reported up to sixty feet long, weighing up to sixty-seven tons. Its home is in the warmer waters of the Atlantic, Pacific, and Indian Oceans.

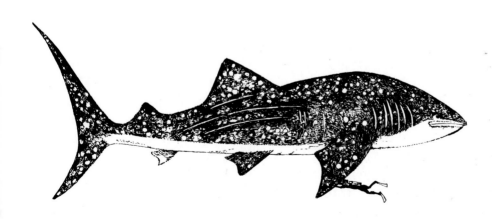

Again nature has produced an anomaly, for in appearance the whale shark is one of the most formidable of all the creatures of the sea, with the shark's typically tall, razory fins; its powerful, vertical tail; its gaping mouth. Actually, no whale shark on record has ever damaged anything larger than a tiny fish or a newborn crab. Mainly the whale shark scoops up plankton — fish eggs, tiny one-celled animals, jellyfish, and newborn shrimp.

Whales themselves, of course, are sea-going mammals, but the whale shark is a true fish — and the largest in all the waters of the earth.

Largest and most fearsome of all the invertebrates is the giant squid, found on the Newfoundland Grand Banks. It is a creature straight from a nightmare or a horror movie. The giant squid has a body more than eight feet long that terminates in ten snakelike arms. Two of the arms are longer than the others and may measure up to thirty-five feet. With this powerful, if unorthodox, equipment the squid can even give a good fight to a sperm whale — his worst natural enemy. ·When feeding, the squid's two longer arms snap out toward its passing prey, sucking disks lock onto the unwary victim, which then is passed along to one or more of the other arms; these, in turn, convey the food to a toothless beak.

Of the flying birds the bird with the largest wingspan is the wandering albatross, that remarkable soarer of the southern seas, which has inspired many a fable and poem. Not only is its wingspan a record-breaker (up to twelve feet or more), but it has the unique ability to drink sea water and separate out the salt.

But man, in all his glory, has made size *unimportant*. Because of its enormity an elephant once could rule its section of the earth without fear; now a pellet no larger than a man's thumb can bring it thundering to earth. The largest creature on this planet once roamed the ice seas in great numbers; now a child's finger on the trigger of a harpoon gun can make those seas run red with the blood of the earth's greatest creature.

Man stands supreme — *the* giant of the earth — except for his greatest enemies, viruses and bacteria so small that we can see them only with the most powerful microscopes. Perhaps not the giants but the midgets may someday inherit the earth the giants once trod.

DISCUSSION

1. What two reasons are given as to why the blue whale may soon vanish?
2. Why is a whale not a fish?
3. How does an elephant provide its own "social security"? What factor may help the elephant to continue to exist?
4. Have you heard the familiar saying "An elephant never forgets"? How is that saying illustrated in this article?
5. Give some of the theories as to why the giraffe has such a long neck.
6. What did the author mean by saying that no one has ever had an undistorted view of the blue whale?
7. What is a practical joke? Why did the author apply this term to the ostrich?
8. The International Whaling Commission attempts to regulate the number of whales caught and to protect the various species in several ways. Why do you think some countries ignore the commission's guidelines? What do you think could be done to enforce the guidelines?
9. What unique ability does the albatross possess? How could man benefit by having this ability?
10. Which one of the animals mentioned in the article do you think has the best chance of surviving? Why?
11. The author spoke of man as being *the* giant of the earth. What did he say may someday conquer him? Why do you agree or disagree? What do you think is man's greatest enemy?

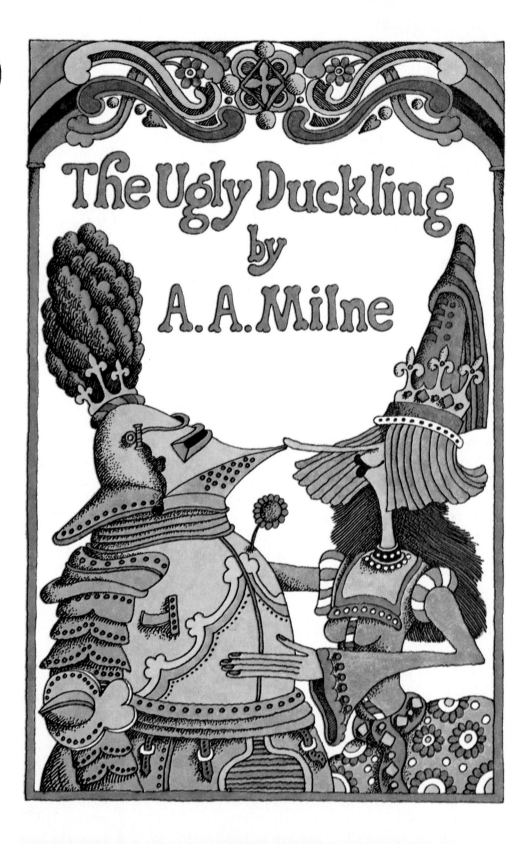

The Ugly Duckling
by
A. A. Milne

masterworks

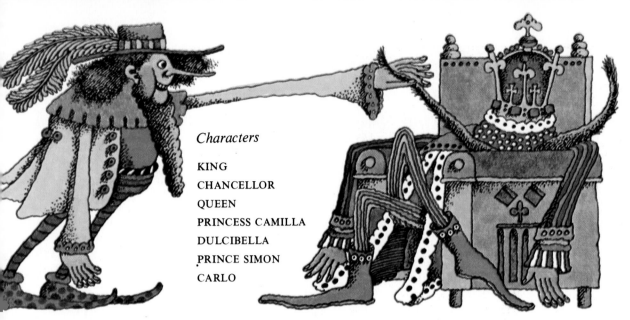

Characters

KING
CHANCELLOR
QUEEN
PRINCESS CAMILLA
DULCIBELLA
PRINCE SIMON
CARLO

The scene is the throne room of the palace — a room of many doors with thrones for the king, the queen, and the princess and a long seat on both sides of the thrones. As the curtain rises, the king is asleep on his throne with a handkerchief over his face.

A VOICE (*announcing*): His Excellency the Chancellor! (*The* CHANCELLOR *enters, bowing. The* KING *wakes up with a start and removes the handkerchief from his face.*)

KING (*with simple dignity*): I was thinking.

CHANCELLOR (*bowing*): Never, Your Majesty, was greater need for thought than now.

KING: That's what I was thinking. (*He struggles into a more dignified position.*) Well, what is it? More trouble?

CHANCELLOR: What we might call the old trouble, Your Majesty.

KING: It's what I was saying last night to the queen. "Uneasy lies the head that wears a crown," was how I put it.

CHANCELLOR: An original thought, which may well go down to posterity.

KING: You mean it may go down well with posterity. I hope so. Remind me to tell you sometime of another little thing I said to Her Majesty: something about a fierce light beating on a throne. Posterity would like that too. Well, what is it?

CHANCELLOR: It is in the matter of Her Royal Highness's wedding.

KING: Oh . . . yes.

CHANCELLOR: As Your Majesty is aware, the young Prince Simon arrives today to seek Her Royal Highness's hand in marriage. He has been travelling in distant lands and, as I understand, has not — er — has not —

383

KING: You mean he hasn't heard anything?

CHANCELLOR: It is a little difficult to put this tactfully, Your Majesty.

KING: Do your best, and I will tell you afterwards how you got on.

CHANCELLOR: Let me put it this way. Prince Simon will naturally assume that Her Royal Highness has the customary — so customary as to be, in my own poor opinion, slightly monotonous — has what one might call the inevitable — so inevitable as to be, in my opinion again, almost mechanical — will assume, that she has the, as *I* think of it, faultily faultless, icily regular, splendidly —

KING: What you are trying to say in the fewest words possible is that my daughter is not beautiful.

CHANCELLOR: Her beauty is certainly elusive, Your Majesty.

KING: It is. It has eluded you; it has eluded me; it has eluded everybody who has seen her. It even eluded the Court Painter. His last words were, "Well, I did my best." His successor is now painting the view across the water-meadows from the west turret. He says that his doctor has advised him to keep to landscape.

CHANCELLOR: It is unfortunate, Your Majesty, but there it is. One just cannot understand how it occurred.

KING: You don't think she takes after *me* at all? You don't detect a likeness?

CHANCELLOR: Most certainly not, Your Majesty.

KING: Good.... Your predecessor did.

CHANCELLOR: I have often wondered what happened to my predecessor.

KING: Well, now you know. (*There is a short silence.*)

CHANCELLOR: Looking at the bright side, although Her Royal Highness is not, strictly speaking, beautiful —

KING: Is not, truthfully speaking, beautiful —

CHANCELLOR: Yet she has great beauty of character.

KING: My dear Chancellor, we are not considering Her Royal Highness's character but her chances of getting married. You observe that there is a distinction.

CHANCELLOR: Yes, Your Majesty.

KING: Look at it from the suitor's point of view. If a girl is beautiful, it is easy to assume that she has, tucked away inside her, an equally beautiful character. But it is impossible to assume that an unattractive girl, however elevated in character, has, tucked away inside her, an equally beautiful face. That is, so to speak, not where you want it — tucked away.

CHANCELLOR: Quite so, Your Majesty.

KING: This doesn't, of course, alter the fact that the Princess Camilla is quite the nicest person in the kingdom.

384

CHANCELLOR (*enthusiastically*): She is indeed, Your Majesty. With the exception, I need hardly say, of Your Majesty — and Her Majesty.

KING: Your exceptions are tolerated for their loyalty and condemned for their stupidity.

CHANCELLOR: Thank you, Your Majesty.

KING: As an adjective for your king the word *nice* is ill-chosen. As an adjective for Her Majesty the word is — ill-chosen. (HER MAJESTY *comes in. The* KING *rises. The* CHANCELLOR *puts himself at right angles.*)

QUEEN (*briskly*): Ah, talking about Camilla? (*She sits down.*)

KING (*returning to his throne*): As always, my dear, you are right.

QUEEN (*to* CHANCELLOR): This fellow, Simon — what's he like?

CHANCELLOR: Nobody has seen him, Your Majesty.

QUEEN: How old is he?

CHANCELLOR: Five-and-twenty, I understand, Your Majesty.

QUEEN: In twenty-five years he must have been seen by somebody.

KING (*to* CHANCELLOR): Just a fleeting glimpse?

CHANCELLOR: I meant, Your Majesty, that no detailed report of him has reached this country, save that he has the usual personal advantages and qualities expected of a prince and has been travelling in distant and dangerous lands.

QUEEN: Ah! Nothing gone wrong with his eyes? Sunstroke or anything?

CHANCELLOR: Not that I am aware of, Your Majesty. At the same time, as I was venturing to say to His Majesty, Her Royal Highness's character and disposition are so outstandingly —

QUEEN: Stuff and nonsense. You remember what happened when we had the Tournament of Love last year.

CHANCELLOR: I was not myself present, Your Majesty. I had not then the honor of — I was abroad and never heard the full story.

QUEEN: No, it was the other fool. They all rode up to Camilla to pay their homage. It was the first time they had seen her. The heralds blew their trumpets and announced that she would marry whichever prince was left master of the field when all but one had been unhorsed. The trumpets were blown again; they charged enthusiastically into the fight, and — (*The* KING *looks at the ceiling and whistles a few bars.*) don't do that.

KING: I'm sorry, my dear.

QUEEN (*to* CHANCELLOR): And what happened? They all simultaneously fell off their horses and assumed a posture of defeat.

KING: One of them was not quite so quick as the others. I was very quick. I proclaimed him the victor.

QUEEN: At the Feast of Betrothal held that night —

KING: We were all very quick.

QUEEN: The Chancellor announced that by the laws of the country the successful suitor had to pass a further test. He had to give the correct answer to a riddle.

CHANCELLOR: Such undoubtedly is the fact, Your Majesty.

KING: There are times for announcing facts and times for looking at things in a broadminded way. Please remember that, Chancellor.

CHANCELLOR: Yes, Your Majesty.

QUEEN: I invented the riddle myself. Quite an easy one. What is it that has four legs and barks like a dog? The answer is "a dog."

KING (*to* CHANCELLOR): You see that?

CHANCELLOR: Yes, Your Majesty.

KING: It isn't difficult.

QUEEN: He, however, seemed to find it so. He said an eagle. Then he said a serpent, a very high mountain with slippery sides, two peacocks, a moonlight night, the day after tomorrow —

KING: Nobody could accuse him of not trying.

QUEEN: *I* did.

KING: I *should* have said that nobody could fail to recognize in his attitude an appearance of doggedness.

QUEEN: Finally he said, "Death." I nudged the king —

KING: Accepting the word *death,* I clapped him on the shoulder and congratulated him on the correct answer. He disappeared under the table, and, personally, I never saw him again.

QUEEN: His body was found in the moat the next morning.

CHANCELLOR: But what was he doing in the moat, Your Majesty?

KING: Bobbing about. Try not to ask needless questions.

CHANCELLOR: It all seems so strange.

QUEEN: What does?

CHANCELLOR: That Her Royal Highness, alone of all the princesses one has ever heard of, should lack that distinctive feature of royalty, supreme beauty.

QUEEN (*to* KING): That was your Great-aunt Malkin. She came to the christening. You know what she said.

KING: It was mysterious. Great-aunt Malkin's besetting weakness. She came to *my* christening. She was one hundred and one then and that was fifty-one years ago. (*to* CHANCELLOR) How old would that make her?

CHANCELLOR: One hundred and fifty-two, Your Majesty.

KING (*after thought*): About that, yes. She promised me that when I grew up I should have all the happiness that my wife deserved. It struck me at the time — well, when I say, "at the time," I was only a week old — but it did strike me as soon as anything could strike me — I mean of that nature — well, work it out for yourself, Chancellor. It opens up a most interesting field of speculation. Though naturally I have not liked to go into it at all deeply with Her Majesty.

QUEEN: I never heard anything less mysterious. She was wishing you extreme happiness.

KING: I don't think she was *wishing* me anything. However.

CHANCELLOR (*to* QUEEN): But what, Your Majesty, did she wish Her Royal Highness?

QUEEN: Her other godmother — on my side — had promised her the dazzling beauty for which all the women in my family are famous —— (*She pauses, and the* KING *snaps his fingers surreptitiously at the* CHANCELLOR.)

CHANCELLOR (*hurriedly*): Indeed, yes, Your Majesty. (*The* KING *relaxes.*)

QUEEN: Great-aunt Malkin said — (*to* KING) what were the words?

KING:

> *I give you with this kiss*
> *A wedding-day surprise.*
> *Where ignorance is bliss,*
> *'Tis folly to be wise.*

I thought the last two lines rather neat. But what it *meant* ——

QUEEN: We can all see what it meant. She was given beauty — and where is it? Great-aunt Malkin took it away from her. The wedding-day surprise is that there will never be a wedding day.

KING: Young men being what they are, my dear, it would be much more surprising if there *were* a wedding day. So how —— (*The* PRINCESS *comes in. She is young, happy, and healthy but not beautiful.*)

PRINCESS (*to* KING): Hullo, darling! (*seeing the others*) Oh, I say! Affairs of state? Sorry.

KING (*holding out his hand*): Don't go, Camilla. (*She takes his hand.*)

CHANCELLOR: Shall I withdraw, Your Majesty?

QUEEN: You are aware, Camilla, that Prince Simon arrives today?

PRINCESS: He has arrived. They're just letting down the drawbridge.

KING (*jumping up quickly*): Arrived! I must ——

PRINCESS: Darling, you know what the drawbridge is like. It takes at *least* half an hour to let it down.

KING (*sitting down*): It wants oil. (*to* CHANCELLOR) Have *you* been grudging it oil?

PRINCESS: It wants a new drawbridge, darling.

CHANCELLOR: Have I Your Majesty's permission ——

KING: Yes, yes. (*The* CHANCELLOR *bows and goes out.*)

QUEEN: You've told him, of course? It's the only chance.

KING: Er — no. I was just going to, when —

QUEEN: Then I'd better. (*She goes to the door.*) I'll explain to the girl. I'll have her sent to you. You've told Camilla?

KING: Er — no. I was just going to, when —

QUEEN: Then you'd better tell her now.

KING: My dear, are you sure —

QUEEN: It's the only chance left. (*dramatically to heaven*) My daughter!

(*She goes out. There is a little silence when she is gone.*)

KING: Camilla, I want to talk seriously to you about marriage.

PRINCESS: Yes, Father.

KING: It is time that you learnt some of the facts of life.

PRINCESS: Yes, Father.

KING: Now, the great fact about marriage is that once you're married you live happily ever after. All our history books affirm this.

PRINCESS: And your own experience, too, darling.

KING (*with dignity*): Let us confine ourselves to history for the moment.

PRINCESS: Yes, Father, to history.

KING: Of course, there *may* be an exception here and there, which, as it were, proves the rule; just as — oh, well, never mind.

PRINCESS (*smiling*): Go on, darling. You were going to say that an exception here and there proves the rule that all princesses are beautiful.

KING: Well — leave that for the moment. The point is that it doesn't matter *how* you marry or *who* you marry as long as you *get* married. Because you'll be happy ever after in any case. Do you follow me so far?

PRINCESS: Yes, Father.

KING: Well, your mother and I have a little plan ——

PRINCESS: Was that it, going out of the door just now?

KING: Er — yes. It concerns your waiting maid.

PRINCESS: Darling, I have several.

KING: Only one that leaps to the eye, so to speak. The one with the — well, with everything.

PRINCESS: Dulcibella?

KING: That's the one. It is our plan that at the first meeting she should pass herself off as the princess — a harmless ruse, of which you will find frequent record in the history books — and allure Prince Simon to his — that is to say, bring him up to the —— In other words the wedding will take place immediately afterwards and as quietly as possible. Well, naturally, in view of the fact that your Aunt Malkin is one hundred and fifty-two, and since you will be wearing the family bridal veil — which is no doubt how the custom arose — the surprise after the ceremony will be his. Are you following me? Your attention seems to be wandering.

PRINCESS: I was wondering why you needed to tell me.

KING: Just a precautionary measure, in case you happened to meet the prince or his attendant before the ceremony; in which case, of course, you would pass yourself off as the maid ——

PRINCESS: A harmless ruse, of which, also, you will find frequent record in the history books.

KING: Exactly. But the occasion need not arise.

A VOICE (*announcing*): The woman Dulcibella!

KING: Ah! (*to* PRINCESS) Now, Camilla, if you will just retire to your own apartments, I will come to you there when we are ready for the actual ceremony. (*He leads her out as he is talking, and as he returns, he calls out.*) Come in, my dear! (DULCIBELLA *comes in. She is beautiful but dumb.*) Now don't be frightened, there is nothing to be frightened about. Has Her Majesty told you what you have to do?

DULCIBELLA: Y — yes, Your Majesty.

KING: Well now, let's see how well you can do it. You are sitting here, we will say. (*He leads her to a seat.*) Now imagine that I am Prince Simon. (*He curls his moustache. She giggles.*) You are the beautiful Princess Camilla, whom he has never seen. (*She giggles again.*) This is a serious moment in your life, and you will find that a giggle will not be helpful. (*He goes to the door.*) I am announced: "His Royal Highness Prince Simon!" That's me being announced. Remember what I said about giggling. You should have a faraway look upon the face. (*She does her best.*) Farther away than that. No, that's too far. You are sitting there, thinking beautiful thoughts but with the mouth definitely shut. That's better. I advance and fall upon one knee. You extend your hand graciously — *graciously;* you're not trying to push him in the face. That's better, and I raise it to my lips — so — and I kiss it — no, perhaps not so ardently as that, more like this, and I say, "Your Royal Highness, this is the most — er —— Your Royal Highness, I shall ever be — no —— Your Royal Highness, it is the proudest ——" Well, the point is that *he* will say it, and it will be something complimentary, and then he will take your hand in both of his and press it to his heart. (*He does so.*) And — what do *you* say?

DULCIBELLA: Coo!

KING: No, *not* Coo.

DULCIBELLA: Never had anyone do *that* to me before.

KING: That also strikes the wrong note. What you want to say is, "Oh, Prince Simon!" . . . Say it.

DULCIBELLA (*loudly*): Oh, Prince Simon!

KING: No, no. You don't need to shout until he has said "What?" two or three times. Always consider the possibility that he *isn't* deaf. Softly, and giving the words a dying fall, letting them play around his head like a flight of doves.

DULCIBELLA: O-o-o-o-h, Prinsimon!

KING: Keep the idea in your mind of a flight of *doves* rather than a flight of panic-stricken elephants, and you will be all right. Now I'm going to get up, and you must, as it were, *waft* me into a seat by your side. (*She starts wafting.*) *Not* rescuing a drowning man, that's another idea altogether, useful at times, but at the moment inappropriate. Wafting. Prince Simon will put the necessary muscles into play — all you are required to do is to indicate by a gracious movement of the hand the seat you require him to take. Now! (*He gets up a little stiffly and sits next to her.*) That was better. Well, here we are. Now, I think you give me a look with an undertone of regal dignity, touched, as it were, with good comradeship. Now try that. (*She gives him a vacant look of bewilderment.*) Frankly, that didn't quite get it. There was just a little something

390

missing. An absence, as it were, of all the qualities I asked for and in their place an odd resemblance to an unsatisfied fish. Let us try to get at it another way. Dulcibella, have you a young man of your own?

DULCIBELLA (*eagerly seizing his hand*): Oo, yes, he's ever so smart; he's an archer, well not as you might say a real archer, and me being maid to Her Royal Highness and can't marry me till he's a real soldier, but ever so loving, and funny like, the things he says. I said to him once, "Eg," I said —

KING (*getting up*): I rather fancy, Dulcibella, that if you think of Eg all the time, *say* as little as possible, and, when thinking of Eg, see that the mouth is not more than partially open, you will do very well. I will show you where you are to sit and wait for His Royal Highness. (*he leads her out, saying*) Now remember — *waft* — *waft* — not *hoick*. (PRINCE SIMON *wanders in from the back unannounced. He is a very ordinary-looking young man in rather dusty clothes. He gives a deep sigh of relief as he sinks into the King's throne. . . .* CAMILLA, *a new and strangely beautiful* CAMILLA, *comes in.*)

PRINCESS (*surprised*): Well!

PRINCE: Oh, hullo!

PRINCESS: Ought you?

PRINCE (*getting up*): Do sit down, won't you?

PRINCESS: Who are you, and how did you get here?

PRINCE: Well, that's rather a long story. Couldn't we sit down? You could sit here if you liked, but it isn't very comfortable.

PRINCESS: That is the king's throne.

PRINCE: Oh, is that what it is?

PRINCESS: Thrones are not meant to be comfortable.

PRINCE: Well, I don't know if they're meant to be, but they certainly aren't.

PRINCESS: Why were you sitting on the king's throne, and who are you?

PRINCE: My name is Carlo.

PRINCESS: Mine is Dulcibella.

PRINCE: Good. And now couldn't we sit down?

PRINCESS (*sitting down on the long seat to the left of the throne, and, as it were, wafting him to a place next to her*): You may sit here, if you like. Why are you so tired? (*He sits down.*)

PRINCE: I've been taking very strenuous exercise.

PRINCESS: Is that part of the long story?

PRINCE: It is.

PRINCESS (*settling herself*): I love stories.

PRINCE: This isn't a story really. You see, I'm attendant on Prince Simon, who is visiting here.

PRINCESS: Oh? I'm attendant on Her Royal Highness.

PRINCE: Then you know what he's here for.

PRINCESS: Yes.

PRINCE: She's very beautiful, I hear.

PRINCESS: Did you hear that? Where have you been lately?

PRINCE: Travelling in distant lands — with Prince Simon.

PRINCESS: Ah! All the same, I don't understand. Is Prince Simon in the palace now? The drawbridge *can't* be down yet!

PRINCE: I don't suppose it is. *And* what a noise it makes coming down!

PRINCESS: Isn't it terrible?

PRINCE: I couldn't stand it any more. I just had to get away. That's why I'm here.

PRINCESS: But how?

PRINCE: Well, there's only one way, isn't there? That beech tree and then a swing and a grab for the battlements, and don't ask me to remember it all — (*He shudders.*)

PRINCESS: You mean you came across the moat by that beech tree?

PRINCE: Yes. I got so tired of hanging about.

PRINCESS: But it's terribly dangerous!

PRINCE: That's why I'm so exhausted. Nervous shock. (*He lies back and breathes loudly.*)

PRINCESS: Of course, it's different for *me*.

PRINCE (*sitting up*): Say that again. I must have got it wrong.

PRINCESS: It's different for me because I'm used to it. Besides, I'm so much lighter.

PRINCE: You don't mean that *you* —

PRINCESS: Oh yes, often.

PRINCE: And I thought I was a brave man! At least, I did until five minutes ago, and now I don't again.

PRINCESS: Oh, but you are! And I think it's wonderful to do it straight off the first time.

PRINCE: Well, *you* did.

PRINCESS: Oh no, not the first time. When I was a child.

PRINCE: You mean that you crashed?

PRINCESS: Well, you only fall into the moat.

PRINCE: Only! Can you *swim?*

PRINCESS: Of course.

PRINCE: So you swam to the castle walls and yelled for help, and they fished you out and walloped you. And the next day you tried again. Well, if *that* isn't pluck —

PRINCESS: Of course I didn't. I swam back and did it at once; I mean I tried again at once. It wasn't until the third time that I actually did it. You see, I was afraid I might lose my nerve.

PRINCE: Afraid she might lose her nerve!

PRINCESS: There's a way of getting over from this side too; a tree grows out from the wall, and you jump into another tree — I don't think it's quite so easy.

PRINCE: Not quite so easy. Good. You must show me.

PRINCESS: Oh, I will.

PRINCE: Perhaps it might be as well if you taught me how to swim first. I've often heard about swimming, but never ——

PRINCESS: You can't swim?

PRINCE: No. Don't look so surprised. There are a lot of other things that I can't do. I'll tell you about them as soon as you have a couple of years to spare.

PRINCESS: You can't swim, and yet you crossed by the beech tree! And you're *ever* so much heavier than I am! Now who's brave?

PRINCE (*getting up*): You keep talking about how light you are. I must see if there's anything in it. Stand up! (*She stands obediently and he picks her up.*) You're right, Dulcibella. I could hold you here forever. (*looking at her*) You're very lovely. Do you know how lovely you are?

PRINCESS: Yes. (*She laughs suddenly and happily.*)

PRINCE: Why do you laugh?

PRINCESS: Aren't you tired of holding me?

PRINCE: Frankly, yes. I exaggerated when I said I could hold you forever. When you've been hanging by the arms for ten minutes over a very deep moat, wondering if it's too late to learn how to swim — (*He puts her down.*) what I meant was that I should *like* to hold you forever. Why did you laugh?

PRINCESS: Oh, well, it was a little private joke of mine.

PRINCE: If it comes to that, I've got a private joke too. Let's exchange them.

PRINCESS: Mine's very private. One other woman in the whole world knows, and that's all.

PRINCE: Mine's just as private. One other man knows, and that's all.

PRINCESS: What fun. I love secrets. . . . Here's mine. When I was born, one of my godmothers promised that I should be very beautiful.

PRINCE: How right she was.

PRINCESS: But the other one said this:

> *I give you with this kiss*
> *A wedding-day surprise.*
> *Where ignorance is bliss,*
> *'Tis folly to be wise.*

And nobody knew what it meant. And I grew up very plain. And then, when I was about ten, I met my godmother in the forest one day. It was my tenth birthday. Nobody knows this — except you.

PRINCE: Except us.

PRINCESS: Except us. And she told me what her gift meant. It meant that I *was* beautiful — but everybody else was to go on being ignorant and thinking me plain until my wedding day. Because, she said, she didn't want me to grow up spoilt and willful and vain as I should have done if everybody had always been saying how beautiful I was; and the best thing in the world, she said, was to be quite sure of yourself but not to expect admiration from other people. So ever since then my mirror has told me I'm beautiful, and everybody else thinks me ugly, and I get a lot of fun out of it.

PRINCE: Well, seeing that Dulcibella is the result, I can only say that your godmother was very, very wise.

PRINCESS: And now you tell me *your* secret.

PRINCE: It isn't such a pretty one. You see, Prince Simon was going to woo Princess Camilla, and he'd heard that she was beautiful and haughty and imperious — all *you* would have been if your godmother hadn't been so wise. And being a very ordinary-looking fellow himself, he was afraid she wouldn't think much of him, so he suggested to one of his attendants, a man called Carlo, of extremely attractive appearance, that *he* should pretend to be the prince and win the princess's hand; and then at the last moment they would change places —

PRINCESS: How would they do that?

PRINCE: The prince was going to have been married in full armor — with his visor down.

PRINCESS (*laughing happily*): Oh, what fun!

PRINCE: Neat, isn't it?

PRINCESS: Oh, very . . . very . . . very.

PRINCE: Neat, but not so terribly *funny.* Why do you keep laughing?

PRINCESS: Well, that's another secret.

PRINCE: If it comes to that, *I've* got another one up my sleeve. Shall we exchange again?

PRINCESS: All right. You go first this time.

PRINCE: Very well. . . . I am not Carlo. (*standing up and speaking dramatically*) I am Simon! *Ow!* (*He sits down and rubs his leg violently.*)

PRINCESS (*alarmed*): What is it?

PRINCE: Cramp. I was saying that I was Prince Simon.

PRINCESS: Is your leg better?

PRINCE (*despairingly*): I am Simon.

PRINCESS: I know.

PRINCE: How did you know?

PRINCESS: Well, you told me.

PRINCE: But oughtn't you to swoon or something?

PRINCESS: Why? History records many similar ruses.

PRINCE (*amazed*): Is that so? I've never read history. I thought I was being very original.

PRINCESS: Oh, no! Now I'll tell you *my* secret. For reasons very much like your own the Princess Camilla, who is held to be extremely plain, feared to meet Prince Simon. Is the drawbridge down yet?

PRINCE: Do your people give a faint, surprised cheer every time it goes down?

PRINCESS: Naturally.

PRINCE: Then it came down about three minutes ago.

PRINCESS: Ah! Then at this very moment your man Carlo is declaring his passionate love for my maid, Dulcibella. That, I think, is funny. (*The* PRINCE *laughs heartily.*) Dulcibella, by the way, is in love with a man she calls Eg, so I hope Carlo isn't getting carried away.

PRINCE: Carlo is married to a girl he calls "the little woman," so Eg has nothing to fear.

PRINCESS: By the way, I don't know if you heard, but I said, or as good as said, that I am the Princess Camilla.

PRINCE: I wasn't surprised. History, of which I read a great deal, records many similar ruses.

PRINCESS (*laughing*): Simon!

PRINCE (*laughing*): Camilla! (*He stands up.*) May I try holding you again? (*She nods. He takes her in his arms.*) Sweetheart!

PRINCESS: You see, when you lifted me up before, you said, "You're very lovely," and my godmother said that the first person to whom I would seem lovely was the man I should marry; so I knew then that you were Simon and I should marry you.

PRINCE: I knew when I saw you that I should marry you even if you were Dulcibella. By the way, which of you *am* I marrying?

PRINCESS: When she lifts her veil, it will be Camilla. (*Voices are heard.*) Until then it will be Dulcibella.

PRINCE (*in a whisper*): Then good-bye, Camilla, until you lift your veil.

PRINCESS: Good-bye, Simon, until you raise your visor. (*The* KING *and* QUEEN *come in arm in arm, followed by* CARLO *and* DULCIBELLA, *also arm in arm. The* CHANCELLOR *precedes them, walking backwards at a loyal angle.*)

PRINCE (*supporting the* CHANCELLOR *as an accident seems inevitable*): Careful! (*The* CHANCELLOR *turns indignantly around.*)

KING: Who and what is this? More accurately, who and what are all these?

CARLO: My attendant, Carlo, Your Majesty. He will, with Your Majesty's permission, prepare me for the ceremony. (*The* PRINCE *bows.*)

KING: Of course, of course, *of course!*

QUEEN (*to* DULCIBELLA): Your maid, Dulcibella, is it not, my love? (DULCIBELLA *nods violently.*) I thought so. (*to* CARLO) *She* will prepare Her Royal Highness. (*The* PRINCESS *curtsies.*)

KING: Ah, yes. Yes. *Most* important.

PRINCESS (*curtsying*): I beg pardon, Your Majesty, if I've done wrong, but I found the gentleman wandering —

KING (*crossing to her*): Quite right, my dear, quite right. (*He pinches her cheek and takes advantage of this kingly gesture to speak in a loud whisper.*) We've pulled it off! (*They sit down — the* KING *and* QUEEN *on their thrones,* DULCIBELLA *on the princess's throne.* CARLO *stands behind* DULCIBELLA, *the* CHANCELLOR *on the right of the* QUEEN, *and the* PRINCE *and* PRINCESS *behind the long seat on the left.*)

CHANCELLOR (*consulting documents*): Hmm! Have I Your Majesty's authority to put the final test to His Royal Highness?

QUEEN (*whispering to* KING): Is this safe?

KING (*whispering*): Perfectly, my dear. I told him the answer a minute ago. (*over his shoulder to* CARLO) Don't forget. *Dog.* (*aloud*) Proceed, Your Excellency. It is my desire that the affairs of my country should ever be conducted in a strictly constitutional manner.

CHANCELLOR (*oratorically*): By the constitution of the country a suitor to Her Royal Highness's hand cannot be deemed successful until he has given the correct answer to a riddle. (*conversationally*) The last suitor answered incorrectly and thus failed to win his bride.

KING: By a coincidence he fell into the moat.

CHANCELLOR (*to* CARLO): I have now to ask Your Royal Highness if you are prepared for the ordeal?

CARLO (*cheerfully*): Absolutely.

CHANCELLOR: I may mention, as a matter, possibly, of some slight historical interest to our visitor, that by the constitution of the country the same riddle is not allowed to be asked on two successive occasions.

KING (*startled*): What's that?

CHANCELLOR: This one, it is interesting to recall, was propounded exactly a century ago; and we must take it as a fortunate omen that it was well and truly solved.

KING (*to* QUEEN): I may want my sword directly.

CHANCELLOR: The riddle is this: What is it that has four legs and mews like a cat?

CARLO (*promptly*): A dog.

KING (*still more promptly*): Bravo, bravo! (*He claps loudly and nudges the* QUEEN, *who claps too.*)

CHANCELLOR (*peering at his documents*): According to the records of the occasion to which I referred, the correct answer would seem to be —

PRINCESS (*to* PRINCE): Say something, quickly!

CHANCELLOR: Not dog, but —

PRINCE: Your Majesty, have I permission to speak? Naturally, His Royal Highness could not think of justifying himself on such an occasion, but I think that with Your Majesty's gracious permission, I could —

KING: Certainly, certainly.

PRINCE: In our country we have an animal to which we have given the name "dog," or, in the local dialect of the more mountainous districts, "doggie." It sits by the fireside and purrs.

CARLO: That's correct. It purrs like anything.

PRINCE: When it needs milk, which is its staple food, it mews.

CARLO (*enthusiastically*): Mews like nobody's business.

PRINCE: It also has four legs.

CARLO: One at each corner.

PRINCE: In some countries, I understand, this animal is called a "cat." In one distant country that His Royal Highness and I visited, it was called by the curious name of "hippopotamus."

CARLO: That's right. (*to* PRINCE) Do you remember that ginger-colored hippopotamus, which used to climb on to my shoulder and lick my ear?

PRINCE: I shall never forget it, sir. (*to* KING) So you see, Your Majesty —

KING: Thank You. I think that makes it perfectly clear. (*firmly to* CHANCELLOR) You are about to agree?

CHANCELLOR: Undoubtedly, Your Majesty. May I be the first to congratulate His Royal Highness on solving the riddle so accurately?

KING: You may be the first to see that all is in order for an immediate wedding.

CHANCELLOR: Thank you, Your Majesty. (*He bows and withdraws. The* KING, QUEEN, *and* DULCIBELLA *rise.*)

KING (*to* CARLO): Doubtless, Prince Simon, you will wish to retire and prepare yourself for the ceremony.

CARLO: Thank you, sir.

PRINCE: Have I Your Majesty's permission to attend His Royal Highness? It is the custom of his country for princes of the royal blood to be married in full armor, a matter that requires a certain adjustment —

KING: Of course, of course. (CARLO *bows to the* KING *and* QUEEN *and goes out. As the* PRINCE *is about to follow, the* KING *stops him.*) Young man, you have a quality of quickness, which I admire. It is my pleasure to reward it in any way which commends itself to you.

PRINCE: Your Majesty is ever gracious. May I ask for my reward *after* the ceremony? (*He catches the eye of the* PRINCESS, *and they give each other a secret smile.*)

KING: Certainly. (*The* PRINCE *bows and goes out. The* KING *speaks to* DULCIBELLA.) Now, young woman, make yourself scarce. You've done your work excellently, and we will see that you and your — what was his name?

DULCIBELLA: Eg, Your Majesty.

KING: That you and your Eg are not forgotten.

DULCIBELLA: Coo! (*She curtsies and goes out.*)

PRINCESS: Wait for me, Dulcibella!

KING (*to* QUEEN): Well, my dear, we may congratulate ourselves. As I remember saying to somebody once, "You have not lost a daughter, you have gained a son." How does he strike you?

QUEEN: Stupid.

KING: They made a very handsome pair, I thought, he and Dulcibella.

QUEEN: Both stupid.

KING: I said nothing about stupidity. What I *said* was that they were both extremely handsome. That is the important thing. Or isn't it?

QUEEN: What do *you* think of Prince Simon, Camilla?

PRINCESS: I adore him. We shall be so happy together.

KING: Well, of course you will. I told you so. Happily ever after.

QUEEN: Run along now and get ready.

PRINCESS: Yes, Mother. (*She throws a kiss to them and goes out.*)

KING (*anxiously*): It seemed to me that Camilla wasn't looking *quite* so plain as usual just now.

QUEEN (*carelessly*): Just the excitement of the marriage.

KING (*relieved*): Ah, yes, that would account for it.

DISCUSSION

1. What was the "old trouble" that the king, queen, and chancellor were discussing when the play opened? Why was Princess Camilla's wedding a problem?
2. At what point in the story was the godmother's gift fulfilled?
3. Princess Camilla told Prince Simon what her godmother meant by the rhyme. What did her godmother mean?

4. What plan did the king and queen have to make sure Princess Camilla married Prince Simon? Why did this plan almost fail? How did Prince Simon get Carlo out of the predicament he was in?

5. How did the speech of the chancellor remind you of a character that you read about earlier in this book?

6. What kind of person was Princess Camilla? What kind of person was Prince Simon?

7. Do you agree with Princess Camilla's godmother that the best thing in the world is to be quite sure of yourself but not to expect admiration from other people? Why or why not?

8. For what reason were Princess Camilla and Prince Simon so impressed with each other at their first meeting? Why do you think they decided to exchange secrets?

9. What special problems might a real prince or princess have today?

10. Many fanciful tales end with "And they lived happily ever after." Do you think all stories should end happily? Why or why not?

AUTHOR

Alan Alexander Milne, more commonly known as A. A. Milne, was born in 1882 in Milburn, a district of central London. He could read before he was three years old, and at the age of eight and a half he submitted his first article to *Chum,* a magazine for boys. After graduating from Cambridge University, he became an assistant editor for *Punch,* a humorous British magazine.

Mr. Milne started writing plays during the four years he served his country in World War I. *Wurzel-Flummery* and *Belinda* were his first, and several other successful plays followed. When the war ended, he started writing full time. Although he wrote various plays, Mr. Milne became best known for his children's verses and stories. He wrote his first children's book of verse, *When We Were Very Young,* about his three-year-old son, Christopher Robin. *Winnie-the-Pooh* and *The House at Pooh Corner* are charming stories about his son's stuffed animals. Mr. Milne's books for children are enjoyed by young and old alike. Christopher Robin, Winnie-the-Pooh, and Piglet are a few of the characters that Mr. Milne has made famous.

FROM THE BOOKSHELF

NUMBER FOUR, *by Molly Cone*

When Benjamin Turner, an American Indian, begins to take pride in his culture and tries to share it with other Indian students, he runs into trouble with the authorities at his high school.

A STAR TO THE NORTH, *by Barbara Corcoran and Bradford Angier*

A courageous brother and sister survive a perilous journey when they leave an unhappy home in California, hoping to find refuge with an uncle in the Canadian woods.

THE SOUL BROTHERS AND SISTER LOU, *by Kristin Hunter*

Louretta Hawkins, a lonely Harlem teen-ager, learns to be proud of the positive values of black life.

MODELS OF AMERICA'S PAST AND HOW TO MAKE THEM, *by C. J. Maginley*

Step-by-step instructions plus detailed diagrams explain how to build to scale models of houses, barns, and furniture of early America.

LOST WILD AMERICA: THE STORY OF OUR EXTINCT AND VANISHING WILDLIFE, *by Robert M. McClung*

The conditions of North American wildlife from the arrival of the first Europeans to the present day are documented in this book.

THE OTHER PEOPLE, *by Janet McNeill*

This suspense story captures the atmosphere of an English seaside resort and the emotions of a sensitive young girl who becomes involved in the lives of others.

FULLBACK FEVER, *by Jackson Scholz*

Chuck Denny has to decide whether he is better qualified to be a football star or president of the student body.

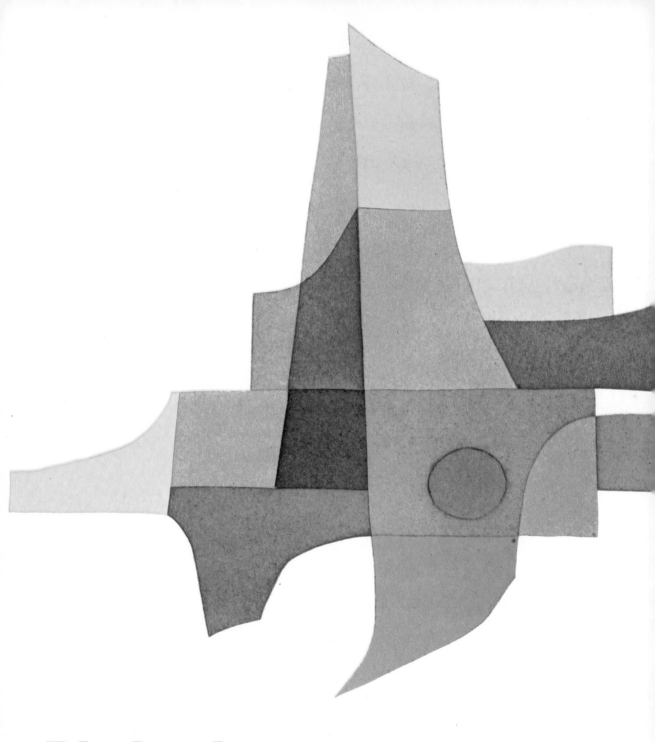

Distinction

Contents

Distinction

The Skating Rink

by Mildred Lee

Fifteen-year-old Tuck Faraday, a speech-handicapped Georgian farm boy, lives with his father, Myron Faraday; his stepmother, Ida; his older twin brothers, Tom and Cletus; and his young half sister, Karen.

Daily, Tuck watched the building of a new roller-skating rink between the highway and his father's peach orchard. There began his friendship with Pete Degley, the owner of the rink, and his wife, Lily.

The fifteenth of January dawned in mizzling rain, harried by mean bursts of wind. The wet cold seeped through Tuck's clothing as he did his morning chores. Karen snuffled and whined with a cold in her head, and her mother said she could not go out if it wasn't better by evening. Clete and Tom gobbled the breakfast Ida set before them and went down to the highway to hitch a ride to town.

The day crawled by, going too fast even so, bringing Tuck's ordeal closer with every tick of the greasy-faced clock. The house was bursting with family, but its discord rose and fell about Tuck without touching him.

At supper Ida tried to coax Karen out of going to the opening of the new roller-skating rink.

"I ab goi'd," Karen muttered on the heels of a sneeze, and her father shouted to her to mind her tongue, or she'd be going to bed.

"You go down there with a lotta riffraff, you're liable to catch wors'n a cold," Ida wheedled. "That rink'll be there when you're shut of your cold. You stay home with me, and we'll make us some syrup candy to pull."

"I doe wadda pull doe caddy," Karen wailed, casting a look of desperation at Tuck. "It's the *opening*, Ma." She stopped short, blew her nose loudly, and added, "I wadda skate."

"Fat lot you know about skating," Tom scoffed.

"Tuck might could teach you," Clete suggested. "All the time he's spent there, he must be an expert."

Karen, red-faced, started to make a retort, and Tuck pushed his chair back from the table, noisily. They all looked at him, but he looked only at Karen as if the others weren't there. She pressed her lips sullenly together, her red face looking ready to burst. Passing her chair, Tuck put his hand on the back of her neck a second, and Karen stuck her tongue out at Clete instead of speaking.

Tuck washed and dressed hurriedly, so he could go down to the rink ahead of the others. He put on a clean shirt and jeans and combed his hair as carefully as if he were Tom or Cletus. There was no real reason for him to get there early. But, apart from feeling that he must go alone, as always, he hoped to find, somehow, in the atmosphere of the rink, the courage that seemed all week to have been dwindling.

At the rink he stood looking about him. All was bustle and strangeness. Behind the cash register was a brassy-haired, stoutish woman. At the snack bar, now amply stocked with the delicacies dear to the stomachs of teen-agers, was a young man in a wild plaid shirt. A spotty-faced boy with hair longer than Tom's checked skate sizes. So it was true that Pete Degley had brought his staff in from outside Wesley. Tuck had never laid eyes on any of them before. The fact that he alone had been chosen from the local scene held only added terror for him at the moment.

Even Pete, whipping about with an air of being everywhere at once, might have been someone Tuck had never seen before. Lily was nowhere in sight. Tuck stiffened his knees against their weak trembles and moved in front of the empty spectators' benches toward the cubicle in the rear, where he was to change his clothes.

His costume hung against the wall: white tights and the scarlet shirt Lily had made and said she would press after the dress rehearsal last night. Tuck touched a satin sleeve tenderly, then scowled at himself in the rectangle of mirror fastened to the door. He could hear Lily moving about on the other side of the thin partition and would have liked to smile at her needing so much time for dressing — in such little scraps of a costume too — but he couldn't make the stiff muscles of his face give.

Tuck and Lily's number was not to be till just before closing time. No use sweating his fancy rig up in this little cell of a dressing room. He felt the need of air and went out the rear door of the building to walk up and down behind it, sucking in the cold, wet air. A car turned off the highway into the parking area, then another, and another. They were coming early enough! Doors slammed; young voices shrilled; headlights swung in bright arcs against the side of the building.

"Tuck? Tucker Faraday —" Lily's voice penetrated his mounting terror. He saw her coming toward him through the dark. She had on a white cape over her tight-fitting, blue bodice and little bob-tailed skirt of fiery fish scales, and she made Tuck think of a big light moth — the kind that blunders into the house on a summer night. "Oh, here you are. Got the jitters? I always have them too, many times as I've been on with Pete. They don't mean a thing. In fact, Pete says they're a healthy sign." He felt her hand clutch his, icy but as steady as a rock.

Tuck gulped, "I'm O.K."

Lily pulled the cape around her arms, shivering. "We'd better go inside. I take cold easy, and you know what Pete's like when I do."

Inside the rink again Tuck left Lily and made his way toward the front of the building. He pressed himself against the wall beside the bulletin board that announced skating lessons on Saturday mornings from ten to twelve. He saw Pete Degley and the spotted boy handing out skates as fast as the brassy-haired cashier could ring up admissions. There were almost as many older people on the spectators' seats as there were young ones reaching for skates. Some of those who were unwilling to risk life and limb but had come for the excitement of watching others do so were already rushing the snack bar, keeping the bright-shirted fellow on the jump.

Tuck saw his father and his stepmother sitting near the door and thought his father had selected a place handy to an exit should the evening prove too great a bore.

A piercing whistle blast brought all eyes to Pete Degley in the center of the rink. He was on skates and a grin split his face. His voice rang out after the whistle, folksy and full of good salesmanship. Wonder at this battled with Tuck's stage fright, making him miss much of what Pete was saying. It came in waves and fragments to his ears, mostly nonsense, but he could see the crowd was lapping it up and loving it.

"... want you all to have a good time tonight ... few regulations to keep in mind ... don't want anybody to get hurt — see you forgot to bring your sofa pillows to fasten on

behind. . . ." Laughter, boisterous and wholehearted. "When this whistle sounds" — he held the police whistle on its cord around his neck for them to get a good look — "you all want to pull up and stop like a traffic cop was on your tail." More laughter. "When it blows next, you that's ready to roll fall in line and come onto the floor *through the break in the railing.* No scrounging or pushing under if you don't want to sit out the first round." A pause for this to sink in. "I repeat: We don't want anybody hurt. You big kids watch out for the little ones, and you limber young folks watch out for us oldsters that's brittle in the bones." Laughter, a few brash remarks, and catcalls from bold local teen-agers.

The whistle shrilled. Pete began to skate backwards, his eyes everywhere. The "Glowworm," though amplified almost beyond bearing, failed to drown out completely the thump and slide of wheels on novice feet. The floor filled; the spills began. Pete Degley whipped in and out among the strugglers, each hand picking a child from the floor.

Tuck saw Karen shuffling along laboriously, one hand gripping the rail, the other making frequent dabs at her troublesome nose. Link Grover glided smoothly past in the inner circle to which Pete was directing the better skaters, Jenny Morrow clinging proudly to his arm. Tuck saw other boys and girls

he knew, some skating in pairs, some singly. Most did better than he had in the beginning but not all. He knew Pete would count on the poor skaters as candidates for instruction — the instruction with which Tuck was to help him. Pete had told him this only a few days ago when he put the bulletin up.

Flattening himself against the wall, Tuck thought how crazy it all was that he was a part of this — or would be if he didn't flub up the works tonight. Nerves twitched in his legs, making them feel weak. The shortness of his breath made him wonder if he might give out of wind and collapse. He imagined himself lying on the floor, gasping like a fish, while the crowd hissed and booed and Pete Degley's dream died a shameful death.

Shaking his head to clear his vision, he had a fleeting glimpse of Tom and Tolly Mayhew, managing to keep on their feet but little more than that. Some experts from beyond Wesley were doing a little showing off — as much as the crowded floor permitted. And Tuck thought how strange it was that Mr. Degley had picked a raw country boy like himself to make into a skater, an artiste, as he always said so proudly. Fright deepened his humility, and he wished Pete had chosen someone else — that guy out there with the blond hair swept carefully back above his sports collar. Mr. Degley could have trained someone like that and saved himself a lot of bother along with Tuck Faraday's present anguish.

Then Tuck saw his brother Cletus and a yellow-headed girl and knew it was Elva Grimes before he saw her face. She was keeping Cletus on his feet by sheer, dogged effort, her legs working stolidly and her hands bracing her unsteady partner.

As they came opposite Tuck, Clete's glazed look strayed from its hazardous course to his brother flattened against the wall. A grin broke the rigid surface of Clete's face. He pulled his hand from Elva's grasp and waved, shouting, "Hey, Tuck! Come on in; the water's fine." It was more than Elva could handle. Clete's feet flew from under him and down he went, pulling Elva on top of him.

The tension flowed out of Tuck as if a plug had been pulled to release it. As if he had waited only for this to happen, he turned, slipped past the seat full of spectators, and shut himself in his dressing room. He sat on the one straight chair and let his thoughts tumble from one thing to another, random and inconsequential. The noise outside beat futilely in his ears, having nothing to do with him. After the anguished week his relief was like sudden freedom from physical pain. He sat there a long while before he put his costume on, not feeling foolish as he had last night — like something escaped from the circus.

Pete Degley thumped on the door once and thrust his head in, his face agleam with perspiration. "You O.K., Faraday?"

"Yes, sir."

"I better send Lily in to make you up a little. I got to get back to see none of those kids bust themselves up."

Lily stood on tiptoe to darken Tuck's eyebrows and elongate the corners of his eyes. She put a little rouge on his cheeks and reddened his lips. Tuck burned with shame and dared not meet his reflection in the glass. She said, impatiently, "You got to have make-up to beat that spot. You'll look green otherwise. How's your nerve?"

Tuck smiled, not wanting to waste himself on talk. But he was no longer afraid. Even when he heard Pete Degley's whistle bring the skaters to a grinding, thumping halt and the hubbub ebbed to comparative silence, he was not afraid.

"And now, ladies and gentlemen," Pete Degley's hoarse but strident voice announced, "I give you that bright Star of the Evening, Queen of Roller-Skating, LILY. And her supporting star — TUCKER HOLLAND FARADAY."

The gasp from the audience, shot through by one raucous bray of laughter, died as Tuck and Lily skated into the rink. The strains of Tchaikovsky's (chī-kôf'skē) "Swan Lake" flowed into the stillness; the lights went down; the spotlight bloomed out of the dark to catch the glitter of sequins on Lily's skirt and the circlet round the smooth knob of hair on the top of her head. Tuck saw their flashing, nothing else. He felt nothing, neither the magic transmitted from the music to his body nor the breathless unbelief of the spectators.

Tuck and Lily circled the rink twice, their motion as of one skater. Tuck had no awareness of Lily's cold little hands in his; they were part of him, as he was part of the act. He saw her spinning round and round in the center of the rink, the spotlight on her like a heatless sun. He could not have counted the times they had gone through each part of the act Pete had so painstakingly choreographed, so relentlessly driven them to perfect. All that lay behind him; the moment was now — his moment and Pete Degley's.

His eyes on Lily's little flashing head, Tuck did not feel the elation building within him, giving lift to his feet, power to his body. They came together; they parted; they performed in a silence somehow more powerful than the sound of the music and the roll of their skate wheels — what they had performed those countless times to Pete Degley's furious shouts and peremptory orders to halt and begin again.

No doubt he was out there in the audience somewhere, watching. But now he did not exist for Tuck,

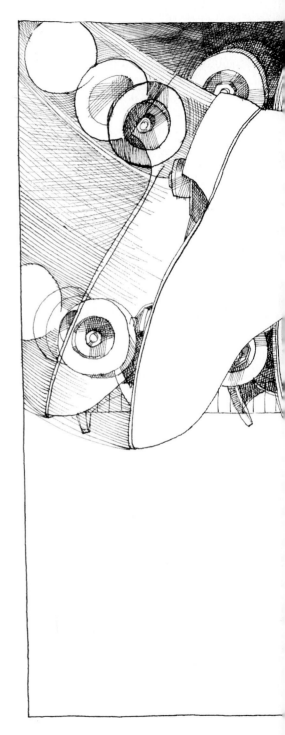

413

moving in the magic circle of the spotlight, unaware of the darkened jungle of eyes.

There was not a sound from the audience till Tuck lifted Lily and swung her at the level of his outstretched arms, unconsciously counting the bars, gradually lowering her till her feet touched the floor and she was skating again beside him. Howls, cheers, stamping, and madly crackling palms brought Tuck to himself.

When the overhead lights sprang on and he saw the faces, his numbness continued for a second; then feeling poured through him. He felt like God, as if nothing ever again would be beyond his grasp. They were pounding and screaming for more — those who had ridiculed him year after dreary year. His awareness sharpened to an ecstasy that was almost pain. He had done it, he, Tucker Holland Faraday. He had made Mr. Degley's dream come true.

Somehow, Tuck and Lily stood in the dim passage between the rink and the dressing rooms, their hard breathing slowing, settling to normal. Tuck could hear Pete's voice announcing that it was closing time, then the babble of talk, the shuffle of feet. He didn't know what the talk was and didn't care. It was done. A faint shadow of regret touched his ecstasy as he wondered if there could ever again be a moment to equal those just passed —

moments swept already into time, gone and behind him.

"You did it, Tucker," Lily said softly, and he looked down to see her eyes shining up at him as if she had had no part in it, as if it were all his show. Shame licked at him, for hadn't he been thinking the same?

"It — you did it, Lily. You were the s-star." The stammer irked him, and he said it over, more carefully. "You were the star."

She shook her head, raised both hands, and wiped her forehead. Something childlike in the gesture moved him. "I never did as well before. Not even when I skated with Pete. He'll tell you; you'll see. He knew you could do it and so did I." She shivered in the drafty passage. "See you later," she said, and went into her dressing room.

Tuck was standing in his dressing room, still bemused, when Pete Degley hurried in. "Well, you pulled it off, Faraday. Not but what I knew you would. Still, I don't know but what you did a better job than I expected — and that's saying a mouthful! Congratulations, man. You're in now. You know that, don't you?"

Tuck shook his head. "It — it was you, Mr. Degley. You and —"

"Say, don't you think it's about time you dropped that 'mister,' Faraday? Pete's the name. We been through enough together that you've earned the right, I'd say."

But the Pete did not come that easily to Tuck; his respect was too nearly reverence. "That crowd out there," Pete went on, "they never seen anything like this, you bet your life. You coulda heard a pin drop if it hadn't been for the music, I swear. You better get into dry clothes. I'll see you later."

He started out the door, then turned, grinning again. "Looks to me like this calls for a little celebration. How about the three of us going out after I get done here? Maybe find a place and dance some.

Dance? Him? Tuck felt a blush crawling over his face. How did he know he couldn't? A short time ago he hadn't been able to skate.... Then — he didn't quite know why — he was shaking his head.

"No, Mr. Degley. Th-thanks just the same. I better get home. It'll be late —"

"Maybe you're right," Pete agreed. "Guess you're mighty near bushed as I am, young as you are. Well, take a rain check on it — and see me in the office, O.K.?"

Tuck changed slowly, tending to fall into reverie, his shirt hanging from his hands, his eyes vacantly on the costume hanging neatly on the wall, still damp from the heat of his body. It had been a night; to prolong it would be a mistake. Besides, he felt the house above the orchard pulling at him, a thing he'd never felt before....

Cars were still waiting their chance to get out onto the highway, honking horns. Voices called; laughter rode the damp air. It did not strike Tuck as strange that none of his family had attempted to seek him out, congratulate him; in their place he wouldn't have ventured behind the scene, either, he thought. And good old Karen, she had kept the secret. He bet she would run her tongue ragged now that it was over. He could just imagine her at school. And what a time she'd give Tom and Clete. He chuckled, slipping his shirt on over chilling shoulders.

The crowd had gone; the skates were put away; two men were cleaning the floor, wan bursts of talk punctuating the sleepy swish of their long-handled brooms. The cashier, the snack bar attendant, and the pimpled boy had gone. Tuck's face still stung from the cold-water scrubbing he had given it to remove Lily's make-up.

Pete Degley laid the bills on the battered old roll-top desk in the box of a room that was his office. They were new ten-dollar bills — ten of them. Tuck had never seen one hundred dollars before, and his eyes seemed glued to them in wonder. He felt this to be unseemly and tried to look elsewhere — at the leather couch as worn as the desk, where Lily sat in her slacks and jacket, a green scarf tied over her hair, at anything but the bills on the desk. It was the first time he had ever been inside the office; he had never thought of its having anything to do with him.

"This do for a starter?" Pete said round the toothpick in his mouth.

Tuck's hands hung numb and heavy at his sides. Pete nudged the pile. "Ain't it satisfactory?" Tuck's face burned.

"It — it's not that, Mr. Degley. You know it's not that. I —" His voice died. How could he tell Pete Degley that what he had given him already was more than the money — much more — that he, Tuck, was the indebted one, the one beholden?

"Well, put it in your jeans then, son." Pete yawned noisily. "Me, I'm beat. Guess the three of us could do with a night's sleep." He looked at Tuck, and something in his eyes, tired but still bright and warm, made Tuck know that he didn't have to be told. Not Mr. Degley, he was a master hand at understanding — without being told. "I don't mind saying I was right proud of you tonight. You'll be a real skater before I get done with you; you keep on working like you have. Reckon we're in business, now." He chuckled. "That crowd was crazy for you. Thought I'd have to carry out some of them screeching girls at the end of the number. Small town boy makes good, heh, heh. Tucker Holland, you'll have to beat those girls off

with a club from now on in." He reached for his jacket. "Me, I got to take my girl home. See you tomorrow, Faraday. Two thirty. I'm looking for a pretty good crowd at the afternoon session."

"Yes, sir. Thanks, Mr. Degley." Tuck pushed the bills into his pocket, still shamefaced. "Night, Mr. Degley — Pete. Night, Lily."

The trees had stopped dripping, and when Tuck came out of the orchard and looked up, he saw a sprinkle of stars between the white clouds that drifted ahead of the wind. He pushed the kitchen door creakingly inward. In the darkness he caught the sound of rough breathing and reached for the fly-spotted cord. Harsh light filled the kitchen, and Tuck saw his father sitting at the end of the table. Staring at the cracked oilcloth, Myron said, "I thought you wasn't coming home."

Without meaning to, Tuck moved his hand to the pocket of his jeans.

"Where else would I g-go, Pa?"

His father still did not look at him. "Off. With that feller and that girl."

Tuck laid the roll of bills on the table. He said, eagerly, "Count it, Pa." But his father only stared at the money, his veined hands lying loosely in front of him. Tuck had never seen him look so tired or so old. There was something else, too, in the dejected slump of the thin shoulders. Was it grief because he had thought Tuck would not be coming home?

"The others," Myron said, as if bound to unburden his mind of what lay upon it, "they waited up to see you — to tell you. Karen said she knew all along it was going to happen. Maybe she made it up — you know kids, and she's half sick with her cold. Ida put her to bed and rubbed her with that croup salve she swears by. Tom and Clete had them girls to see home, I reckon." He rubbed a thumb over a break in the oilcloth.

Tuck leaned across the table, and the room seemed to sway as fatigue descended suddenly upon him. His father had waited up. Blurrily, Tuck saw him slowly part the bills, his fingers shaking. His face was gray when he looked up.

"A hundred dollars. All that money for prancin' round a skating rink with a girl?" He shook his head, unbelieving.

"Take it," Tuck said on a long sigh.

"It's yore money," his father protested, embarrassed. "You earned it honest, I reckon."

"There'll be more. Mr. Degley — he's hired me to help with skating lessons, Saturday mornings. I — I'll be working regular at the rink."

"Working." Myron shook his head. "They call that working."

Struggling with his own sudden embarrassment, Tuck scarcely heard him. "Pa — Burl Wilson's got a kitchen stove at his place. Electric. It's in pretty fair s-shape, I reckon. You get it. M-Ma wants one bad. This one — it — it's pink."

"A pink cook stove." Myron's faded eyes, coming slowly from the bills to study Tuck's face, were uncomprehending.

"Yeah, a pink cook stove," Tuck said so loudly he was afraid he'd wakened Ida. "They make them that way now. Well I'd be p-proud if you'd use some of the money I made tonight for it. Don't t-tell her that; just get it, like it was your idea." Hot as his face was, he kept commanding eyes on his father. Myron's look fell.

"If that's what you want."

"It's what I w-want." Tuck picked one of the bills from the table. "I need some shoes too," he said. "You keep the rest."

He was halfway across the room when his father called to him, and he turned to see Myron drawing himself erect, tears creeping through the stubble on his lean cheeks. "I hear how much better you talk. Good as anybody, might' near. I always said you could if you was of a mind to, but still — it's kind of a miracle, seems like."

Tuck was silent, feeling an immense weariness and a wisdom he could not share with his father.

"I 'preciate the money," Myron brought out with difficulty. "Tom or Clete wouldn't of give up a dollar if it was theirs. Not without the law made them." Bitterness cracked his voice. "But you're not like them, Tuck. You never was like them."

"Good night, Pa." Tuck steadied himself against the door frame. He couldn't remember ever having said good night to his father before; the Faradays did not bother with such niceties.

"Good night, son," his father said.

Tuck undressed quickly in the dark. He fumbled in the pocket of the jeans he had just taken off, extracted the ten-dollar bill, and pushed it under his pillow. A good pair of shoes like Mr. Degley's would last a long time because he would be riding the bus to school.

Maybe he was crazy. He had looked forward to quitting school. But with everything different he might as well change that too. He heard his father's slow steps taking him to the room where Ida lay snoring, heard his shoes, one and then the other, hit the floor.

Tuck pulled the covers over his throbbing body. His head swam with weariness, but he saw a little way beyond tonight. Only a little way but it was enough. Thoughts drifted through his head, random, unimportant thoughts, pleasing because they did not disturb him. Yesterday they had, but that was yesterday and now was now.

DISCUSSION

1. Why did Tuck want to go to the skating rink alone?
2. What was Tuck afraid might happen to him during the performance? What incident made him lose his tension and fear?
3. Why did Tuck have a difficult time calling Mr. Degley by his first name?
4. Why did Tuck's family not go backstage to congratulate him? Do you think his family was proud of him? Why do you think that?
5. What did Tuck mean when he said Pete had given him much more than money?
6. What was the miracle Tuck's father spoke of? Why do you think it happened?
7. How had Tuck and his father's relationship changed at the end of the story? What do you think caused the change?
8. Why do you think some people go to an event to get enjoyment from watching others "risk life and limb"?

9. Why do you think Tuck didn't want to take the credit for getting the new cook stove? Would you have given the credit to someone else or taken the credit yourself? Why?
10. Why do you think Tuck had decided to quit school? Why did he change his mind? Do you think this was wise? Why? How do you think his classmates acted toward him the next day?
11. What do you think was the most important result of Tuck's success?

AUTHOR

Mildred Lee, one of four children of a southern Baptist minister, was born and grew up in Alabama. Although the family's income was low, Miss Lee says, "We did not think of ourselves as 'poor.' We had advantages most of our friends had not . . . the example of good vocabularies and books."

Her interest in reading and telling stories to her younger brother and sister are the two things that most inspired Mildred Lee to write stories of her own. However, she wrote thousands of words just for the fun of writing them before she tried to have any of her stories published. She was married and the mother of two children before she sold her first magazine story. Although Miss Lee is now Mrs. James H. H. Scudder, she uses her maiden name for her pen name. In addition to many magazine stories and one adult novel, she has written several books for young people. Besides *The Skating Rink,* from which the excerpt you have just read was taken, she has written *Honor Sands, The Rock and the Willow,* and *Fog.* In 1963, *The Rock and the Willow* won a Child Study Association Children's Book Award.

Mr. and Mrs. Scudder lived for many years in the New York-New England area before moving to Florida, where they now make their home.

Music

The neighbor sits in his window and
  plays the flute.
From my bed I can hear him,
And the round notes flutter and tap about
  the room,
And hit against each other,
Blurring to unexpected chords.
It is very beautiful,
With the little flute-notes all about me,
In the darkness.

In the daytime,
The neighbor eats bread and onions with
  one hand
And copies music with the other.
He is fat and has a bald head,
So I do not look at him,
But run quickly past his window.
There is always the sky to look at,
Or the water in the well!

But when night comes and he plays his
  flute,
I think of him as a young man,
With gold seals hanging from his watch.
And a blue coat with silver buttons.
As I lie in my bed
The flute-notes push against my ears and
  lips,
And I go to sleep, dreaming.

Amy Lowell

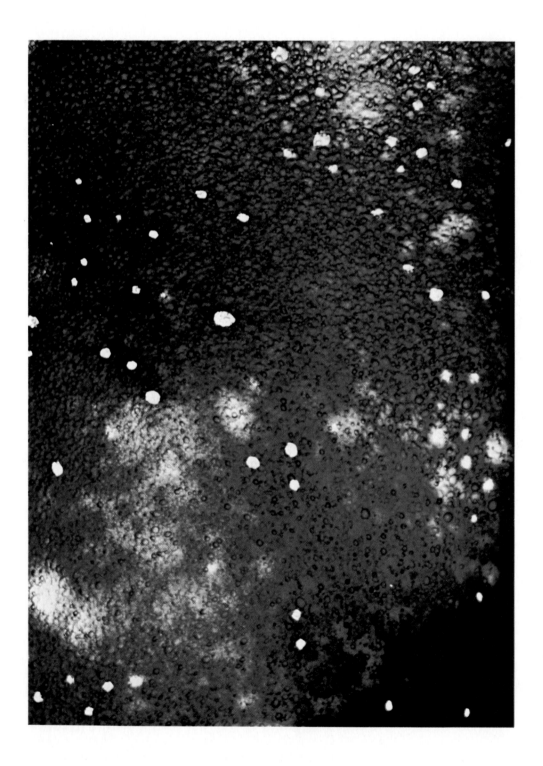

422

LIFE ON OTHER WORLDS

by Robert Silverberg

When we reach the other planets of our solar system — or those of other stars — will we find living creatures dwelling on them? Will we find, perhaps, strange beings who have developed rich, complex civilizations totally unlike ours? Or is life a cosmic accident, confined only to our world?

This is the most exciting of the questions whose answers we seek as we move into the era of space. Soon we will begin to learn whether we are alone in the vastness of the universe or about to meet at last the alien life-forms with whom we share it.

Man has long loved to speculate on this theme. Greek philosophers 2,500 years ago argued the likelihood of finding other inhabited worlds. Though some religious thinkers argued that the creation of life had taken place only once — in the Garden of Eden, on Earth — others readily accepted the idea that there might be life on other worlds. And in the seventeenth century, after Copernicus (kō-pûr'nə-kəs), Kepler, and Galileo (găl'ə-lā'ō) had shown that the Earth and all the other planets revolve about the sun, many men turned to the question of what beings might dwell on our neighbors in space.

So Kepler seriously discussed the possibility of life on the moon. Bernard de Fontenelle's (fônt'něl') entertaining book of 1686,

"Life on Other Worlds," from The World of Space, *by Robert Silverberg. Copyright © 1969 by Robert Silverberg. Reprinted by permission of the author and his agents, Scott Meredith Literary Agency, Inc., 580 Fifth Avenue, New York, New York 10036.*

Conversations on the Plurality of Worlds, attempted to describe the beings that might be found on the various planets. The people of Mercury, he said, "are so full of fire that they are absolutely mad; I fancy they have no memory at all . . . and what they do is by sudden starts and perfectly haphazard; in short, Mercury is the bedlam of the universe." Because Mercury is so small, all of its inhabitants know one another, but on huge Jupiter the situation is quite the opposite. As for Saturn it is so cold that a Saturnian brought to Earth would perish from the heat, even at the North Pole.

Christian Huygens's (hī'gənz) *The Celestial Worlds Discovered* covered the same topic in a much more scientific way. It was first published in 1698, a few years after its author's death. "A man that is of Copernicus's opinion, that this Earth of ours is a planet carried round and enlightened by the Sun, like the rest of them, cannot but sometimes have a fancy that it's not improbable that the rest of the planets have their dress and furniture, nay and their inhabitants, too, as well as this Earth of ours," Huygens began. But he observed that there were certain necessary conditions for life and rejected the idea that the moon, for example, could be inhabited because "it has no seas, no rivers, nor clouds, nor air and water."

Huygens was one of the first to sound this note of caution. However, as scientists learned more, both about the nature of life on Earth and about the conditions existing on the other planets, they grew increasingly doubtful that those planets could support life of the kind found on our world.

What is meant by "life," though?

There are three basic requirements for the development of life on any planet. First, a building-block substance is needed — a plentiful, readily available element that is chemically able to join with other elements to form complex compounds. These compounds must be stable enough to keep from breaking up but just unstable enough to be capable of undergoing the chemical changes that sustain life.

Second, a solvent is needed — a substance in which the building-block element can exist and in which atoms and molecules can move about freely to take part in chemical reactions.

Third, there must be chemical reactions that result in the production of energy, so that the vital processes of life can be carried out.

On Earth the building-block substance is carbon, which has an unusual ability to combine with other elements. The solvent is a liquid compound formed from hydrogen and oxygen: water. The energy-producing chemical reactions are brought about by oxygen, which releases heat when it combines with other elements.

Carbon, water, and oxygen — without them there can be no Earth-type life. But temperature is also a factor, if only because it sets a limit to the places where water can be found. The need for water in liquid form immediately eliminates most of the planets of the solar system as possible sites for our kind of life. Water freezes at 32° F. and turns to a gas at 212° F. Earth, luckily, is so placed in relation to the sun that most points on its surface have average temperatures in the middle of this range; except at the poles few places on Earth experience prolonged periods of below-freezing temperature, and except in the desert regions there are few places where the temperature regularly goes above 100° F.

The other planets are either too close to the sun or too far from it to have water. Mercury and Venus must be disqualified as too hot for water to remain liquid; and Jupiter, Saturn, Neptune, Uranus, and Pluto, as too cold. (Some scientists think there is a possibility that Jupiter, under its heavy atmosphere, is warmer than we think and may have water; but those holding this belief are in a minority, as are those who think parts of Venus may not be as hot as our space probes suggest.)

Only Mars is close to the right temperature range. In the daytime it is well above the freezing point in most places. At night the temperature plunges to 100° F. below zero and colder; but Martian organisms might be able to cope with this if their internal fluids contained some substance that could act as an antifreeze, such as lithium chloride, which keeps water from freezing even at 100° F. below zero. The fact that Mars has practically no water in the first place could also, perhaps, be dealt with; such plants as cacti survive quite well on Earth in environments that may be nearly as dry as that of Mars. The scarcity of oxygen on Mars is a more difficult problem to overcome and leads many scientists to think that the red planet must be as lifeless as the moon. But there is at least a chance that Mars does have life — bacteria or simple plants — that operates on the carbon-oxygen-water system as life on Earth does. Nowhere else in the solar system is that possibility thought to be very great.

However, the other planets may have life based on some entirely different scheme. Alternatives to the carbon-oxygen-water system can be considered, at least in theory.

Life based on silicon rather than carbon is one possibility. Silicon has many of the same chemical properties as carbon. At our temperature range silicon-based life would be impossible, but at much higher temperatures, 800° F. and up, it might work. Of course, water would not be available at such temperatures, requiring some other solvent, perhaps liquid sulfur.

On cold worlds carbon-based life might exist with liquid ammonia as its solvent; ammonia is liquid from −28° F. to −108° F. On very cold worlds methane, which remains liquid down to −300° F., might suffice. Chemical reactions proceed extremely slowly at low temperatures, and oxygen might not be a suitable energy source; fluorine, the most reactive of all elements, is a possible substitute.

Inventing such chemistries is an interesting exercise in science fiction. We can design life-forms to fit the special conditions of our eight fellow planets and several of their moons, and perhaps nature's ingenuity has matched our own, so that we will find living creatures surviving even under the conditions — so hostile to us — that those planets and moons afford. For the moment, though, little optimism is felt that life will be discovered elsewhere in the solar system. Certainly, we do not expect to find the cities and highways of alien beings. Simple plants on Mars, and perhaps microscopic creatures drifting in the atmosphere of Venus or Jupiter, are the best we can realistically hope for. It seems more likely that the Earth is a rare island of life in a sterile family of planets, though some great surprises may be in store for us.

When we look toward the stars, however, we see a more encouraging picture — or maybe a more frightening one. The chances are excellent that the universe teems with life and that it will be carbon-oxygen-water-based life, operating on principles similar to those of life on Earth.

Simple probabilities appear to favor it. There are so many billions of stars, and so many of them — we suspect — have planets, that there must be a multitude of worlds where conditions of temperature and atmosphere are not too different from Earth's.

We can eliminate all the stars less than three-fourths as massive as the sun. They are too dim to provide enough heat to sustain life, except for planets quite close to them; and a planet that close to its star will almost certainly be caught in a gravitational lock, always keeping one face to its sun. The extremes of temperature that such a situation causes are not favorable to the development of life.

We can also eliminate all the stars that are brighter, hotter, and larger than the sun. The larger a star is, the faster it uses up its hydrogen fuel; and when this happens, the star becomes unstable, changing in size and making life impossible on its planets. In stars more than one and a half times as massive as the sun, this instability sets in when the star is less than three billion years old. Scientists believe that more than three billion years is necessary for planets to cool and become receptive to life; so the emergence of life on planets of an unstable sun is most unlikely.

Discarding the stars that are too small and the stars that are too big, we find that we have rejected seven stars out of eight as possible sites for life-bearing planets. But the number of stars not rejected is vast — more than twelve billion in our galaxy alone.

Suppose that half of these have systems of planets. That gives us six billion solar systems. Suppose that half of these have planets that lie at the correct distance to maintain water in its liquid state. That gives us three billion potential Earths. Suppose that half of these are too small to retain an atmosphere. That leaves us with a billion and a half planets. Say that a billion of these must be rejected because they are too big, because they do not rotate on their axes, because they have no water, or because they are in some other way unsuitable for Earth-type life. That still leaves 500 million Earth-type planets in our own galaxy! And there are millions of galaxies.

Completely leaving out of account the chances of strange silicon-based or ammonia-solvent life-forms, then, we see that the probability is great that many worlds exist whose inhabitants are biologically similar to the life-forms of Earth. Every stage of evolution may be represented among them. Some worlds may be populated only by simple one-celled creatures; others may have seas swarming with fish and crustaceans; others may be worlds of insects or reptiles or amphibians or birds. In some there may be intelligent civilized beings at about the same level of development we have reached. And there may also be planets whose inhabitants are as far beyond us in their achievements as we are beyond the first primitive ape-men.

If such superraces exist elsewhere in the galaxy, though, why have we not heard from them by now?

Possibly we have — without understanding the message or even realizing a message has been sent. Or perhaps they simply have no wish to talk with creatures as backward as we are. Maybe they prefer to keep away from us until they are sure we have learned to control our hydrogen bombs and our other dangerous toys.

Such speculations, of course, are in the realm of science fiction. But there is no doubt at all that we have made a very serious, scientific effort to make contact with possible intelligent neighbors in the universe.

The first such project was proposed in 1869 by the French inventor Charles Cros. He wanted the French government to pay for the construction of a gigantic mirror capable of focusing a beam of light and transmitting it to Mars. The heat of this beam would be used to burn messages into the sands of the Martian deserts: geometrical figures like triangles and circles, then more complex designs — the head of a man, the outline of a house, and so forth.

It would have been technically impossible to build such a mirror, even if a nineteenth-century government could have been persuaded to put up the cash for such a wild scheme. And, if there are any Martians, one wonders if they would react with much enthusiasm to a fiery beam of light aimed at them from Earth, even if it did sketch geometrical figures in the deserts. Cros, nevertheless, devoted many years of his life to his campaign, which won no support at all.

Nearly a century later the United States carried out the first official attempt to discover if there are other intelligent races in the universe. This was Project Ozma, carried out at the National Radio Astronomy Observatory, Green Bank, West Virginia. The Ozma scientists suggested that it might be possible to tune in on the radio broadcasts of another civilization, using a device called a radio telescope. They

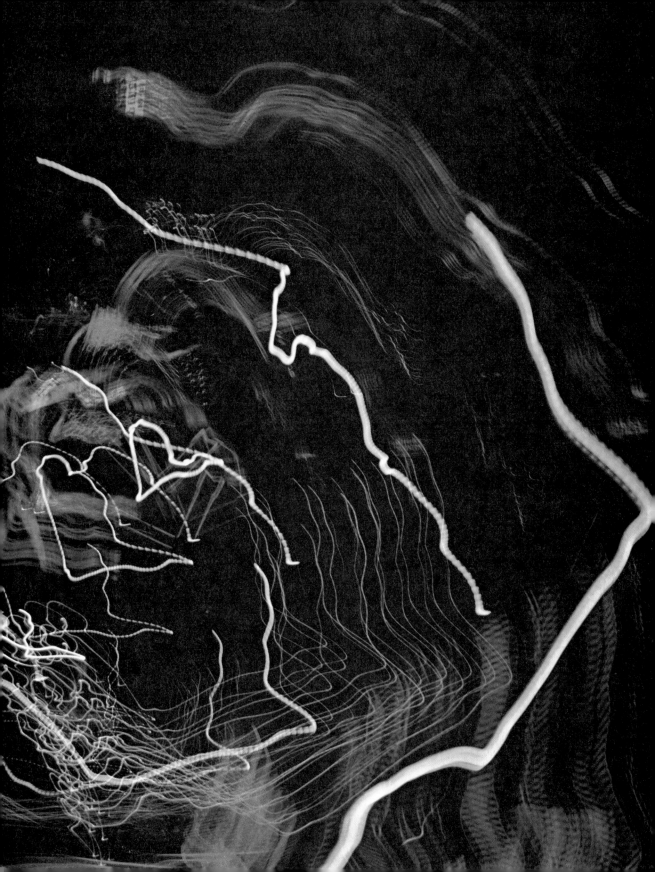

spent three months in 1960 aiming the eighty-five-foot-diameter receiving antenna of the Green Bank radio telescope at stars that are thought particularly likely to have Earthlike planets, but there were no results. This does not necessarily mean that there were no broadcasts to intercept; the radio telescope used was simply too small to offer much hope of success. The giant radio telescopes we now have, such as the 1,000-foot-diameter one at Arecibo (ă'rā-sē' bō), Puerto Rico, may be more helpful when Project Ozma is revived.

We are also considering various plans for aiming messages of our own at the stars — the Charles Cros project brought up to date. One possibility is to make use of the brilliant beams of light produced by lasers, employing them not to burn pictures on other worlds but to flash rhythmic signals in Morse code or some other system. Presumably a race intelligent enough to monitor such signals would be aware that the rhythmic flashes of light must be coming from another civilization; and they might reply with some code of their own, ultimately leading to interstellar communication.

Whether we use laser beams or conventional radio waves, we will find it maddeningly slow to "talk" to dwellers in other solar systems. The trouble is that we are limited by the speed of light, which is also the speed at which radio waves travel — 186,000 miles a second. Although this is fast enough to send a message completely around the world seven times in a single second, it is much too slow for any meaningful conversation across the gulfs of interstellar space.

A message to the nearest star — Proxima Centauri — would take about four years to get there, and then we would have to wait four more years for an answer. A message to a star like Capella would have to spend forty-five years on its journey. Contact with another galaxy would be inconceivable; if we sent a message to the closest galaxy, the Magellanic (măj'ə-lăn'ĭk) Clouds, it would not arrive for 200,000 years.

These figures indicate why no scientists are speaking yet in a serious way about actual expeditions to other stars. The relativity theories of Albert Einstein indicate that nothing in the universe can travel faster than light — and thus that 186,000-mile-a-*second* speed becomes an inflexible barrier, cutting us off from dreams of voyages to the stars.

In the present primitive state of rocketry even the speed of light seems impossible for us to attain in spaceships. If we could reach it, we could get to Pluto in a few hours; but with our current equipment the trip would last forty-five years. We are still in a very early stage of our space adventure, and great improvements in rocket speeds undoubtedly are coming. Even so, it will be a while before we have moved past today's 25,000-mile-an-*hour* speeds to the velocities that can enable us to think about exploring the outer worlds of our solar system, let alone the stars.

We have the capacity now to send rockets on the way to the stars. The Saturn V rocket could lift a ten-ton truck and ship it to Proxima Centauri; but it would take half a million years to reach its destination. By the end of this century we may have more efficient vehicles capable of reaching speeds of ten million miles an hour, and this would allow us to make trips to the closer stars in one hundred and fifty years or less. Robot explorers might be the first to go forth, programmed to relay information about their discoveries homeward to the great-grandchildren of their designers. Human astronauts, placed in a kind of deep freeze, might sleep away the entire long voyage, awakening at its climax — the landing on a planet of some other star. Or, maybe, whole generations of explorers will be born, live, and die aboard the same ship as it makes its centuries-long voyage to the stars, and those who are on board at the time of the historic landing will be the distant descendants of those who, centuries before, blasted off from Earth.

We of the twentieth century can only guess how it will come to pass. But we know that it *will* come to pass and that we will have had something to do with making it happen. In our own lifetimes, in an astonishingly brief interval, we have moved from the first wobbly rockets and the first tiny space satellites to the conquest of the moon. Millions of us will live to see the next phase unfold, as we take the giant step to the nearer planets.

The universe is great, and man is very small. But we are on our way — outward, into the most vast of all seas, toward a frontier without end.

DISCUSSION

1. What has caused doubt about the possibility of an Earth-based life on the other planets in our solar system?
2. What are the three basic requirements for the development of life on any planet? How are these requirements met on Earth?
3. Which planet in our solar system, other than earth, has the greatest possibility of having some sort of life? Why?
4. Where, other than in our solar system, may we look for more possibilities of finding carbon-oxygen-water-based life, such as exists on Earth? How may we attempt to communicate with dwellers outside of our own solar system? Why might this communication be maddening?
5. Did any part of this article remind you of "The Great Hoax," an earlier selection in this book? If so, which part?
6. Why do we of the twentieth century think that some day our distant descendants will be making voyages to the stars?
7. Would you be willing to work toward a goal that would not be realized for several generations after you? Why or why not?
8. Given the size of the Earth and the vastness of the universe, what would you say man's chances are for conquering all the mysteries of the universe? Why do you think that?

ESP IMPRESSIONS

by Larry Kettelkamp

The most common of the extrasensory perceptions (ESP) is probably telepathy. This term comes from the Greek words *tele* and *pathy,* which mean "distant" and "feeling." It is used to describe an incident in which a person receives information from the thoughts of another person in another place. The experience seems strongest when intense emotional feelings are involved.

One of the most famous experiments in telepathy was carried out by two men, Harold Sherman, an American author and psychic, and Sir Hubert Wilkins, an English explorer, who had a common interest in the study of ESP. Sir Hubert was to go on an expedition to the Arctic, starting in the fall of 1937. He planned to keep a diary of his day-to-day activities. Accordingly, he and Sherman agreed that three nights each week when Sir Hubert sat down to write his diary notes hundreds or thousands of miles away, Sherman also would sit down at the same time and wait quietly. Sherman was to record whatever impressions came to him. Sir Hubert would mail his diary notes to Sherman, and Sherman would mail copies of his own notes to the psychologist, Dr. Gardner Murphy, an American who pioneered in the study of psi. (Psi is a shortened form of the word *psychic,* which means literally "of the mind or soul.") Then the sets were kept for comparison. After the expedition the men found that many of Sherman's remarks agreed exactly with entries in Sir Hubert's diary.

One night when he sat down at the scheduled time, Sherman felt as if he suddenly had a toothache. He sensed that Sir Hubert's tooth, three thousand miles away, was the one that actually was aching. Sherman wrote down "Have feeling you have had a bad toothache today. . . ." A few weeks later Sherman received Sir Hubert's diary notes for that day in the mail. They included the entry "Had severe toothache today. Flew to Edmonton to get tooth filled. . . ."

On another evening Sherman wrote that Sir Hubert had made a forced airplane landing at the town of Regina. Sherman "saw" Sir Hubert appearing at an Armistice Day dance there in a dress suit. Although he was sure Sir Hubert didn't have such a suit with him, Sherman put down his strange impression anyway. Later Sir Hubert's mailed report matched exactly. In it he said he had been forced down in that town, and while there someone had loaned him a dress suit so he could attend the dance.

Sherman and Sir Hubert found that the accuracy of the telepathic impressions had little to do with the extent of the distance between them. The impressions were most accurate when there was a strong emotion involved. The toothache, the only one Sir Hubert had on the entire trip, and the forced plane landing were both extremely emotional experiences. Accordingly, Sherman sensed what was happening to Sir Hubert at these times.

Just as Sir Hubert Wilkins and Harold Sherman were able to convey diary notes through telepathy, other teams have had some success at sending and receiving simple drawings. Such a team was the noted author Upton Sinclair and his wife. Sinclair found that his wife was able to pick up his thoughts unusually well. They worked out a series of experiments in which Sinclair would make a simple drawing and his wife, without seeing it and without knowing what was to be drawn, would try to make a copy of it. In some of the tests Mrs. Sinclair was in a neighboring room with doors closed and could not see her husband's drawing. In others she was as far as forty miles away. The distance seemed to have no particular effect on the results. After nearly three hundred tests had been made, Sinclair wrote a book about the experiments called *Mental Radio.*

Four pairs of drawings from the book are shown on page 435. In each pair the one on the left is the drawing made by Upton Sinclair, and the one on the right is the drawing his wife made from her

The sketches at the left were made by Mr. Sinclair. The matching sketches at the right were made by Mrs. Sinclair.

mental impression without seeing his. These four pairs suggest the kinds of results that can be called hits or near matches. The first drawing is of a knight's helmet, and Mrs. Sinclair's impression is an almost exact duplicate. The next pair shows Mr. Sinclair's drawing of a volcano. His wife thought of a beetle with feelers but drew it in the shape of a volcano. In the next pair Mr. Sinclair drew a fishhook, and his wife drew two flowers in the shape of fishhooks. The last pair shows Mr. Sinclair's drawing of an umbrella and Mrs. Sinclair's drawing, which has much the same shape. She said of this one, "I feel that it is a snake crawling out of something, but it looks like a cat's tail."

The fact that many of Mrs. Sinclair's impressions were similar to her husband's drawings, but also different, tells us much about the nature of ESP. As with the famous Sherman-Wilkins experiments, emotions seemed to be very important. The umbrella handle was interpreted as a snake because Mrs. Sinclair always had been afraid of snakes, and this shape reminded her of the fear. The beetle and the flowers also suggested Mrs. Sinclair's feelings about living things.

DISCUSSION

1. What is meant by telepathy? When are telepathic impressions the strongest?
2. Give two examples of telepathic impressions that Sir Hubert Wilkins and Harold Sherman were able to convey to each other.
3. Why do you think distance seems to be an unimportant factor in telepathy?
4. Do you think the fact that the Sinclairs were married, and therefore knew each other well, had anything to do with their ability to convey messages to each other? Why do you think that?
5. Do you think a person can learn telepathy, or is it strictly an innate characteristic? Why do you think that?

SKILL LESSON 7

IDENTIFYING PROPAGANDA TECHNIQUES

Some reading materials, such as stories, have been written primarily to provide enjoyment. Other materials, such as many of your school textbooks, have been written to provide information. But some reading matter has been deliberately written to influence your opinion or behavior, to cause you to be for or against something or someone.

In the following political advertisement what do you think the writer is trying to influence you to do?

Joe Brown has clearly shown that he is for all the people, not just a few. If he is elected next Tuesday, he will be the finest District Attorney our city has ever had.

The writer is certainly not trying to entertain you. If he simply intended to inform you about Joe Brown, he could have provided many other kinds of information even in that short advertisement. The advertisement is obviously intended to influence you to vote for Joe Brown.

Material which is primarily written to get you to be for or against something or someone is called PROPAGANDA. Sometimes, as in the above advertisement, its purpose is quite clear to the reader. At other times, however, the writer may be so skillful that you have to read very carefully before you know that he is trying to influence your opinion.

If you are going to make choices wisely on the basis of your reading, you should be able to decide when a writer is trying to influence you.

You may choose to think the way he wants you to or you may not, but you cannot make this decision wisely unless you are able to recognize how the writer is using propaganda to direct your thinking.

You will be more skillful in recognizing propaganda as you read if you know some of the most common propaganda techniques. One such technique is called the "Bandwagon" approach. The writer hopes to influence you by causing you to think, "Everyone else is doing it; maybe I should too."

Read the following advertisement that appeared on the television page of a newspaper to see how the writer uses the "Bandwagon" approach:

Tonight, 100,000 of your friends and neighbors will be watching "Clyde" on Channel 9.

The writer does not tell you what the television show will be about. He doesn't even ask you to watch it. But, by telling you that so many other people will be watching it, he hopes that you will want to "get on the bandwagon" too.

Another propaganda technique is the "Testimonial." Here the writer uses an endorsement of an idea, a course of action, or a product by someone he thinks you may admire or respect. He hopes that you will then support it too.

The following political advertisement is an example of this approach:

Bonnie Smith, the lovely television and movie star, says, "President Watson has shown in his first term that he is the finest President our country has ever had. I will support the President for reelection."

The writer of that advertisement hopes to influence you to vote for President Watson simply because Bonnie Smith intends to vote for him. He hopes that her testimonial will influence you, even though she may have no special qualifications to judge which person is most suited to be President.

"Transfer" is another propaganda technique that you sometimes see, particularly in advertisements. While in the "Testimonial" approach a well-known figure actually endorses a person, a thing, or an

438

action, the "Transfer" approach simply uses a pictured association, which is intended to influence you.

For example, the following picture shows Sam Padding, the well-known football quarterback, standing beside his brand-new Evernick lawnmower:

Although Sam is not telling you that you should buy an Evernick lawnmower or even that he likes it, the writer of the advertisement hopes that you will transfer any admiration you have for Sam to the lawnmower.

Still another propaganda technique is called "Repetition." As you might suspect, in this approach the writer hopes that the repetition of a word or phrase will cause you to remember it.

In the following political advertisement note how the writer uses this technique:

Bob Smart is for the little man.
Bob Smart is for the big man.
Bob Smart is for every man.
Bob Smart is for you.
Vote Smart: Bob Smart.

Although the writer has told you little or nothing about Bob Smart that would help you decide for yourself whether you should vote for him, he has used his name six times in five short lines. He hopes that this repetition will cause you to remember the name Bob Smart and to vote for him on election day.

Sometimes a writer hopes to influence you to be for or against something by using "Emotional Words." In this technique words are very carefully chosen, not to inform you but to arouse your emotions.

The "Emotional Words" technique is often used in advertising products, as in this example:

Luxurious suits in rich fabrics and exciting patterns. Handsomely tailored with luxury details. Only $44.95.

The writer of that advertisement hopes to persuade you to buy a suit. To accomplish that purpose, he used words and phrases that he believes will appeal to your emotions — *luxurious, rich fabrics, exciting patterns, handsomely tailored,* and *luxury details.*

The following paragraph is from a "Letters to the Editor" column in a newspaper. Notice how the writer has used emotional words to try to influence your thinking.

The biased editorial in favor of increasing the already burdensome tax load in our city has many unforgivable mistakes. Our overstaffed city street department does not need more loafing employees. Their wild story that they need more hard-earned tax dollars is stupidly untrue.

By using such words as *biased, burdensome,* and *unforgivable,* the writer hopes to stir your emotions. You can probably see this more clearly by reading the following paragraph and comparing it with the one above. The one below contains exactly the same information as the one you have just read; however, the emotional words have been left out.

> The editorial in favor of increasing the tax load in our city has many mistakes. Our city street department does not need more employees. Their story that they need more tax dollars is untrue.

The second paragraph clearly indicates the writer's disagreement with the editorial, but the position is stated without resorting to words designed to appeal to the emotions.

"Name Calling," as its title implies, is designed to substitute the calling of names for information. The following paragraph from a "Letters to the Editor" column in a newspaper shows one way in which this technique is used:

> The voters of this city should show Mayor Cratchett exactly what they think of him when they go to the polls next week. Mayor Cratchett has been a burden to the taxpayer. He has been a dictator in his dealings with city employees and dishonest in his dealings with the public.

The writer of that letter obviously wants to influence you to vote against Mayor Cratchett. However, instead of providing specific information about Mayor Cratchett's weaknesses or his opponent's strengths, he has resorted to using such words as *burden, dictator,* and *dishonest* with the hope that these will influence your opinion.

Still another propaganda technique that you sometimes see is called "Faulty Cause and Effect." In this approach the writer tries to get you to believe that some action or situation has caused a certain result, even though no relationship between the two is actually explained.

For example, read the paragraph on the following page from a political speech as it was reprinted in a newspaper.

Since I became governor of this state, many good things have happened. We now have more people employed than ever before. The average family income has gone up. People are now able to buy things that they couldn't afford before. The voters of this state should elect me to another four-year term.

The writer has strongly hinted that *because* he was governor all the good things he mentioned have happened. Although this may be true, he has given no evidence to support it. All those things might have happened whether he was governor or not. He has not shown that his election as governor was the cause for the desirable things that happened while he was in office.

At the beginning of this lesson you learned that propaganda is a method of trying to influence you to be for or against something or someone. Although most of the examples you have read thus far might be considered as "bad" propaganda because they tried to hide information from you, propaganda may also be used for your benefit.

For example, a professional organization of dentists might try to influence you to take proper care of your teeth; or a health organization might try to influence you to drink orange juice because it is good for your health. Since such efforts are trying to influence your thinking, they could be called propaganda, but the results of your being influenced by such propaganda could be beneficial to you.

The important point is that you should be able to recognize propaganda when you read it. You may or may not decide to act in the way that the writer hopes you will, but, whatever your decision, it should be made with an understanding of the methods being used to influence your thinking.

Discussion

Help your class answer these questions:
1. What is propaganda? Why should you be able to recognize it in your reading?

2. How is a writer trying to influence you when he uses the "Band-wagon" technique?
3. How are the "Testimonial" and "Transfer" techniques alike? How are they different?
4. What is the "Repetition" approach in propaganda?
5. When a writer uses the "Emotional Words" approach, what is he trying to do to influence you?
6. What is the "Name Calling" technique?
7. What is a writer trying to get you to believe when he uses the "Faulty Cause and Effect" approach?
8. Is all propaganda designed to be harmful to the reader? Why or why not?

On your own

The picture below illustrates a propaganda technique. Write the numeral 1 on a sheet of paper and beside it the name of the technique.

Here are six other examples of propaganda techniques. In each example try to identify the particular propaganda technique used by the writer. On the same sheet of paper number and write the names of the techniques.

2. The softest, warmest, most comfortable sheets in the world are made by the Eversoft Company. As you quietly slip into a blissful sleep on these heavenly sheets, you will know the meaning of true peace.
3. Bill Clutz, a famous home-run hitter for the Farm City Redbirds, says, "Whenever I brush my teeth, I always use Soapy toothpaste. You should too."
4. Each day thousands of people are discovering the pleasure and the healthful benefits of drinking milk. Have you discovered milk yet?
5. The new Crashmobile automobile is the finest Crashmobile that the Crashmobile Company has built in its long history of building Crashmobiles.
6. Since we introduced our new line of bread in this city, the number of tooth cavities in children under ten has gone down.
7. Jim Hill should not be reelected. He is a wasteful spendthrift and a puppet for big business.

Checking your work

If you are asked to do so, read aloud one or more of your answers. If you made a mistake in any, find out why it is a mistake.

MR. STRANG FINDS THE ANSWERS

by William Brittain

Mr. Strang walked up the steps through a haze that might have been fog and onto the decorated and flag-draped platform. Three men wearing high silk hats and cutaways smiled at him. He wondered if his old tweed jacket with the leather patches at the elbows was suitable for the occasion, but there really hadn't been time to change. Amid thunderous applause he was awarded the Nobel prize in chemistry, and then the main speaker rose and approached the microphone, which would carry his words of praise for Leonard Strang, Aldershot High School's veteran science teacher, all over the planet. . . .

"Mr. Strang, waddya use lime-water for?"

With an almost audible "pop" Mr. Strang's dream of glory faded into the reality of the classroom. He raised his head and considered his Lilies of the Field.

Guy Oringer, Ward Hilditch, and Alan Speed — in mentally dubbing them the Lilies of the Field, Mr. Strang was only half correct. For while it was certain that in the academic sense they toiled not, their ability to spin was amply proved by fantastic yarns concerning undone homework and late entrances to class. In fact, it was their unique ability to

Copyright © 1967 by Davis Publications, Inc. Reprinted by permission of the author and the author's agents, Scott Meredith Literary Agency, Inc., 580 Fifth Avenue, New York, New York 10036.

procrastinate that accounted for their presence in Mr. Strang's classroom at a time when all other students and teachers had long since left.

"Carbon dioxide bubbled through limewater will turn it a milky white, Guy," Mr. Strang replied wearily, "and if it doesn't work, you get an incomplete in chemistry. That experiment should have been done two weeks ago."

"Well, you see, Mr. Strang," he said, "I was sick when you assigned it, and —"

"And in about five minutes I'm going home whether you're finished or not. I hate to hurry you, boys, but it's after five o'clock, and you've been here since three thirty. Now either finish those experiments or take the consequences."

Each boy bent to his assigned task with a diligence that would have guaranteed a listing on the honor roll, if the diligence could have been maintained for more than ten minutes at a time.

Finally, the three approached Mr. Strang's desk. Ward Hilditch held out a flask of Benedict's solution with one hand while he nervously inspected the fingers of the other in a fruitless search for a fingernail that hadn't already been gnawed to the quick. Guy Oringer presented a beaker of limewater of a satisfactory whitish color with the élan of one who had discovered a cure for an incurable disease. And with a cackle that any mad scien-

tist in a horror movie would have been proud to utter, Alan Speed exhibited a lump of black, spongy carbon as proof that he had been able to separate table sugar into its component elements.

"Gentlemen, I'd like to say I'm proud of you," sighed Mr. Strang. "Unfortunately, the words would stick in my throat. However, you will be allowed to take the final examination next week."

"Will you tell my mom and dad I can take the test?" asked Ward, still nibbling on a nonexistent fingernail. "They were real sore when they found out I might have to go to summer school."

"I've already written letters to your families, telling them the good news," Mr. Strang replied, "but up to now it's been questionable whether they'd ever be sent. I'll mail them on my way home. Now wait until I get my briefcase, and I'll walk you as far as the door of the school."

He went to a door at the rear of the classroom, which led to the chemistry storage closet, where he had left his briefcase. He opened the door wide, took a deep breath, and stepped back, coughing and gasping.

"What's the matter, Mr. Strang?" asked Alan, finding it hard to keep from laughing.

Quickly removing his black-rimmed glasses, Mr. Strang rubbed his eyes with his handkerchief. "Ether!" he gasped when he could catch his breath. "The whole closet reeks of ether! Is this your idea of a joke, Mr. Speed?"

Alan's smile faded from his face as he understood what the teacher was implying. "Oh, gee, Mr. Strang," he wailed. "I didn't do anything. It's just that you were hopping around rubbing at your eyes and — well, you looked so funny that — oh, gee!"

Holding the handkerchief firmly over his nose, Mr. Strang entered the closet. It was deep enough so that he was out of the boys' sight for several seconds. When he came back through the door, his mouth was set in a grim line, and his eyes glittered menacingly. "Ward Hilditch, Guy Oringer, Alan Speed — sit down!" he said slowly and distinctly, pointing to each one in turn with a rigid index finger.

Trouble! Mr. Strang usually called students by their first names. On rare occasions when formality was necessary, he used last names but always preceded them with "Mr." or "Miss." The last time he had addressed a student by both first and last name, that student had been expelled. The three boys knew that whatever was the matter, it involved something more serious than spilled ether.

"I've cleaned up the ether," said the teacher thickly, "and almost asphyxiated myself in the process. The fumes should dissipate in a few minutes. Then I have something for you to see."

The classroom clock ticked off three minutes, while Mr. Strang fanned the closet door back and forth vigorously to force fresher air into the small room. Then, he beckoned to the boys.

Most of the wall space in the storage closet was lined with shelves containing a variety of scientific supplies and apparatus. An empty ether can lay in the tiny sink along with several cleaning rags. In one corner of the room was a coatrack on which hung Mr. Strang's overcoat and battered felt hat.

"Look!" said the teacher, pointing one slender finger at the floor below the coatrack, where his briefcase lay on its side. And then the boys knew the reason for his anger.

Although the briefcase was still locked, one side was wide open. It had been cut through with a knife or some other sharp instrument.

"Now who did that?" barked Mr. Strang. For one of the few times in his teaching career, he was dangerously close to losing his temper.

Silence. The boys looked at one another. Even Alan Speed, who normally had a quip for every occasion, knew better than to open his mouth. But finally Guy Oringer asked, "Why would anybody do a thing like that?"

"Correction, Mr. Oringer," said Mr. Strang. "The question is, Why would one of you three do a thing like that? I didn't put my briefcase in here until after you were in the room, and no one else came in.

"But for the benefit of the two innocent parties, let me explain. Inside

447

that tan briefcase is — was — a copy of the final exam in chemistry, which you will take next week. As the senior member of the department I was going to take it home this evening to check it for possible typographic errors, a fact that was not unknown to the students. Attached to the examination was a test key — a single sheet of paper containing the answers to all the questions except the essays. I'd be very much surprised if one of those items isn't missing — or both of them!"

Quickly the teacher leafed through the contents of the mutilated case. A set of essays, still uncorrected, was in order. A packet of letters still had its rubber band around it. Privately, Mr. Strang hoped that the letter to the parents of one of the three boys might be missing, but no such luck. Even the final exam was there. The answer key, however, was gone.

"Well, at least, whichever one of you took it was intelligent enough not to try to get out with the exam itself," said the teacher. "Ten pages would have been quite a wad to slip past me. I suppose the guilty one expected to be well away from here before I discovered my damaged briefcase."

"Does — does this mean we can't take the final exam after all?" asked Alan, now almost in tears.

"That exam took more than six weeks to make up," replied Mr. Strang. "It's impossible to replace it at this late date. And if there's a possibility of the answers having been ex-posed, it may be that nobody will take the final exam. Now who has that answer key?"

Mr. Strang suspected that he would get nowhere by appealing to the boys' sense of honor. In his years of teaching he had tried it too many times with at best only negative results; he was no longer shocked by the idea that teen-agers are not wholly honest and truthful.

"May I suggest," he continued, "that each of you submit to a search?"

The boys gave frightened nods. A few minutes later they were dressed only in their shorts, and all their clothing had been examined; the contents of their pockets were on Mr. Strang's desk, and the answer key was still missing. Guy Oringer and Alan Speed laughed nervously at their near-naked condition, while Ward Hilditch munched at the end of one finger and stared at the floor.

"Protozoa, Metazoa, Porifera," muttered Mr. Strang. This recitation of animal phyla made him feel no better. He had lost the answers, and he had asked three of his students to strip in his classroom. There would be telephone calls from irate parents. And Marvin W. Guthrey, Aldershot High School's principal, was not known for taking a firm stand in adversity. He would call Mr. Strang to his office the following morning. The teacher winced at the thought of Guthrey's sarcasm, which could cut like a knife.

A knife — that was it. Whoever cut

open the briefcase must have used a knife. All he had to do was search the three piles of belongings on his desk.

As he did this, Mr. Strang smiled broadly at his own cleverness. Ward Hilditch had a folding knife. It was tiny, but when the teacher got it open at the cost of a broken thumbnail, he found that its scratched and battered blade would easily have been able to cut through the soft leather of the briefcase.

When he had finished sorting through the second pile, Mr. Strang's smile slipped a bit, for Guy Oringer also carried a knife. It was bulky and had enough gadgets to equip a machine shop. Guy insisted on displaying each of them and explaining its use. There were no less than six different tools that might have been used to slit the case.

By the time Mr. Strang examined Alan Speed's belongings, he was right back where he had started. By pressing a catch on Alan's knife, the teacher almost succeeded in amputating one of his fingers. Switchblades were forbidden in Aldershot High School, but this did not concern Mr. Strang at the moment. The fact was that each of the three boys carried equipment capable of having cut open the case.

Mr. Strang looked at the boys. The room still reeked of ether, and his head had begun to ache. The ether bothered him in another way. What was the point of it? The can had been kept on the highest shelf in the closet, so it certainly hadn't been spilled accidentally. Whoever had slit the case must have used the ether for something. But what? Was it supposed to put the teacher to sleep?

Mr. Strang shook his head in annoyance and spoke to the boys. "I don't suppose any of you remember who was the last one to be in the storage closet before I went in?" he drawled, his voice dripping with irony.

They didn't.

"Well, at least I know the answer key won't be going out with you," he continued. "I'll go on with my search after you leave. Now get dressed."

After he had escorted the boys, once again fully clothed, to the door of the school, Mr. Strang checked the classroom and the storage closet with a thoroughness that would have turned a customs inspector green with envy. He scrutinized the desks, he opened and peered into the bottles of chemicals, he probed the cracks in the woodwork, and he pulled down the window shades to see if the missing sheet of paper had been rolled up in one of them. Mr. Strang even searched his own pockets on the off chance that he himself had inadvertently taken the answers from his briefcase.

At the end of a frustrating hour he reluctantly came to two inescapable conclusions:

First, none of the boys could possibly have taken the answer key away with him when he left the classroom.

And second, the missing answers were no longer in either the classroom or the storage closet.

For a moment Mr. Strang seriously considered the possibility that one of the boys had chewed and swallowed it. But there would have been no point in doing that *before* the teacher had found his damaged briefcase, and there had been no opportunity afterward. Marching into the closet, he jammed his arms into the sleeves of his coat, crushed his hat down onto his head, and then, in a burst of irritation, he kicked viciously at the briefcase. It skittered across the black-tile floor, and Mr. Strang saw the glint of a metal object that had remained hidden beneath the briefcase throughout his search.

His stiff joints cracking, he knelt and picked up the object. It was a dime. And Mr. Strang was sure it hadn't been there when he had first placed the briefcase on the floor. He put the coin on the briefcase and shoved at it with a finger, listening to the small, sharp clink it made when it hit the floor. "Funny," he muttered. "It seems to me that if it was dropped, anybody in here would have heard it hit the floor." Thoughtfully he put the dime in his pocket.

Mr. Strang consigned the three boys, the answer key, and Mr. Guthrey's temper to the devil and prepared to leave. Absent-mindedly he grasped the briefcase by the handle, lifted it, and was rewarded by a cascade of papers, which poured through the gaping hole in its side. Unmarked assignments, the bundle of letters, and the final examination lay strewn across the floor of the closet.

"Oh, Coelenterata (sĭ-lĕn-tə′rāt′ə)!" he cried out at this latest outrage against his dignity. He retrieved the final exam, put it into a cupboard, and snapped the lock. Then he gathered the uncorrected papers into a pile, folded the pile in half, and stuffed it into a coat pocket. He debated whether or not to mail the letters on his way home, decided that since he had to go to the drugstore anyway he might as well, and crammed them into his pocket on top of the other papers. "With my luck," he growled, "I'll drop the wrong thing through the slot, and tomorrow there'll be twenty-eight essays delivered to homes all over town."

He walked out of the building to his battered automobile. Roaring angrily out of the parking lot, he yanked at the steering wheel and headed toward the business district of Aldershot. There he stole a parking space from under the headlights of a waiting taxi. Then, still fuming over the loss of the answers, he completed his errands, treating the druggist with lofty disdain and leaving the man behind the stamp window at the post office an amazed and innocent victim of one of Mr. Strang's rare temper tantrums.

When he reached his rooming house, he rocketed into the driveway, narrowly missing the yellow cat, which belonged to his landlady, Mrs.

Mackey, and stopped the car with a screech of brakes. He entered the house prepared to oppose any views Mrs. Mackey might make concerning the weather, only to find her on her hands and knees, fumbling in the pile of the living-room rug.

Mrs. Mackey knew better than to ask what the trouble was; she could almost see the steam coming out from under Mr. Strang's collar. She limited herself to a noncommittal, "Hello," and continued prowling over the rug, an envelope clutched in one fist.

"Picking daisies, Mrs. Mackey?" asked Mr. Strang sarcastically, and was immediately ashamed of himself.

Mrs. Mackey stopped, picked up something from the rug, and placed it in the envelope. "Not daisies — pearls," she answered.

"What?"

"Pearls. The string on my necklace broke, and the pearls went all over the rug. I just found the last one." She held up the envelope triumphantly.

Mr. Strang nodded and headed for the stairway. He was halfway up when he turned his head to where Mrs. Mackey, in the living room below, was pouring the pearls into the palm of her left hand. A wide smile crossed the teacher's face.

"Of course," he said to himself. "That must have been the way it was done."

He climbed the rest of the stairs, did a little dance step at the top, and said happily, "Leonard Strang, you are a fat-headed idiot."

Once in his room he took a copy of his class list from a bureau, looked up Ward Hilditch's telephone number, and began to dial the instrument next to his bed. "Mr. Hilditch, please," he said a moment later. "This is Mr. Strang, Ward's chemistry teacher."

He made two more phone calls — to the other two fathers — and then sat back to await his visitors.

It was past eight o'clock when Mrs. Mackey called Mr. Strang to greet the first of his guests. "Mr. Oringer," he said to the scowling man removing his overcoat, "good of you to come."

"Good, my foot!" rumbled Paul Oringer. "What did you expect me to do? The idea, threatening to fail Guy without even letting him take the final examination." Removing a comb from his pocket, Oringer began to draw his hair over an incipient bald spot. "I heard about what happened in school today," he continued as he combed. "You should be ashamed of yourself, making Guy take his clothes off in the classroom. As a lawyer, Mr. Strang, I ought to —"

Whatever Mr. Oringer was planning for the teacher was interrupted by the arrival of Benjamin Hilditch. Hilditch's hands shook visibly as he unbuttoned his coat, and he had a habit of clutching at one ear, much as a drowning man might grasp a life preserver. Mr. Strang remembered Ward Hilditch's almost nonexistent fingernails and wondered if his father's ear was the adult equivalent of a "security blanket."

Before Hilditch could do more than mumble a polite greeting, Winslow Speed entered the living room. More reasonable than Oringer and more vocal than Hilditch, he admitted that his boy might be capable of stealing the answers, but he wanted to know what proof the teacher had of his son's guilt.

Mr. Strang led the three men to his room. Warning them not to trip on the threadbare spot in his rug, he offered them seats, while he himself perched on the edge of the bed.

"Now I'm willing to keep an open mind about this, Mr. Strang," began Oringer. "Only tell me, where do you get off, acting like a —"

"Paul Oringer, close your mouth," said Mr. Strang. "You always were too talkative, even when I taught you physics in high school. I see maturity hasn't changed you much."

"That's one on you, Paul," chortled Hilditch, still holding his ear.

"Look, Mr. Strang, you called us here, so let's get down to business," said Speed. "I'm not too happy about the way you handled things with our boys today — at least, from the way Alan tells it. But I'd like to hear your side of the story."

"For the benefit of anyone whose child may have given a slightly biased view of the day's events, let me review exactly what did happen," said the teacher. Swiftly he described what had gone on in the classroom before and after the disappearance of the answer key. "So you see," he concluded, "it's obvious not only that one of the boys made arrangements to get the answers but that those arrangements were successful."

"You made my boy strip," said Oringer. "Right there in the classroom."

"Oh, come off it, Paul," said Speed. "This thing involves every kid who's taking chemistry. What did you expect him to do, just let someone leave with all the answers? What about it, Hilditch? If you caught three guys in your store, and you knew one of 'em was a shoplifter, what would you do? Just let 'em walk out on you?"

"No, I suppose not," said Hilditch nervously. Mr. Strang was afraid the ear would come away in his hand.

"That's very different!" shouted Oringer. "Mr. Strang is —"

"How is it different?" asked Mr. Strang softly. "The stolen answer key represents, I'd say, a great deal more work on the part of various individuals than one of the keys Mr. Hilditch sells in his hardware store."

"Look," said Oringer, "kids are going to cheat, right? You did it, I did it, we all do it. Can it be that wrong?"

"Yes," said Mr. Strang simply.

"Oh, come on!" Oringer shook his head impatiently. "Everything today is test, test, test. Schools, jobs, the army — everything. And if a kid fails, the doors start closing. All he gets are the dirty jobs."

"I'm inclined to agree that testing can be overdone," said Mr. Strang, "but does that mean we should do away with it entirely? Mr. Oringer, if you took on a partner in your legal work, wouldn't you sometimes like to know what kind of job he was doing, just out of curiosity if for no other reason? Most businesses have a quality check on the products they manufacture, don't they? And the product which, hopefully, the schools produce is educated citizens."

"Oh, for Pete's sake, be reasonable. Do you mean to tell me, Mr. Strang, that you never sneaked a look at an answer while you were taking an exam? Never?"

"What we're talking about," said the teacher, "is not a weak-willed individual suddenly giving in to temptation. We are talking about a deliberate plan to steal —"

"I still don't think it's stealing," said Oringer.

"What would you call it, Paul?" Winslow Speed asked grimly.

"Why – why — "

"It is stealing and nothing less," said Mr. Strang. "It was the theft of a year's work in chemistry from those students who may not now be allowed to take the final exam."

"All right," said Oringer in his best cross-examination manner, "let's say it was – er – stealing and get down to cases. I'm even willing, under the circumstances, to overlook the impromptu striptease in the classroom. But I'd like to ask one question: Why should all three boys be punished for what only one of them did?"

"A good point," said Mr. Strang. "So if one of you should be on hand when the thief picks up the missing answer key, we'd all know who the guilty one is, wouldn't we?"

The three men sat forward in their seats. "You mean you know where the answers are?" asked Speed finally.

"Yes, I know."

"Then why don't you get them?"

"Impossible. The men guarding them —"

"What!" Paul Oringer stood up and looked down at the teacher. "You mean whoever stole the answers had a gang working for him?"

"In a sense, yes."

"I think you're cracking up, Mr. Strang," said Oringer, sitting down again.

Benjamin Hilditch detached his hand from his ear and drummed his fingers nervously on the arm of the chair. "This is more serious than I thought," he said. "A gang. I had no idea. . . . You can prove what you're saying, of course."

"Certainly." Mr. Strang stood up, jerked his black-rimmed glasses from his nose, polished them on his necktie, and held them tightly between the thumb and forefinger of his right hand. Thrusting his left hand deep into his jacket pocket, he looked at the men in front of him. Oringer vaguely remembered Mr. Strang performing these rites in the classroom.

"Fact one," began the teacher, holding up the glasses dramatically,

"the missing answers did not leave the room when the boys left. Even a single sheet of paper has a certain amount of bulk to it, however tightly it is folded. And I went over the clothing and possessions of the boys with a fine-toothed comb. No, the answer key was still in school when I searched the classroom and the storage closet."

"Then, why didn't the key turn up?" asked Speed.

"Because there was one place I didn't search."

"All right, Mr. Strang, I'll bite. First you say you looked *all* over the classroom and the closet. Now you say you didn't look *everywhere*. If that's the case, why don't you go back right now and get it?"

"Because it's no longer there."

There was a murmuring of voices. Then Oringer quieted the others. "You mean the guilty boy sneaked back and —"

"Of course not. Even if he'd been able to unlock my door, one of the custodians would have been sure to see him."

"Then who took the answers out of the room?" shouted Oringer.

Mr. Strang looked ruefully at the men. "I did," he said softly.

"You? Oh, come on, Mr. Strang, make sense. You took the answer key, but now a gang has it, and you know where it is but you can't find it. What's going on, anyway?"

"I didn't find the key in my classroom," said Mr. Strang, "because

it never left my briefcase — at least, until I myself took it out."

"But you said you *looked* in your briefcase."

"I did. But not in the right place."

After a short silence Hilditch snapped his fingers. "The letters!" he cried.

"Go to the head of the class, Mr. Hilditch," said Mr. Strang. "Of course. The answer key was in one of those sealed envelopes I had prepared to mail to you three."

"Then the 'gang' is —"

"Our faithful postmen," replied Mr. Strang. " 'Neither sleet, nor storm, nor hail,' and so on. It was a beautiful plan, really. Once the thief put the answer key in the envelope addressed to his own parents, I, myself, would carry it out, mail it, and the next day it would be delivered right to his door. All he had to do was be the first one to get the mail. He would be able to take the final exam, if it were given, and I would have no reason to suspect him more than the other two. It would have worked, too, if I hadn't seen my landlady earlier this evening putting some pearls into an envelope. That got me thinking about what else might have been stuffed into an envelope — and suddenly the whole scheme was crystal clear."

"Wait a minute," said Oringer. "You said the envelopes were sealed. How could they have been opened without tearing the paper, to say nothing about resealing them?"

456

"Ether," said Mr. Strang. "What do you think of when I mention ether?"

"Why, putting people to sleep."

"Unfortunately, that was my first reaction too. But ether is also an excellent solvent. A very small amount applied to the outside of the envelope flap would have softened the glue to the point where the envelope could be opened. It would have been easy for the thief to insert the answer key and then reseal the letter. As soon as the ether dried, the glue would harden again, and there would be nothing to show what had been done."

It was Winslow Speed who finally asked the question in the minds of the three fathers. "Who did it, Mr. Strang? Which one of our boys —"

"I don't know, Mr. Speed."

"What?"

"I don't know. But it shouldn't be too hard for you to find out. I suggest all three of you make a point of being on hand when your mail is delivered for the next day or so. There will be a letter from me addressed to each of you. But, in the case of the guilty boy, the parent will get something additional. Finding the answer key in your envelope should be convincing enough proof for any of you. From then on, whatever action you wish to take will be up to you."

When the men had left, Mr. Strang sat at his desk, idly flipping the dime he had found under the briefcase. As proof, the dime wouldn't hold up in a court of law for thirty seconds. After all, it might have been dropped in the closet accidentally. But the science teacher was sure that the thief had taken the dime out of his pocket deliberately.

It was because of the knife, of course. Two of the knives had opened easily — one much too easily, thought Mr. Strang, remembering the near miss with the switchblade. But one knife had been hard to open. It was tiny, and the blade was difficult to grip in its closed position. It would have been difficult to open it, he thought, especially if its owner had bitten his fingernails to a point where they were too short to hook under the notch in the tiny blade. He would have needed a tool — and a dime was thin enough to insert in the notch and flick the blade open.

But Mr. Strang had not had the heart to mention it and break a father's heart in front of the other men. "I must be getting old," Mr. Strang whispered to himself. "Now what should I do about giving the students the final exam?"

It was two days later when he found the package on his desk. Tearing off the wrapping paper, he found a new and expensive leather briefcase with the initials *L. S.* stamped in gold on one side.

There were two pieces of paper in it. One of them had printed at the top: *Chemistry — Final Examination — Aldershot High School.* The other was a handwritten letter that was addressed to Mr. Strang. It read:

Mr. Strang,

My father told me what you said the other night. But I saw the postman a block before he got to our house, and he gave me the mail with your letter in it. I didn't have any more ether to get it open, but the steam from a teakettle worked just as well, so my father was pretty happy when he opened the envelope and there was nothing inside but your letter. As for me I haven't been too happy about anything since I took the answers to the exam out of your briefcase.

Honest, I didn't look at any of the answers, but if you don't want me to take the final exam, I won't squawk.

And I'll accept any punishment the school feels I've got coming. But is there any way to keep my folks from finding out who took the answers? I'm not afraid of what they'll do to me, but it would just about kill my father and mother to find out what I did.

The letter was signed by Ward Hilditch.

Mr. Strang looked at the letter again, remembering a scared little man tugging nervously at one ear. Maybe something *could* be worked out. . . .

He decided that he would have to drastically alter his dim views concerning honor among teen-agers.

DISCUSSION

1. How did Mr. Strang plan to notify the parents that the boys would be allowed to take the final examination? How was this plan the key to the mystery?
2. How did the landlady's broken necklace help Mr. Strang in solving the mystery?
3. How did the ether and the dime that were found underneath the briefcase fit into the mystery?
4. Why did Ward Hilditch intercept the letter to his father? How did he remove the answer key without his father knowing it?
5. What effect do you think this event had on each of the boys?
6. Was there any point in the story where you guessed which boy had taken the answer key? If so, where?
7. Do you agree with Mr. Oringer or Mr. Strang about the value of testing? Why do you think as you do?

8. Do you think that taking the answer key was stealing or cheating or both? Why do you think that?
9. Do you think Ward Hilditch did the right thing when he opened his father's mail? Why or why not?
10. Why do some pupils try to cheat on examinations? Do you think doing so can ever be justified? Why or why not?

AUTHOR

William Brittain, the author of the story you have just read, is a junior-high schoolteacher. After reading many stories in popular mystery magazines, Mr. Brittain decided he could write better ones himself. Unfortunately, this opinion was not shared right away by the editors to whom he sent his first attempts. It took him seven years to sell his first Mr. Strang story to *Ellery Queen's Mystery Magazine.* Since then he has written and sold many Mr. Strang stories, including *Mr. Strang Pulls a Switch, Mr. Strang Sees a Play,* and *Mr. Strang Takes a Trip.*

Mr. Brittain, his wife, and two children live in New York State in a tiny village, which he says can only be found on a very large map.

the sniffle

In spite of her sniffle,
Isabel's chiffle.
Some girls with a sniffle
Would be weepy and tiffle;
They would look awful,
Like a rained-on waffle,
But Isabel's chiffle
In spite of her sniffle.
Her nose is more red
With a cold in her head,
But then, to be sure,
Her eyes are bluer.
Some girls with a snuffle,
Their tempers are uffle,
But when Isabel's snivelly
She's snivelly civilly,
And when she is snuffly
She's perfectly luffly.

OGDEN NASH

The Long Iron Trail

by Daniel Chu and Samuel Chu

California in the 1860's was an exciting place to be. The Western frontier was being settled, and the California gold rush was in its final surge. The government was anxious to join the vast, teeming territory with the East through some means of transportation that would facilitate travel and also provide a more direct trade route to the Orient. The fruit of this idea was the transcontinental railroad. This monumental achievement involved the efforts of thousands of men. The Chinese contributed most vitally to the building of the railroad. Thousands had immigrated to California in search of gold. After the gold supply dwindled, many Chinese remained permanently in the new country, working at a number of jobs, such as laundering, saddlemaking, farming, and woodchopping. Their resourcefulness, however, did not always assure them of steady jobs. Often the Chinese were employed only in emergency situations, when there was a scarcity of other workers or when the work to be done was dangerous and difficult. The story of their perseverance and courage under trying conditions is told in the following excerpt.

On July 1, 1862, President Abraham Lincoln signed into law a Pacific Railway Act. This act chartered two railroad construction companies to build and operate a cross-continental line. The Central Pacific Railroad Company would begin construction in California, at Sacramento, and work eastward. A second company, the Union Pacific, would start near Omaha, Nebraska, and build westward until its line met with the CP's. As originally planned, the two rail lines were supposed to meet somewhere near the California-Nevada border.

On January 8, 1863, officials of the CP, joined by a large number of Sacramento's population, broke ground to mark the start of the great iron trail in the West.

To big, cheerful Charles Crocker, a local dry-goods merchant, went the job of directing the actual construction work on the CP. He was said to be full of energy and surprisingly light-footed for a man weighing more than 240 pounds. At one time or another Crocker had worked at a half-dozen different jobs, from farming to foundry work to storekeeping. True, he had never built a railroad. But his lack of railroading experience bothered him not at all. "I know," Crocker explained with his usual confidence, "how to manage men."

Though Charlie Crocker later admitted that he had to learn how to build a railroad as he went along, Crocker's construction crews gradually pushed the tracks eastward. By April 1864, Sacramento and the town of Roseville were connected by eighteen miles of track. Soon, the CP had enough rolling stock to begin regular passenger service — service regular enough to warrant the publishing of a timetable.

Crocker moved up and down the track, in his own words, "bellowing like a bull" to urge his work crews on to greater efforts. But as the trackage became longer, he found that he couldn't be everywhere at once. Thereupon, he hired James Harvey Strobridge to take command of the work crews at the end of the track. A tall, angular, fierce-looking man, Strobridge had a terrible temper and a choice collection of cuss words. When men worked for Strobridge, they worked hard — just out of sheer fright.

Even with Crocker bellowing and Strobridge cussing, the construction pace was not fast enough. Government money flowed into the CP's treasury only as fast as each mile of track could be put down. At the rate the CP was moving forward, it was in no danger of becoming rich.

Railroad builders in those days did not have steam shovels or bulldozers or power drills. All they had were hand tools — picks and shovels, crowbars, axes, and sledge hammers — and blasting powder. Mounds of dirt and rocks were hauled by wheelbarrows and by one-horse dump carts. Most of all, railroad construction depended on the muscles and sweat of men.

The Central Pacific needed an army of workmen. But it could barely muster a regiment-sized working force. The glitter of silver and gold in Nevada's Comstock Lode[1] across the mountains had lured away hundreds of workers. They all dreamed of fast fortunes and high living in boom towns, such as Virginia City and Carson City.

By 1865, the CP's labor problems became so serious that its directors even played with the idea of asking the United States Government to send Confederate prisoners of war out west to work on the railroad. But the idea was never carried out because the Civil War ended in that year.

At this point Charlie Crocker came up with an answer to the CP's labor shortage. Over the objections of Strobridge, Crocker issued an order to his construction superintendent: "Hire the Chinese."

Within six months after the first group of Chinese arrived in the CP's work camp, they had been joined by two thousand more of their countrymen. Each work train arriving at the railhead brought more of the blue-shirted, basket-hatted Oriental workmen to the construction site.

The reinforcement from the Orient was arriving at a critical time. By now the CP's railhead was at Clipper Gap, forty-three miles out of Sacramento. Graders building the roadbed ahead of the track-laying crews were climbing up the ridges into the high country. The work grew more difficult with each passing mile, for the CP had come face to face with a solid wall of granite — a mountain range called the Sierra Nevada.

The Sierra Nevada Range was well named. Translated into English, the words mean "snow-capped saw." The Sierra Nevada is just that — a range of saw-toothed peaks and ridges jutting up suddenly from the valley floor. During most winters, the mountain passes there became clogged with tons and tons of snow, a death trap for those caught or lost in it.

On the route of the CP the high Sierras crested at more than seven thousand feet above sea level. But there was no way to get around them. The CP had to go over them and through the mountains. It meant tunneling and bridging on a scale never before tried.

Directed by Crocker and Strobridge, the Chinese workmen began a massed human assault against the mountains. The hillsides rang with the sound of a thousand picks and drills pecking away. The moun-

---

[1] **Comstock Lode** (kŭm'stŏk lōd), a rich silver and gold vein discovered in 1859 at Virginia City by Henry Comstock.

tains echoed with constant thunder
of exploding gunpowder. Inch by
inch, the workmen gouged and
carved a path for the railroad up the
steep cliffs.

Along some stretches the cliff-
sides provided no footholds at all —
not even for mountain goats. The
Chinese found a clever way to
overcome this problem.

With reeds sent up from San
Francisco, the Chinese wove big
round wicker baskets with sides
about waist-high. The baskets were
then hauled up to the top of the
mountain. There, one or two Chinese workmen climbed into each

basket, and the rig — men and basket — was lowered by rope and pul-
ley over the side of the cliff.

Dangling dangerously in their
baskets thousands of feet above the
valley floor, the Chinese workmen
chipped a series of holes in the
cliffside, stuffing each hole with
blasting powder. The fuse was lit,
a hand signal given, and the baskets
were quickly hauled up in a frantic
scramble to safety. The explosion
that followed announced that a few
more feet of ledge had been blasted
out of the mountainside.

Sometimes the baskets were not
hauled up fast enough. Sometimes

the ropes snapped, and men and baskets tumbled thousands of feet down the cliffside. The number of Chinese who fell to their deaths in the high Sierras will never be known. The CP kept no records of casualties among its work force. But these were only the first of an estimated five hundred to one thousand Chinese workmen who were to lose their lives before the mountains were finally conquered.

The courage of the Chinese workmen in the mountains proved a real eye opener to the other men working for the CP.

When the Chinese first arrived on the scene, the white workers had greeted them with howling laughter and catcalls. Some of the whites swore that they would not work within a hundred yards of a "heathen Chinese." Others grumbled that the willingness of the Chinese to work for less pay held down their own wage scale.

But Crocker met these grumblings head on. The CP had to hire the Chinese, he explained, because it couldn't get nearly enough white workers to do the job. And if the whites couldn't learn to get along with the Chinese — well, then, the CP would have to let the white workers go and hire only the Chinese. Crocker's threat hit its mark. The grumbling ended.

In any event the white workers soon discovered that their Oriental companions proved inoffensive. They kept to themselves. They bothered no one. Moreover, they freed the white workers from the drudgery of the pick and shovel. Many of the whites found themselves promoted to foremen and crew chiefs to supervise the work of the Chinese crews. With the increase in pay and self-respect of the white workers, labor peace prevailed on the CP.

The Chinese workmen were themselves organized into crews numbering twelve to twenty members. Each crew worked and lived together as a unit. They lived in tents or huts. They slept on simple wooden cots.

Each crew was led by a Chinese headman who kept discipline among his men. On pay days the headman collected the wages for his entire crew, later distributing the money to each member. Most of the headmen could speak just enough English to do a little translating. But language rarely proved a problem. The Chinese workers learned quickly through watching others. Once shown how to do a job, they were fast to figure out the rest of it by themselves.

Each crew also hired its own Chinese cook. Imported Chinese groceries were sent up the line periodically by merchants in San Francisco. Each member of the crew shared in the cost of his food. For the Chinese workers the main diet included dried oysters, abalone, bamboo shoots and bean sprouts, crackers and noodles, Chinese bacon, pork and poultry. To the CP's white workers, surviving on a diet of boiled beef, bread, potatoes, and coffee, the menus of the Chinese crews were a source of endless wonderment.

In addition, the Chinese drank tea by the gallons. Even while they worked, "tea boys" trotted up to the Chinese work gangs dispensing hot tea, transported in old whiskey barrels suspended from the ends of a long pole.

One other thing about the Chinese amazed their fellow workers on the CP. Before supper each night the members of the Chinese work crews lined up before barrels filled with warm water. Then, one after another, they stripped off their dirty clothing, bathed themselves, and changed into clean clothes. Out in the rough and rugged West during those frontier days, such personal cleanliness was considered somewhat unusual.

Indeed, to the casual observer, the Chinese work crews appeared to be disciplined, smooth-working human machines. They worked from dawn to dusk with few breaks and fewer complaints. They hardly ever seemed to get sick or even tired.

Those who watched more carefully, however, knew that this wasn't quite so. One of these, a Swiss student named Hemmann Hoffmann, who worked for a while on the CP, noted that each Chinese crew kept a few spare workers available. When one of the regular workers became ill — or if he just didn't feel like working on a particular day — a substitute would take his place. This made the Chinese able to report with a full work crew each morning.

The hard work and endurance of the Chinese who were working for the CP needed no apologies. As Charles Crocker wrote of his Chinese crews: "Wherever we put them, we found them good; and they worked themselves into our favor to such an extent that if we found we were in a hurry for a job of work, it was better to put Chinese on at once." Little wonder that from this time on the CP's Chinese workers were called Crocker's Pets.

In 1866, the CP's Chinese work force swelled to ten thousand strong. Crocker's Pets seemed to be swarming all over the high Sierras, doing whatever the CP wanted done.

They toppled the tall trees and rooted out the stumps. They broke and carted rock. They graded the climbing roadbed, put down the ties, and spiked home the rails. But the hardest job of all was tunneling.

The Sierra crossing called for a dozen tunnels before the tracks reached the Nevada border (and

three more after that). The tunnels were of different lengths. Seven of them clustered within two miles of the place where the CP's cross-mountain route climbed to its highest point. The longest one, called the Summit Tunnel, meant drilling 1,659 feet through solid granite. This was no easy task.

The CP's engineers figured that it might take as long as a year and a half to bore the Summit Tunnel. They put five hundred Chinese on the job at once, organizing them into three eight-hour shifts, working around the clock. The Chinese worked at both ends of the tunnel at the same time, digging toward the middle. Later, a shaft was sunk down to the center of the tunnel, and work crews were lowered into the hole to dig from the inside out as well.

Still, progress was agonizingly slow. The rock proved so hard that black powder simply blew out of the drill holes without shattering the rock face. Despite the unending labor of the Chinese work crews, progress through the rock was measured at only seven or eight inches a day!

As the year 1866 wore on, the weather became more and more of a problem. The rains came down in torrents, causing washouts, turning roads into mud baths, and fouling up the CP's supply system.

In colder, higher ground the dampness from the skies came down as snow, snow, and more snow. The Sierra Range was living up to its name. From November until the following May the clouds would dump some forty-five feet of snow on the mountains.

Soon even the snowplows could not get through the clogged mountain passes. Work along the rail line came to a standstill. Crocker was forced to send the main part of his work force back down from the mountains. But he kept several hundred of his strongest Chinese laborers up in the cliffs to work on the tunnels all through the wintry months.

Wind-whipped snowdrifts soon buried the camps, entirely covering the huts of the workmen. They had to bore through the packed snow for air shafts to the surface. To get to and back from work, they had to carve out a maze of snow tunnels, some of them two hundred feet long.

Through the terrible winter the Chinese workers burrowed under the piles of snow almost like human moles. They lived through the bitter cold, never seeing sunshine or the open sky. Often the food supply ran short, and the men survived on daily doses of cornmeal and tea.

Now, as the snow piled higher and higher, a new danger arose: avalanche! Tons of snow came sliding down from the higher cliffs, sweeping and burying all before it. Snow tunnels caved in. Men disappeared entirely under the roaring, tumbling snowslides. Their frozen bodies would not be found until the snow began to melt in the thaw of the following spring. Some of them would be found still tightly clutching picks and shovels in their lifeless hands.

But spring came at last. And Crocker threw his army of Chinese laborers into a renewed assault against the Sierras. Normally, the work went on six days a week, pausing only on Sunday. Sometimes, however, it didn't even stop on Sunday.

Finally, on August 29, 1867, came cause for rejoicing. The men boring the tunnel at the summit broke through. The Summit Tunnel was quickly finished off. By November 30, the men had completed laying track through this granite cavern.

As the year 1867 ended, the builders of the Central Pacific could at last enjoy a measure of pride. The CP had laid down about 130 miles of track from Sacramento across the mountains. Except for a seven-mile gap and some smaller tunnels to be finished later, the CP had crossed the high Sierras and reached the Nevada border. The men who challenged the mountains had won.

When the Pacific Railway Act was first passed in 1862, most observers had expected the Central Pacific and the Union Pacific to link up somewhere in the vicinity of the California-Nevada line. They thought that the Sierra crossing was about as much as the CP would be able to finish before it bumped into the UP's tracks streaking westward from Nebraska.

In 1866, however, Collis Huntington, CP vice president, went to work in Washington, D.C., to get Congress to change the ground rules. He was very convincing. Congress changed the Railway Act to allow each company to continue laying tracks until the two lines met — wherever that might be.

Under these rules the Central Pacific and the Union Pacific no longer looked upon each other as partners in the transcontinental railroad. They now considered each other as competitors.

Every mile of track that each company put down meant more government money flowing into the company's treasury (and that much less money flowing into the other company's treasury). Each mile meant more free land for the railroads — land that could later be sold to the public at a huge profit. And the mileage that each company completed would determine how much of the transcontinental line each would control when the long, long railroad was finished.

Charlie Crocker confidently predicted that his crews would average a mile of track for every working day in 1868. The race was on between the CP and the UP.

The Central Pacific now had a labor force numbering some fourteen thousand, about twelve thousand of them Chinese. Most of them by now were veteran railroaders, toughened by the rigors of the Sierra crossing. Month after month, the miles ticked by. By the end of the year 1868, the Central Pacific's tracks reached Elko, three-quarters of the way across Nevada. The CP's work crews had made good Crocker's boast. In a year's time they had completed more than 350 miles of track!

But as the two railroads sprinted into Utah, strange things were beginning to happen. The CP and the UP surveying teams passed each other going in opposite directions. It became obvious that the Union Pacific planned to continue westward until its own tracks reached the Pacific Coast. And the Central Pacific, likewise, would keep going eastward until somebody stopped it, somewhere.

By the spring of 1869, both the Central Pacific's grading crews (made up mostly of Chinese) and the Union Pacific's graders (made up mostly of Irishmen) were working in Utah. Often they built roadbeds that ran side by side, sometimes only one hundred feet or so apart.

From far away in Washington, D.C., Congress ordered the two railroads to cut out the foolishness. The lawmakers picked out a spot in Utah, just north of the Great Salt Lake, as the place where the tracks of the two railroads would join. It was a place called Promontory.

The "Last Rail" ceremonies were scheduled to take place on May 8, 1869. Officers of the Central Pacific who could not make it out to Promontory arranged for elaborate ceremonies to be held at the same time in California.

But complications set in, and the Promontory ceremonies had to be put off a day or two. It was too late to change the plans of the Californians. So they went ahead and began their celebrations as planned on May 8 — two days before the rest of the country.

In Sacramento it was a time for marching bands, parades, cheers, backslapping, and speechmaking. In a proud speech Crocker praised his "Pets."

"In the midst of our rejoicing, I wish to call to mind that the early completion of this railroad we have built has been in a great measure due to that poor, destitute class of laborers called the Chinese — to the fidelity and industry they have shown — and the great amount of laborers of this land that have been employed upon this work."

His was the only speech that told of the contributions of Chinese labor in the building of the transcontinental rail link.

Two days later, on May 10, six

and a half years of determined effort were reaching a climax at Promontory, Utah. A Central Pacific locomotive, the *Jupiter,* and a Union Pacific locomotive, *No. 119,* sat almost headlamp to headlamp. Behind the *Jupiter* the Central Pacific tracks stretched 690 miles back to Sacramento. Behind the *119,* the Union Pacific tracks stretched 1,086 miles toward Omaha. Between the two locomotives a gap of one rail-length remained.

CP President Leland Stanford came to Promontory well equipped with expensive hardware: two gold spikes from California, a gold and silver spike (the gift of Nevada), and a gold, silver, and iron spike (the gift of Arizona). To drive home the last spikes, Stanford had a silver-plated sledgehammer. The final tie, made just for the occasion, was of polished California laurel with a silver plate suitably inscribed. (This expensive material could hardly be left to rot under the tracks. It was removed for safekeeping after the ceremonies and replaced by cheaper hardware.)

The Golden Spike ceremonies officially got under way shortly after high noon. James Strobridge and his counterpart on the UP, Samuel Reed, set the laurel tie in place. A team of Irish trackmen hefted the last rail into place for the Union Pacific, while a crew of Chinese did the same for the Central Pacific. The honor of tapping in the golden spikes was shared by Stanford and Dr. Thomas C. Durant, vice president of the UP.

At about 12:40 P.M., the railroad was finished. The message was flashed along the telegraph wires. In cities from coast to coast fire whistles shrieked, church bells pealed, and cannons boomed out a roaring salute.

Perhaps the Chinese laborers — the thousands who crossed an ocean to work in a strange land far from their homes — never fully understood what a continent-spanning railroad was all about. Yet, their courage, hard work, and endurance had helped to turn the dream of a long iron trail into reality.

DISCUSSION

1. Why was it hard to get workers to build the transcontinental railroad? How was the labor problem solved? Why did the solution prove to be a good one?
2. What was the initial reaction of the white workers to the hiring of the Chinese? Why did their opinion change?
3. What was the most challenging obstacle that the Central Pacific railroad builders encountered? How did the weather add to their problem?
4. Why did the Central Pacific and the Union Pacific come to regard each other as competitors rather than partners? What new problem did this create? How was it solved?
5. Why did the Chinese crews come to be known as Crocker's Pets? Did this term mean they received special treatment from Mr. Crocker? Why do you think that?
6. Why might it be difficult for the Chinese laborers to understand what a continent-spanning railroad was all about?

7. What factors showed that the Chinese were well organized? Why do you think the white workers did not profit from their example?
8. At the celebration for the completion of the railroad, only Crocker mentioned the contributions of the Chinese workers. In your opinion should other recognition have been given? Why or why not?
9. What needs were satisfied by the transcontinental railroad in those days?

AUTHORS

Daniel Chu and Samuel Chu, who are brothers, were born in China and lived there and in Paris and Moscow before coming to the United States in 1941. *Passage to the Golden Gate: A History of the Chinese in America to 1910,* from which the selection you have just read was taken, was written by them in 1967.

Daniel Chu has been a staff writer and an editor for several weekly magazines, including *Scholastic.* At the present time he is an associate editor with a national magazine in New York City. He is also co-author, with Elliott Skinner, of *The Glorious Age in Africa: The Story of Three Great African Empires,* a book which is used as a supplementary text in some schools. His most recent book for young people is about China.

Samuel Chu is a professor of history and director of the Asian Studies Program at Ohio State University in Columbus, Ohio.

In addition to writing, both brothers are interested in music, reading, sailing, skiing, and spectator sports, especially football.

EQUAL RIGHTS FOR WOMEN

by Edwin D. Hoffman

On May 27, 1851, the young Ohio town of Akron was bursting with excitement. Throughout the day carriages and wagons rolled down its unpaved streets, bringing delegates to the second "Annual Convention of the Women of Ohio." At the corner of Market and Main Streets many Akron farmers and artisans were gathered, awaiting the arrival of that strange new species of American, the women who asked for equality with men. What sort of costume would the feminists be wearing? Would it be the "Turkish costume" introduced last year in the East by Mrs. Bloomer?[1] And what sort of women would they be? Would decent married women leave their families to go to a two-day gathering?

America in the years 1830–1860 was stirring with social reform move-ments. Women joined in these reform movements. But women quickly found that if they wished to be reformers, they first had to establish the right of their sex to speak in public at all. America, including most women of the day, believed that a woman's place was in the home and that no "lady" exposed herself to public life. She was idealized as a lovely, delicate creature who lacked the intelligence and capability to enter the political and business worlds of men. Those women who refused to accept this inferior role in society decided that one more reform movement was needed, to obtain equal rights for women.

When the townsfolk, gathered on Akron's wooden sidewalks, saw the delegates, they were sorely disappointed that no one was wearing the sensational Bloomer Girl costume. Practically all the delegates were matronly housewives and mothers of large families. A few in the crowd recognized Mrs. Frances Gage. She

---

[1] Bloomer, Amelia Jenks (bloo'mər), temperance reformer and advocate of women's rights.

was "Aunt Fanny," a popular writer for children and farm women and the mother of eight children. Temperance, as well as women's rights and the abolition of slavery, stirred her to action. Later, a most determined-looking woman drove by, and rumor had it that she was a lady newspaper editor. The lady editor was Mrs. Jane Grey Swisshelm. Her paper, the *Pittsburgh Saturday Visitor,* was the first political paper edited by a woman. The arrival of Alfred and Martha Elwell caused the greatest stir. The Elwells were newlyweds from Cleveland and had come to spend their honeymoon at this women's rights convention!

The visitors to Akron surely were agitating for a great deal. They wanted the vote for all women but not only that. They wanted work in many trades and professions to be opened to women, and they wanted women to be paid the same as men for equal work. They wanted married women to be able to own property and be equal to their husbands before the law. To many Akron families, especially their womenfolk, this talk seemed aimed at destroying the family and the respectability of women. Akron was suspicious, but Akron was also curious.

Rain fell heavily on the morning of May 28, 1851, as the delegates drove up the hill to the Universalist Church, the site of the convention. Despite the rain the church filled rapidly. Many men attended as well as the early feminists. One could easily note a number of ministers by their black suits.

Frances Gage was elected chairman. She had never attended a convention before, and she had never presided over a meeting. These activities were not the business of American women in that day. She was a large, vigorous farm woman, and upon election she made a strong extemporaneous speech of acceptance. Mrs. Gage came right to the point of the convention. She compared the struggle for women's rights with that of the American pioneers against the wilderness. Here too "there are mountains of established law and custom to overcome; a wilderness of prejudice to be subdued; a powerful foe of selfishness and self-interest to overthrow; wild beasts of pride, envy, malice, and hate to destroy." Women, like the pioneers, would accept the challenge to overcome these obstacles.

"We will be accused of being discontented spirits, striving to disturb the public order and tear up the roots of society," Mrs. Gage went on. "So it was said of Jesus Christ and His followers when they taught peace on earth and good will to all men. So it was said of our forefathers in the great struggle for freedom. So it has been said of every reformer that has ever started the car of progress on a new and untried track!

"Oh, if all women could be impressed with the importance of their own action and with one united voice speak out in their own behalf, in behalf of humanity, they could create a revolution without armies, without bloodshed, that would do more to ameliorate the conditions of mankind, to purify, elevate, ennoble humanity, than all that has been done by reformers in the last century."

After Mrs. Gage had spoken, the morning session ended. That afternoon the church was even more crowded. The session was opened with a prayer, and then the Hutchinson family, folk singers at many conventions of reformers, sang some lively songs. The resolutions were then read, fifteen long and inclusive statements. Each began with a bold declaration of equality of the sexes: "Inasmuch as it is self-evident that woman has been created with as high intellectual and moral endowments and subject to similar necessities as man, it is also self-evident that she is possessed naturally of a perfect equality with him in her legal, political, pecuniary, ecclesiastical, and social rights."

In the resolutions men were accused of "criminal injustice" and women of "reprehensible submissiveness." Religious leaders, editors, teachers, and parents were charged with the task of changing public opinion to favor equality for women.

The resolutions called for the immediate repeal of all laws and constitutional provisions that favored the male sex over the female. Philanthropic men were urged to employ women without prejudice and to give them equal wages for equal work. And one resolution even urged women who worked to form trade unions, "labor partnerships in which each can obtain all that her labors can obtain in the markets of the world."

Discussion began after the reading of the resolutions. The ministers were almost all highly critical of the movement, and even some of the women felt that they were asking for too much at once. Especially vocal in attacking the resolutions was Jane Grey Swisshelm, the editor from Pittsburgh. She later wrote that she attended the convention to "mollify the madness" of the suffragettes. Mrs. Swisshelm believed in going slowly, and she took exception to the idea of equality of the sexes. "There is a male mind and a female mind, and man is a man and woman a woman, and these conventions cannot make it otherwise.... Woman was made for domestic duties and man for the stern labor of the field and the shop." Since women could not do equal mental work with men, she pointed out, women must train for the vote. Let women vote first on whether the dram shop (saloon) should be allowed to exist. Mrs. Swisshelm went on to ridicule the women who were eager to get before the public by any means and "to wear its most stinging sarcasms as they would a new dress cap." This was Mrs. Swisshelm's first public speech, and part of the audience greeted it heartily.

Up rose Emma Coe, destined to become an early woman lawyer, to answer Jane Swisshelm. She, too, was new to public speaking. If men were tyrannical, she said, she was ready to call them tyrants. Women would win the greatest respect from mankind in America when they went to the polls and voted.

And so the delegates went on debating, quoting Scripture, appealing first to reason and then to emotion. There was an evening session that day, and the debate continued into the night. By this time people were being turned away from the overcrowded church. Mrs. Swisshelm and Mrs. Coe still led in the debate. Emma Coe compared the position of a woman to that of a slave. "The master exacts the labor of the slave, so the husband has the right to exact the labor of his wife. The master may chastise the slave, so may the husband chastise the wife. The slave has no rights under the law to his own earnings, neither has the wife to hers."

Mrs. Swisshelm continued her criticism of the resolutions. She vigorously denied that the differences in the sexes included one of education. She would concede that women property owners should have the vote in town elections but no more. Her wit and clever sarcasm won her frequent applause, and the first day of the convention closed with the principles of women's rights still subject to sharp attack.

The second morning of the convention opened with a prayer and some hymn singing by the Hutchinsons. The committee on education for women reported. Emma Coe, always eager to make the strongest possible case for full equality of the sexes, criticized the resolution. "Do not say that women have nothing to do with colleges for men," she pointed out. "Is not woman taxed to support these institutions? Now man is guilty of a two-fold act of injustice toward her, first crippling the energies of her mind by depriving her of the benefits to be derived from these seminaries and then sneering at the imbecility of character she afterward exhibits. Is this not grinding with the heel and then spurning with the hand the crushed being?" She went on to say that if men were to claim superior native intelligence to women, then women should be given an equal or superior education, for the purpose of an education in a democracy is to create greater equality. "The presumed mental inferiority of women," Emma Coe argued, "furnishes one of the strongest arguments in favor of a superior instead of an inferior education, since she must depend on culture instead of native strength of mind, while man, being born with superior wit and wisdom, as is argued, has less need of cultivation."

Mrs. Coe enjoyed using men's arguments against themselves. If men were always limiting the spheres in which women might move, she welcomed proposals to limit men's life as well. She vigorously proposed that men's insatiable quest to make money be restricted. To the delight of the feminists she said that if man "were to have a life's lease on heaven, on condition of being perfectly content with it, and should hear a sixpence drop on the floor of hell, he would feel an itching palm until he had contrived some means to slip down and pick it up." This greed for money is written into a young boy's heart from the moment he leaves his mother's apron strings, Emma Coe noted. And to make her point, she quoted a little poem:

Go get your gold, no matter how,
No questions asked of the rich I trow,
Steal by night and steal by day,
Doing it all in a legal way.
Be hypocrite, liar, knave, or fool,
But don't be poor (remember the rule),
Dimes and dollars, and dollars and dimes.
An empty pocket is the worst of crimes.

As discussion continued that morning, Methodist, Baptist, Episcopal, Presbyterian, and Universalist ministers rose to question the resolutions. One claimed superior rights and privileges for man on the ground of superior intellect. Another said that if God had desired the equality of women, he would have shown it through the birth, life, and death of Jesus. Another reminded the audience of the sins of the first mother, Eve.

The persuasive oratory of the ministers almost overwhelmed the convention. Very few women dared to "speak in meeting" and especially in opposition to clergymen. The boys in the galleries and the sneerers in the pews were enjoying the obvious embarrassment of the "strong-minded" women. At any moment the convention might have gotten out of hand completely. It was an elderly and uneducated Negro woman, Sojourner Truth, who saved the day for the hard-pressed feminists.

Sojourner Truth (sō-jûrn'ər trōoth) had been born a slave in New York, and her back still bore the lash marks of early whippings. She had escaped from her master, changed her name, and begun to speak for the freedom of her people at abolitionist meetings. Since she had learned Dutch as a mother language and had received no formal education, her English was unusual.

On the opening day of the convention this tall, gaunt Negro woman, dressed in a gray dress and a white turban with a large sunbonnet atop the turban, had entered the church. She had walked with the air of a queen up the aisle and had taken her seat upon the pulpit steps. The delegates were plainly worried by her presence. Women's rights would be linked with another struggling reform, freedom for the slave. The Akron convention would be called an "abolitionist affair."

Throughout the first day's debate Sojourner Truth had sat quietly on the pulpit steps. She had just listened

intently, her elbows on her knees, her chin resting upon her broad hard palms. During an intermission she had been selling the *Life of Sojourner Truth,* a highly religious account of her early adventurous life.

Delegate after delegate urged the chairman not to let Sojourner Truth address the convention: "Don't let her speak, Mrs. Gage, it will ruin us. Every newspaper in the land will have our cause mixed up with abolition and Negroes, and we shall be utterly denounced." But Sojourner Truth did speak. On that crucial second morning when the clergy were so righteously and successfully urging that woman's place was in the home, the old Negro woman slowly rose from her seat. She moved slowly and solemnly up the platform, laid her bonnet at her feet, and raised her eyes to ask recognition from Mrs. Gage. You could hear the audience hissing and murmuring, "Don't let that woman speak." Frances Gage simply announced, "Sojourner Truth," and asked the audience to be silent for a few minutes.

Sojourner Truth made an impressive sight on the rostrum. She was almost six feet tall with an Amazon-like form, a deep-brown skin, and flashing eyes. She spoke in deep tones which, though not loud, reached every ear in the house and even those at the doors and windows outside.

"Well, children, where there is so much racket, there must be something out of kilter. I think that between Negroes of the South and the women of the North, all talking about rights, the white men will be in a pretty fix soon. But what is all this talking about?

"That man over there says a woman needs to be helped into carriages and lifted over ditches and have the best places everywhere. No one ever helps me into carriages or over mud puddles or gives me any best place!" And raising herself to her full height, her voice resounding through the church, she asked, "And aren't I a woman? Look at me! Look at my arm!" And she bared her right arm to the shoulder, showing her tremendous muscular power. "I have plowed and planted and gathered into barns, and no man could head me! And aren't I a woman? I could work as much and eat as much as a man — when I could get it — and bear the lash as well! And aren't I a woman? I have borne thirteen children and seen most all of them sold off to slavery, and when I cried out with my mother's grief, none but Jesus heard me! And aren't I a woman?

"Then they talk about this thing in the head; what's this they call it?" ("Intellect," whispered someone nearby.) "That's it, honey. What's that got to do with women's rights or Negroes' rights? If my cup won't hold but a pint and yours holds a quart, wouldn't you be mean not to let me have my little half-measure full?" And she pointed her significant finger and sent a keen glance toward the minister who had argued against women's rights because women were less intelligent. The cheering was loud and long.

"Then that little man in black there, he says women cannot have as much rights as men because Christ wasn't a woman! Where did your Christ come from?" Rolling thunder could not have stilled the crowd as she stood there with outstretched arms and eyes of fire. Raising her voice still louder, she repeated, "Where did your Christ come from? From God and a woman! Man had nothing to do with Him!"

And then Sojourner Truth turned toward another clerical objector who had spoken of the original evil of Eve. She said she could not read but she could hear. She had heard the Bible read and had been told that Eve had caused the fall of man. "If the first woman God ever made was strong enough to turn the world upside down all alone, these women together" (and she glanced over the platform) "ought to be able to turn it back and get it right side up again! And now that they are asking to do it, the men better let them." Amid cheering, Sojourner

Truth finished. "Blessed be you for listening to me, and now old Sojourner has nothing more to say."

Leaving many delegates with streaming eyes, she returned to her seat amid roars of applause. She had turned the tide. An old ex-slave woman, who could neither read nor write, had won respect and admiration for the cause of women's rights when the Ohio women had almost failed. Her speech had completely subdued the mobbish spirit of that morning and turned the sneers and jeers of the audience to friendship. Hundreds rushed over to shake the hand of this dynamic old mother. She had won their minds and their hearts.

And so the convention went on with far greater unanimity. That afternoon the resolutions were called to a vote, and all were passed. The delegates made farewell speeches and the convention ended. Another part of America had heard the demands of the feminists ably presented; another group of campaigners for women's rights went forth better equipped to battle for equality of the sexes.

DISCUSSION

1. What was the role of women in America in the period 1830–1860?
2. What were some of the reforms the visitors to Akron were working toward? How did the families of Akron feel about these reforms?
3. What made the ministers so effective in swaying the convention? What arguments did they use against the proposed resolutions?

4. Why were the delegates to the convention at first worried by the presence of Sojourner Truth? How did she deal with the opposition of the ministers? What effect did she have on the outcome of the convention?

5. Why do you think Sojourner Truth was silent during the first day of the convention? At what time during the convention did she decide to speak? Why was that the right time for her to do so?

6. What kind of impression did Sojourner Truth make on the audience at the convention? Why do you think her speech was so effective?

7. What resemblance do you see between the women who met in Akron, Ohio, in 1851 and the women who are involved in women's liberation movements of today? How are their goals alike? How are they different?

8. What factors have helped women to achieve the goals of equal rights? What factors have hindered them?

9. Do you think there are some jobs or professions at which women are more capable than men? Are there any at which men are more capable than women? Give your reasons for thinking as you do.

AUTHOR

Currently the Dean of Instruction at West Virginia State College, Edwin D. Hoffman has been Assistant Professor of History at Long Island University, New York; Professor of History and Chairman of the Division of Teacher Education at Allen University, South Carolina; and Professor of History and Chairman of the Division of Social Science at Pembroke State College, North Carolina.

Pathways to Freedom, from which "Equal Rights for Women" was taken, was published in 1964. A French translation of the book appeared in 1966. Dr. Hoffman has also contributed many articles to magazines, including *The Journal of Negro History* and *The West Virginia School Journal.*

ROLAND AND OLIVER

by Barbara Leonie Picard

In the days of the Emperor Charlemagne (shär'lə-mān'), Charles the Great of the Franks, who ruled France and Germany and fought so mightily against the enemies of Christendom, there lived a count named Girard. Count Girard held the city and the castle of Vienne (vyĕn) and the land that lay about it, but he was no friend to his Emperor; and with his vassals and his knights he rebelled and made war on him. Charlemagne, much angered, called together his army and marched against Vienne, whilst Girard and his followers retreated into the city, defending the walls bravely. For many months the advantage fell to neither side, and time passed until the siege had lasted for two whole years; and many there were among the besiegers, as well as among the besieged, who longed for the war to be over. Yet the city could not be taken, so well was it defended; and Charlemagne, glad though he would have been to be at peace with all his subjects, could not bring himself to withdraw his army, lest it should seem as though he acknowledged himself defeated by a rebel.

With the Emperor's army were those who were considered the ten greatest champions of France. There, too, with Charlemagne was his young nephew Roland, son of the Emperor's sister Berthe. Roland had but lately been knighted, and he was anxious to prove himself; yet so long as the siege lasted, it seemed as though he would have little chance of showing his worth. The days went slowly for him, and with the other young knights and the squires he often left the camp and hunted in the woods near Vienne or jousted with his companions; and among them there was no one more skilled at feats of arms than he.

Count Girard also had a nephew, Oliver, of an age with Roland; and one day for an adventure, carrying plain arms that he might be unknown, Oliver slipped unseen through the gates of Vienne and wandered into the Emperor's camp. Here in an open space he found Roland and his companions tilting together, and after watching for a while, he asked if he might join them. Though he was a stranger to them, they thought him one of the Emperor's men, and they lent him a horse and let him tilt with them. Soon it was apparent that Oliver surpassed them all. Not even Roland, who was accounted the best among them, was more skilled with lance and sword.

The youths were loud in admiration of the stranger and asked his name, but he only smiled and would not answer. Then someone whispered that he might be an enemy, since in two years no one of them had seen him before. And the murmur went round amongst them, so that their friendly smiles were changed to suspicious frowns, and they crowded about him, demanding his name. Rough hands were laid upon him; but he broke free and, leaping on a horse, rode for his life toward the walls of Vienne.

"After him!" cried Roland. "He must not escape. He is too good a prize to lose." And the young knights rode after him swiftly with Roland at their head. Steadily Roland gained on Oliver until he was upon him; and close beneath the city walls Oliver turned to face his pursuers, and Roland, in triumph, raised his sword to strike. But at that moment there came a cry of terror from the walls above, and Roland looked up and saw a maiden, the fairest he had ever seen, standing on the ramparts, her hands clasped in supplication and her face pale with fear. It was lovely Aude, the sister of Oliver.

"Spare my brother Oliver," she pleaded. And Roland, staring at her, slowly lowered his sword and let Oliver ride on to the gates unharmed.

"I surely could not bring grief to so fair a maiden," Roland said to himself.

During the days that followed, Roland thought much about Oliver and Aude and wished that they had not been the Emperor's enemies. And for their part they thought of Roland and wished the war were at an end, and Oliver sought to persuade his uncle to peace.

After a time his nephew's counsels prevailed, and Count Girard sent Oliver, well attended, to Charlemagne to ask that they might be accorded. "If you will withdraw your army, sire, my uncle the count will come forth from Vienne and swear allegiance, and he will serve you faithfully for all his life," said Oliver.

But the Emperor, for all that he hated warring against his own vassals, could not find it in his heart to forgive Girard his rebellion so easily. "Let Count Girard humble himself before me, and I will consider pardoning him," he said.

"Sire," replied Oliver, "that my uncle would never do."

"Then the war goes on," said Charlemagne. But Duke Naimes spoke to him, counselling peace.

Oliver, standing before the Emperor, turned his head and looked at Roland and saw how he was watching him. He smiled and said impulsively, "You and I are of an age and well matched. How say you, if our uncles are willing, shall we settle this war in single combat?"

"Gladly," said Roland, and he begged the Emperor's permission. After thought, Charlemagne agreed. "Go back and tell Count Girard," he said to Oliver, "that if you are victorious in this contest, I will depart from his lands with all my army and leave him in peace forever. But if my nephew Roland is the victor, then Count Girard must lose Vienne and all his lands to me."

"I shall tell him," said Oliver, and he returned to the city.

And so it was decided that the outcome of the war should be determined by single combat between the two young knights, and a day was named upon which they should meet on a little islet in a river that ran between the camp and the city walls.

On the appointed day Roland, armed and carrying his sword Durendal, which no blade could withstand, went to the islet to await Oliver. Soon Count Girard's nephew came out through the city gates, wearing armor and bearing a sword, which had been given to him on the day he had been made a knight.

Eagerly, all those from the Emperor's camp crowded about Charlemagne and the champions of France upon the bank of the river to watch the fight, whilst Count Girard and his family, and Aude with them, stood upon the walls of Vienne with the defenders of the city.

The two young men greeted each other courteously, and at once the battle began. They were indeed well matched, giving blow for blow; and at any one of their strokes a lesser knight would have fallen. Soon their shields were dented and their armor battered, links from their chain mail falling about them as they hacked with their good swords. But at last with a great stroke from Durendal, the strongest sword in all France, Oliver's blade was broken; and he fell to his knees with the force of the blow. A cry of fear went up from the watchers on the walls of Vienne, but from the Emperor's knights a shout of triumph rose. Oliver thought, "My last moment is come," and he braced himself to meet the stroke which would end his life.

But Roland flung Durendal aside. "I cannot slay an unarmed man," he said.

Oliver rose, and he and Roland tore up two saplings to serve them as clubs, and with these they continued their fight until the green wood was broken all to splinters. And then the young knights wrestled together, each striving unsuccessfully to throw the other, until at midday, both locked in each other's grip, they fell to the ground at the same time so that neither could be said to have thrown the other. They stood up, breathless and exhausted. "The sun is high," said Roland. "It is too hot for fighting. Let us rest awhile."

They took off their helmets and smiled at one another. "I am happy," said Oliver, "that I am privileged to fight with so worthy an enemy." And the two young men embraced and sat down upon the grass and talked together as though they had been old friends. Wine was brought to them from the city and another sword for Oliver; and when an hour or two had passed and the sun was lower in the sky, they helped each other to arm again and once more began their fight.

As before, neither proved the better, and for long the battle raged; until suddenly, stepping aside to avoid a blow from Oliver, Roland lowered his sword and said, "Stay your hand awhile, for I feel a weakness come over me as though I had a fever, and I would rest."

With courtesy Oliver set aside his sword. "Rest for as long as you need, good Roland. I would not wish to be victor because you are not well. Lie down and I will watch over you."

Roland, who was merely feigning sickness in order to test Oliver, took off his helmet and lay down upon the grass. Oliver placed his shield beneath his head to serve him as a pillow and fetched water for him from the river in his own helmet.

Watching, Charlemagne thought, "My nephew is vanquished and I have lost the day." While from the walls of Vienne fair Aude watched with pity; for though her brother's cause was hers, from her first sight of him she had felt a great admiration for Roland, an admiration which she knew could very easily turn to love.

But Roland sprang to his feet and laughed. "I did but try you, Oliver. And so courteously have you treated me that I wish we were brothers or friends and not enemies."

"Brothers we could be," replied Oliver. "If we both live through this battle, I will give you my sister for your wife, since there is no other to whom I would rather see her wed. And as for friends, are we not friends already in our hearts?"

They fell once more to fighting, and again the advantage lay with neither, and still they fought as the sun went down the sky and sank from sight. Through the twilight they fought, while the watchers strained their eyes to see them and could not tell one from the other, and on into the darkness, so that only the sound of metal clashing upon metal told that the battle still went on.

And then at last from the darkness there was silence, as with one accord they ceased their strife. "Heaven does not mean that to either of us shall be the victory," they said. And they threw down their weapons and embraced, swearing friendship forever. "Never again shall we take arms against each other," they vowed.

Each of them persuaded his uncle to be at peace, and for love of them Charlemagne and Count Girard were accorded, uniting against their common enemies, the Saracens, who held all Spain and were

attacking France. And on a happy May morning Roland and Aude were betrothed, to their great joy and Oliver's.

From the day of their battle Roland and Oliver were comrades in arms, riding together against the Saracens and fighting side by side, winning such fame that they were accounted amongst the champions of France, the foremost of the twelve.

DISCUSSION

1. At the beginning of the story how long had the army of the Emperor Charlemagne besieged the city and castle of Count Girard? Why did Charlemagne not withdraw?

2. At the beginning of the story there were ten men who were considered the greatest champions of France; at the end of the story there were twelve. Who were the two additions?

3. When Charlemagne rejected Count Girard's offer of peace, how did Oliver propose that the war be settled? What were the terms agreed upon? At the end of the story why were the terms not strictly carried out?

4. At the beginning of the story what made Roland and Oliver respect each other? Later on, what made them respect each other even more?

5. Why did Roland spare Oliver's life beneath the city walls? What does this tell you about Roland?

6. What reasons do you think Roland had for wanting the war to end? Which reason do you think was the most important to him? Why?

7. Do you think pride is a good enough reason to continue a war as Charlemagne did? Why do you think that?

8. Imagine that you were either Roland or Oliver. Do you think you could have fought very effectively under the circumstances? Why or why not?

9. Do you respect a person most because of some superior skill or ability he possesses, because of his personal characteristics, or because of a combination of both? Why do you think as you do?

AUTHOR

Barbara Leonie Picard was born in Surrey, England, and since the age of three has lived in one part or another of Sussex, England. Miss Picard, who had always wanted to be an author, became a writer for young people quite by accident. She had long been interested in folktales, mythology, and original fairy tales, but she had never been able to find enough of the Hans Christian Andersen type of fairy tale to satisfy her own reading interest. During World War II she decided to try writing a few for her own amusement and to pass the time between air-raid alarms on her weekly "fire-watching night." At first she wrote four stories, each based on some theme connected with one of the four elements: fire, water, earth, and air.

The Mermaid and the Simpleton was Miss Picard's first collection of fairy tales to be published. This was followed by the publication of several other collections, including her retelling of myths and legends from many lands. Her first full-length novel for young people, *Ransom for a Knight,* appeared in 1956, and in 1965 another of her novels, *One Is One,* was a runner-up for the Carnegie Medal. Her most recent book is *Three Ancient Kings,* a collection of retold stories about three legendary kings, each of whom was persecuted by a deity he had angered.

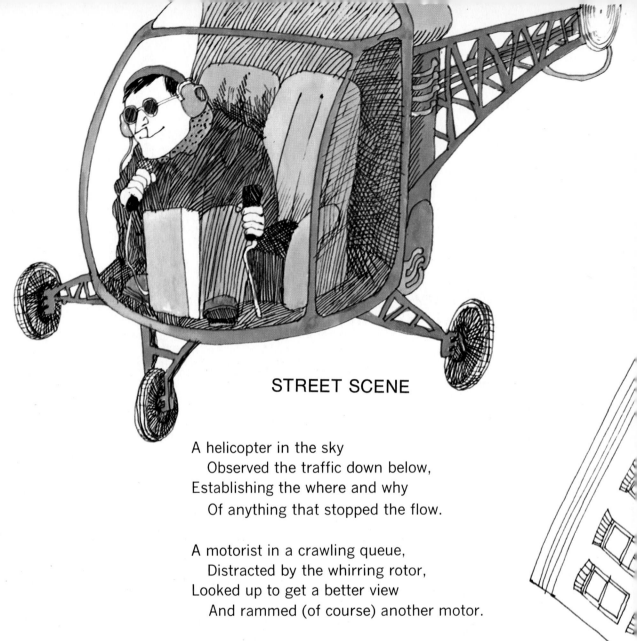

STREET SCENE

A helicopter in the sky
   Observed the traffic down below,
Establishing the where and why
   Of anything that stopped the flow.

A motorist in a crawling queue,
   Distracted by the whirring rotor,
Looked up to get a better view
   And rammed (of course) another motor.

Policemen worked for half the day
   To clear things, and at last succeeded.
The helicopter whirled away
   To see where else it might be needed.

PETER SUFFOLK

SKILL LESSON 8

USING ORGANIZATIONAL CLUES

PART ONE

Take a quick look at the list that follows. Then close your book and try to recall as many of the names as you can.

Greenland
New Guinea
Borneo
Madagascar
Tasmania
Japan
Sumatra
New Zealand
Victoria
Iceland
Corsica

When you looked quickly at the list, did you think of any way in which the names were related to one another? Probably not, since there was nothing to give you a hint of what they all told about. Did you remember many of the names? Perhaps you just thought you were looking at a list of random names that did not seem to be connected in any way.

Often in a chapter that you need to study well, there will be clues that can help you see the relationships among pieces of information that the chapter gives. There may also be clues that help you note quickly the organization of the chapter and clues that help you remember much about what it says. Such clues are the chapter title, the major headings, and the subheadings.

Suppose you saw the following as the title of a chapter:

MAJOR ISLANDS OF THE WORLD

What would you expect the chapter to tell about? A good title for a chapter almost always is a strong clue to what the chapter tells about.

Do you think the chapter would be organized so that it tells about the islands in just any order? Probably not, because most chapters are organized according to some pattern. Look again now at the chapter title with its major headings and see if you can decide what the pattern is:

MAJOR ISLANDS OF THE WORLD

ATLANTIC ISLANDS
PACIFIC ISLANDS
ISLANDS OF THE EAST INDIES
ISLANDS OF THE ARCTIC
ISLANDS IN OTHER OCEANS AND SEAS

The organization of the chapter is geographic; that is, islands are presented according to the oceans in which they are located. The title of the chapter together with its major headings gives you clues to the organization of the material or information that the chapter is likely to contain.

A quick way of determining the organization of a book and its chapters is by looking at the TABLE OF CONTENTS. Located at the front of a book, a table of contents lists the contents of the book by chapters, units, or sections, which may be further divided into smaller parts. Look at the table of contents on the following page to see what the main headings are and what islands are discussed as subheadings under each main heading.

MAJOR ISLANDS OF THE WORLD

If the book that you are reading does not have a table of contents, you can use the chapter titles and headings within chapters to learn how the book is organized and what kind of information it contains.

Just by studying the table of contents or the title and headings for a chapter, you can learn many facts. For example, use the table of contents above to answer these questions:

1. *In what ocean are the British Isles located?*
2. *What is the world's largest island?*
3. *What is the world's most populated island?*
4. *What is a major island in the East Indies?*
5. *What three islands are located in the Arctic Ocean?*
6. *What two seas contain major islands?*

You can use a table of contents or the headings within a chapter to find out in general what information the chapter contains. If it seems to have the information you are looking for, you will probably need to use the index in the book to find the specific pages that will help you.

Discussion

Help your class answer these questions:
1. What information can the title of a chapter give you?
2. How do the major headings for a chapter relate to the chapter title?
3. How do the subheadings under a given main heading relate to that main heading?
4. What is a table of contents?
5. For what purpose can you use a table of contents?

PART TWO

After you have found the information you need, what can you do to insure that you will remember much of it for a report or a class discussion? One way is by MAKING NOTES about the information you read and organizing those notes into an OUTLINE that will help you recall the information any time you need it.

Suppose that you wanted information about only one part of the chapter about the major islands of the world — the islands of the Mediterranean Sea. Here is what your notes might look like for that section of the chapter.

ISLANDS OF THE MEDITERRANEAN SEA

1. Important islands include Corsica, Sardinia, Sicily, and Crete.
2. Corsica, located between France and northwest coast of Italy.
3. Corsica is fourth largest island.

4. Corsica, a French possession. Capital, Ajaccio.
5. Major exports of Corsica — wool, cheese.
6. Mines of Corsica produce granite, marble.
7. Sardinia is second largest island.
8. Sardinia, located west of Italy and south of Corsica.
9. Mining products of Sardinia — lead, iron, copper.
10. Major fishing products — tuna and sardines.
11. Important farm animals of Sardinia — goats, sheep.
12. Sicily is largest island.
13. Sicily, located at southern tip of Italy.
14. Mt. Etna, highest active volcano in Europe, located in Sicily.
15. Farming and fishing major occupations of Sicily.
16. Crete, a Greek island. Largest of Greek islands.
17. Crete, one of the earliest civilizations of the world.
18. Major exports of Crete — olive oil, wine, cheese, citrus fruits.

Generally, notes that you make on informative material are not organized in any special order except the order in which you found the information. When you outline the information, you will then be concerned with identifying and arranging in good order the MAIN TOPICS, SUBTOPICS, and DETAILS. In making notes, you may write whole sentences, but usually you write down the basic information without including unimportant words.

The notes on Islands of the Mediterranean Sea will not be difficult to organize into an outline since the very first note tells what those islands are and the other notes give information about the islands. The title for the notes will be the title for the outline. The main topics within the outline will be the four islands named. Each main topic is numbered with a Roman numeral followed by a period. Here is how the title and main topics would look in outline form:

ISLANDS OF THE MEDITERRANEAN SEA

I. Corsica
II. Sardinia
III. Sicily
IV. Crete

The main ideas about each main topic will be the subtopics in the outline. Each subtopic is indented under the main topic it tells about, is labeled with the correct capital letter, and is followed by a period. This is how the first part of an outline of the main topic and subtopics for the notes on pages 499–500 would look:

ISLANDS OF THE MEDITERRANEAN SEA

I. Corsica
    A. Located between France and northwest coast of Italy
    B. Fourth largest island
    C. French possession
    D. Capital, Ajaccio
    E. Major exports
    F. Mining products

In most outlines you will probably need to include points about the subtopics. Such points are called details. Each detail is indented under the subtopic it tells about and is labeled with the correct Arabic numeral followed by a period. For which subtopics about Corsica is there more information in the notes? Note 5 tells what the major exports are; and note 6 tells what the mines produce. With those points as details, an outline of the first main topic, Corsica, and its five subtopics would look like this:

ISLANDS OF THE MEDITERRANEAN SEA

I. Corsica
    A. Located between France and northwest coast of Italy
    B. Fourth largest island
    C. French possession
    D. Capital, Ajaccio
    E. Major exports
        1. Wool
        2. Cheese
    F. Mining products
        1. Granite
        2. Marble

With such an outline available, you can go over it as many times as you wish to help you fix in your mind important facts about a subject for a class discussion or a report.

Discussion

Help your class answer these questions:
1. Why is it sometimes important to make notes about informative material?
2. How are notes usually listed?
3. Why is it helpful to organize notes into an outline?
4. How are main topics, subtopics, and details labeled in an outline?

On your own

Copy from page 501 the title of the outline and the main topics, subtopics, and details about Corsica. Then use the information you find in the notes on page 500 to complete the section of the outline below about Sardinia. Complete the outline by listing the information about Sicily and Crete on your own. Be sure to use capital letters, Roman numerals, and Arabic numerals properly.

II. Sardinia
  A.
  B.
  C.
    1.
    2.
    3.
  D.
    1.
    2.
  E.
    1.
    2.

Checking your work

If you are asked to do so, read aloud the sections of your outline about Sardinia, Sicily, and Crete. Include the Roman numerals, Arabic numerals, capital letters, and punctuation as you read each main topic, subtopic, and detail.

Check your paper as others read their outlines. If their outlines differ from yours, check to see which wording gives the most information by using the fewest words.

Be sure to find out why any mistake you made is a mistake.

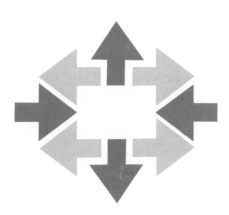

Meet the Armored Spoof

by Mary Sayre Haverstock

What has the ears of a donkey, the tail of a possum, the eyes of a pig, the hide of a Sherman tank, and the undying optimism of a near-sighted dachshund?

The armadillo is a riddle all right but not just because it presents such a whimsical appearance. The real riddle of the armadillo, as every Southern motorist knows, is, What is that critter doing *here?*

A good question. At one time the armadillo was the private property of the Lone Star State, like the blue bonnet and the yellow rose. Yet today the armadillo is becoming a more and more familiar sight throughout the southern and southwestern states, waddling purposefully along the highways at dusk, deeply intent on its own purposes. In less than a century the armadillo has marched far from its traditional home in Central and South America, north to the land of the cowboys, who tolerated it, and on to the plowed fields of the farmers, who detested it for its digging and rooting.

It has crossed the wide Mississippi River, ventured east all the way to Georgia and as far north as Kansas. Only ice and snow prevent this miniaturized Panzer tank from invading more distant territory.

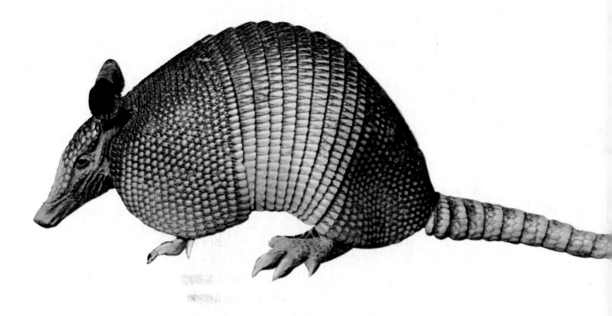

The armadillo, then, poses a challenging riddle indeed. All over the earth wildlife is in retreat; hundreds of species are fighting for their very survival. And yet the armadillo, which possesses no particular supernatural power, is not only surviving but flourishing and in regions that have proved increasingly inhospitable to other forms of wildlife. Naturally, the armadillo is now attracting the attention of a number of ecologists, mammalogists, and even some psychologists, who are trying to piece together an answer to the riddle.

But one does not need a Ph.D. to appreciate the novelty of this curious little twelve-pound tank. Many rural Southerners, when visited by their first armadillo, decided that it must be some sort of reptile or amphibian because of its scaly covering. The armadillo's armor is quite solid over the shoulders and haunches and face. The nine parallel bands over the abdomen from which the species gets its name (literally, "nine belts") are flexible, allowing the animal to roll up in a most unreptilelike fashion when necessary. The armadillo also sports a few sparse hairs on its belly — not what one would call fur exactly but enough to set this creature apart from the lizards and alligators. What, then, is it? In Mississippi they have named it "gravedigger" and "poor man's pig." In other localities it became known as "ground hog," a name that would fit the armadillo to perfection were it not already assigned elsewhere. Certainly, the armadillo's life-style resembles the hog's: It has the same preoccupied way of rooting for its food, and it speaks with a very piglike grunt. Too, it shares the pig's nearsighted, nose-to-the-ground demeanor, and people who have sampled the flesh of the armadillo say that it even tastes a little like pork.

The armadillo is neither lizard nor pig but America's only living representative of the strange mammalian order called *Edentata* (ē'-dĕn-tāt'-ə). Of the three families in the order it would be hard to decide which is the most bizarre in appearance or habits: the anteaters, the sloths, or the armadillos. Though *edentate* means "toothless," the nine-banded armadillo has thirty-two rudimentary teeth; and its cousin, the giant armadillo of South America, has more teeth than any other mammal. These are not biting teeth, however, but primitive molars of uncertain usefulness.

Despite the armadillo's dental problems it manages to enjoy a varied and tasty diet, including beetles, ants, scorpions, spiders, skinks, snakes (small ones), berries, earthworms, mushrooms, and termites. These delicacies it seeks out by twilight and after dark — unless the weather is very cold — grunting and rooting through the underbrush, rattling dry leaves and crunching twigs as if oblivious to all enemies. Stealth seems to be unknown to the armadillo, and hunters will swear that one can make as much noise as a whole family of deer and usually does. But the armadillo can well afford to be self-confident, and even cocky, for it has two highly effective defense mechanisms ready in case of human or animal threat and a third to use in case of flash floods.

First in the armadillo's line of defense is escape. Its sharp claws make this one of the most phenomenal earthmovers in the animal kingdom! In less time than it takes to tell about it, a frightened armadillo can dig itself completely out of sight. Even in hard ground the disappearing act can be accomplished in a minute or two.

Second in its line of defense, if the danger is so imminent or the

earth so impregnable that digging fails, the armadillo simply curls up into a ball, so that it is almost completely encased in leather-hard armor. Faced with this jaw-breaking prospect, most would-be predators are willing to look elsewhere for their dinner.

Third in the armadillo's bag of tricks is the talent which may have brought the first of these animals across the Mississippi back in the 1920's and which keeps it from drowning when floodwaters inundate the riverbanks and lowlands of which it is so fond. At such times it fills its stomach and intestine with gulp after gulp of air and, thus inflated, floats serenely to safety.

These ingenious defenses may explain some of the armadillo's staying power, but other mammals have evolved equally effective survival techniques, and still their range and number decline. What, then, is the armadillo's secret?

Scientists tend to agree that the armadillo is one animal that has been helped, not hindered, by man's encroachment on the wilderness. As man cleared the lowlands and cut down the forests, he inadvertently created an ideal environment for the armadillo, which is happiest in cut-over and second-growth areas. And, fortunately for the armadillo, man's plans for developing the land have had little effect on the armadillo's nesting places, which are located in underground burrows or little rocky niches.

Man's crops have also lured the armadillo into new regions, for this animal is inordinately fond of peanuts, cantaloupe, watermelon, and tomatoes, as well as the beetles that abound in cane fields.

Man has even provided the armadillo with transportation from time to time. A good many found their way east in cattle cars from Texas, from which they disembarked along with the official cargo at station stops throughout the Gulf States.

Then there is the strange case of the East Florida colony. One legend has it that a young Marine from Texas brought a pair of armadillos with him when he was quartered in Florida during World War I. When the war was over, he left his pets behind. Another story tells of a pair brought in 1922 for exhibition at a private zoo in the town of Cocoa. They soon dug their way to freedom, and a year or so later there were lots of little armadillos in the neighborhood. There is no reason to doubt these origin-myths, for the reproductive capacity of the nine-banded armadillo is as impressive as its workings. Each pair of armadillos can be counted upon to produce four identical offspring in a season. In early spring four females or four males, all exactly alike, join the family circle. The quadruplets arrive with their eyes open and are up and around in a day or two, growing rapidly.

But of all man's contributions to the armadillo's welfare, none has been as spectacular as the virtual elimination of all the armadillo's natural enemies. It was only after the retreat of the wildcats, wolves, bears, and coyotes that the great armadillo advance could begin, for these were the only animals capable of penetrating the armadillo's defenses, whether by stealth or by strength or by swiftness of attack. Now that they have effectively passed from the scene, the armadillo needs to fear only freezing weather and the farmer's shotgun. Heavy frost is the armadillo's greatest danger; hundreds are found dead after every bad cold spell. And man, who for so long unwittingly encouraged the armadillo in its forward march, now finds that the animal can make quite a nuisance of itself. Although by its incessant rooting and digging the armadillo serves the farmer as an energetic, if unpaid, tiller of soil, and although it makes significant inroads on crop-damaging insects, it tears up many a field.

Yet it seems certain that without the coyote, bobcat, jaguar, and bear to thin its numbers, and with man's continued cooperation, the armadillo is here to stay.

DISCUSSION

1. Why is the armadillo a challenging riddle?
2. What are the armadillo's three defense mechanisms?
3. What are the armadillo's secrets of survival?
4. Why does the author call the armadillo a "miniaturized Panzer tank"?
5. What do you think scientists will do with the knowledge they get from studying the armadillo?
6. What two things could cause the armadillo's extinction? Do you think "the armadillo is here to stay"? Why or why not?
7. Are there other members of the animal world that you think would be more important to save from extinction than the armadillo? Why do you think as you do?

BITTER IS THE HAWK'S PATH

by Jean McCord

"In May," Miss Waterman announced one day in class, "there will be a play put on down at the university. The lines will all be in French, and although you might not understand every word, still you are second-year students and should be able to get the gist of it."

She looked down her rows of sleepy students, February's dullness lying over them like a damp blanket.

"Especially since," she said, "we will read the play first, taking turns in speaking the parts."

Here she looked hard at Sam Joe Falcon and Billy Joe Reed. These two were best friends, although they were about as much alike as a giraffe and a snake. The only thing they really had in common was their middle name.

Sam Joe was dark, rawboned, and unfinished yet. His mother had come right off the Indian reservation ten miles outside of town. His last name wasn't even Falcon, but he had liked the sound of that, so he had given it to himself. His father had long since left the country.

Billy Joe's father owned the biggest general store in the whole northern part of the state. Billy Joe owned a car but, as yet, had no license to drive. He came and went as he pleased. He was small, all knit-up as if he already had all his growth in this fourteenth year, and tense all the time, even in his sleep. His mother had died when he was very little. Sometimes in the middle of the night he cried. No one knew this, not even himself.

Miss Waterman looked on them both with a jaundiced eye. It wasn't that they were insolent or disorderly — she wouldn't have stood for that — only that neither of them ever did what he was really capable of.

From his mother Sam Joe knew French, probably better than the teacher. She didn't even know why he was in her class, unless it was to give himself a snap course with an easy grade. Why, then, did he sit at the back of the room like a big buffoon and laugh softly every time she pronounced a new word and when she called on him to recite, stumble and falter over the words?

And Billy Joe was no better. Miss Waterman knew he had the highest I.Q. in her class. Yet he turned in sloppy work that barely gave him a passing grade.

Well, Miss Waterman often thought to herself, she did what she could. She taught. It was up to the student to open his mind and receive. And if he wouldn't . . . there was no key yet made for teachers that could open a closed and locked mind.

"That's all," Miss Waterman said in a final tone. "Make your plans, then, for the weekend of the twenty-fifth of May. We will leave here Friday after classes, attend the play on Saturday afternoon, and return home on Sunday. Transportation on the school bus has been arranged. Class dismissed."

Ordinarily she spoke to them in French, but on occasions like this or in announcing a test, she used English so no one could claim later he hadn't understood. Miss Waterman was not one to let the wool be pulled over her eyes.

Sam Joe and Billy Joe were the first ones out of the room. That was half the reason they had chosen their seats at the back. The other half was a vain hope that Miss Waterman might not call on them as often, but she had scotched this at the very beginning. She went up and down the rows in turn, skipping no one.

In the corridor Billy Joe said, "Let's go down to the gym and shoot a few baskets." He liked to play the game but was constantly handicapped by his lack of wind and his short legs.

Sam Joe was the top scorer on the team, with his accurate eye and long reach. He had helped boost the school to second place in the northern league. He was conscious that he was *somebody* as far as athletics went, though he scorned to fill any hero's role. And he ignored the girls that clustered in knots in the hallways, laughing and talking like a gaggle of geese till a fellow walked by; then they would drop into hissing whispers. Was it his imagination that always made him feel they were whispering about him? He would straighten his back and shove his thumbs deep into his pants waist — a dangerous move, since he wore his blue jeans low on his narrow hips, and it looked as if he so much as shivered, they might drop completely.

The two of them practiced in the gym till it was dark, and the janitor, finishing his chores, turned off the lights. Then they sauntered uptown, still warm enough from their exercise to ignore the biting cold.

"Listen, friend." Billy Joe's words made smoke clouds in front of his face. "Are you going on that trip? I mean, do you really want to go?"

"Well, maybe. I guess my rich old lady could spare me the dough." This was a joke, and they both knew it. Sam Joe's mother didn't make a living for them working at her chambermaid job at the local hotel. Whenever Sam Joe made any money, he gave it to her, keeping only a dollar for himself.

In the winter there was little he could do to make money. He ran a single trapline out by Lake Little Bear, but this winter had been extremely hard. His total catch was two muskrats and a fox, and he hadn't sold the skins yet. He was looking forward to summer when he was sure he could make some real money guiding the tourists who came to fish. Last summer he had guided three parties and done well. Now he was older and had grown much bigger. In June, when the season opened, he would put a sign in the general store window. Billy Joe, who worked there when he felt like it, would steer Sam Joe's way any fishermen who asked for a guide.

But right now he was dead broke. And his boots had rips along the seams, where the snow crept in. It was seeping in now, wetting his socks. "Probably get chilblains before winter's over," he thought grumpily.

The boys walked to the post-office corner and stood silently for a moment before parting. Neither of them kept any regular hours for meals. Billy Joe's father would still be in the store. He worked long hours there, using the store for a home and using his home as he would a hotel — to sleep.

"Well, see you." Billy Joe spun on his heel and set off for the store. He would wait around until his father closed up, and they would go home together. They seldom cooked a meal. If they did attempt it, it was only to open a can of sardines or heat up a can of beans. But mostly they went to a restaurant, always the same one, the Pickerel Cafe. They had become used to the food and the waitress there.

Sam Joe stamped his feet unfeelingly on the icy sidewalk, undecided where to go. He could sneak round to the side door of the hotel kitchen and see if his mother could smuggle him something to eat. He could go on home to the two cold rooms they rented over a garage. Or he could wander on down to the firehouse where it was warm, and sometimes one of the men offered him a sandwich from a lunch basket, and the big blue enamel coffeepot was always full.

Automatically, he started for there but then stopped a moment, hunched up in his jacket to think. He'd gone there last night, and Jim Boyd had passed him his whole supper, saying, "Sam Joe, my wife's a terrible cook. Get rid of this, will you, as a favor to me? And I'll step across the street to the diner for some decent grub."

Sam Joe had eaten it all, shoveled it down, he remembered, because he'd felt like a starving wolf. It wasn't the first time Jim Boyd had said the same thing to him. But tonight standing here, the dry cold had cleared his head or something, and he realized that Jim's food wasn't all that bad. In fact, Mrs. Boyd seemed to be a pretty darned good cook.

Immediately, he turned around and headed for home. An angry flush spread down his neck as he realized the firemen fed him as they did a hungry dog who also showed up there once in a while.

His mother wasn't home. He hadn't expected her to be. When her work shift was over, she usually stayed on in the kitchen, talking and playing rummy with the other women.

There were a few things in the cupboard, mostly staples. A pan of cold cornmeal sat on the sink, left over from breakfast. Sam Joe fried this in grease, turned it out on a piece of bread, and spread peanut butter on top. He liked odd food combinations, his favorite being potatoes and honey.

With the edge taken off his hunger, he set about making a fire in the pot-bellied wood stove that was their heat source. While the fire caught, he peeled five potatoes to make into a soup. This he would sweeten with a big dollop of honey, and it would fill him up until breakfast.

He sat down on a kitchen chair and, leaning back, stretched his legs out with his boots on top of the stove. A box of hazelnuts dried behind the stove, and seeing them turned his thoughts to summer and the good times he had with Billy Joe. They knew every bit of the country for miles around, had tramped around in it first as small boys looking for adventure and now as fishermen and the big hunters they fancied themselves to be. Sam Joe knew he was going to be a good hunter; he had all the natural instincts of patience, stealth, and interest in the habits of animals. And he deeply wished that there were someone who could teach him the things that he was working hard to teach himself. He could have gone out to the reservation, but he had no real ties there.

One time he and Billy Joe had gone there, hiking part of the way and then catching a ride with a family coming back from town. They had walked around, looking hard at the clapboard shacks and the broken windows patched with cardboard.

"Wow!" Billy Joe snubbed up his nose. "Did your mother really come from here? I mean, no offense, but no wonder she moved into town. Don't your people . . ."

Sam Joe's eyes narrowed in anger, and he kicked an empty oil can out of the dirt road up onto someone's front steps. "They aren't my people," he muttered. "I got no people. Just me. I'm a lone wolf." He'd doubled up his fist and shoved it under Billy Joe's nose. "But you say one more word about me, and I'll let you have it."

"OK! OK!" Billy Joe wanted no fight. He always lost. "But if they're not your people, then we're not talking about you, are we?"

"Just never mind. Your old man's quick enough to take their money when they go into his store."

"Yeah." Billy Joe laughed. "He sure don't run 'em out."

"Come on." Sam Joe spun around, his mouth set in a slit. "What we doin' here, anyway? We got no business here. Let's get off the place."

They had walked all the way back to town in silence, and every step of the way Sam Joe had fought a terrible urge to set upon his friend and beat him senseless.

Billy Joe must have known it. He never mentioned the reservation again, and they never went back there. But they went everywhere else together. Billy Joe's quick tongue and sense of sarcasm brought him to the verge of many fights, but the offended person always backed off when he saw that he would also have to fight Sam Joe.

Together they constituted a gang of two.

In summer if they hiked down to their favorite swimming place at the lake and found it occupied, they either drove the other boys off, if there weren't too many, or went on farther around the lake where they could swim in splendid solitude.

Sam Joe was a phenomenal swimmer. He beat Billy Joe in every race and could swim under water for a hundred feet, popping to the surface like a loon and going down again before Billy Joe could spot him.

"Some day that guy's going to drown himself," Billy Joe would sputter. The thought half-pleased him; but then, thinking of what it would be like without his pal, he would drag himself up on the bank until he could spot Sam Joe's head.

In the winter they didn't do much. Billy Joe had sinus and respiratory problems. He had never even gone with Sam Joe to check on the trapline, and neither one of them, out of some sense of awkwardness, ever went to the other's home.

The stove was smoking. As in a dream Sam Joe leaned forward, fixed the draft, and reached into the box for a handful of nuts. He cracked them with his teeth and rolled the nuts around his tongue. He remembered the day he and Billy Joe had picked them. Hot. The sun rolling high overhead like a flaming beachball. Their shirts sticking to the middle of their backs, till with unspoken accord, they stopped and stripped them off. He intended to fill his gunny sack if Billy Joe would cooperate a little.

They rambled out a dirt road, away from town, toward a large stand of the wild hazel bushes growing in someone's pasture land. They didn't know whose. It didn't matter. These bushes grew all over the country, a pest to most farmers.

They'd started picking and kept going till the sack was half filled. Then they stopped to rest awhile. They were in a central clearing, encircled, the bushes growing in massive clumps higher than their heads. The sun beat down as if they were beneath a magnifying glass. Sam Joe's head began to ache, and a pulse throbbed deeply in his throat. He sat, face turned up to the sky, eyes closed, until the sun burned through his lids, and he could see it as a double image, incandescent ... floating.... Then a feeling shook him, and he shivered slightly from the strangeness of it. He wanted to jump up, fling off his clothes, and do a dance to the sun god. He wanted to stomp and howl and stretch himself out upon the earth as a living sacrifice. His fingers dug into the dirt to restrain himself.

"Nuts!" groaned Billy Joe. "We're crazy for working in this heat. Let's give it up and go for a swim." He rose to his feet listlessly. "Come on. I'll have a stroke if we don't get out of this sun."

They'd headed for the lake, a mile away, leaving the bag of nuts behind. Sam Joe had gone back for it later.

But thinking about that experience in the days that passed made him wonder about himself. Was he that much different from the other boys he knew? Was there really something in his blood that he would never escape, an ancient knowledge of old customs, old beliefs? In short, was he an Indian? Or was he a white man? Or did he even have a choice?

The stench of his boots burning on the stove brought him abruptly back to the moment. Now he had done it! If his boots had been bad before, they were ruined now. In their sodden condition he had baked them into shapeless lumps. It was all he could do to pull them off his feet.

The next morning, dressing for school, he looked at them, despair pulling down the corners of his mouth. But again, as in many times past, he had no choice. It was either put them on in their ruined condition or pad off to school barefooted.

At the end of the third period Billy Joe caught up with him. They had had no classes together before then.

Sam Joe's feet were killing him. They were chafed raw in spots and felt like a vise had tightened on each of them. He limped wearily down the hallway.

"Hey," Billy Joe said, looking down, "what's the matter? Cut your foot or something?"

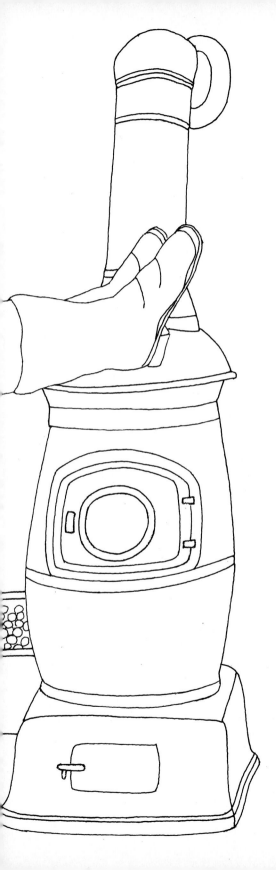

"No!" Sam Joe laughed shortly. "Baked my boots. Turned 'em into cast iron."

"Well, for Pete's sake! You can't walk around in those things. And just what'll you wear on our trip to the big city? Look," he said, "we'll go down to the store after last class. You can pick out a pair, and my dad can give you credit. Just till you get a summer guide job," he put in hastily as he saw Sam Joe's face darken.

"I don't want charity!" Sam Joe forced himself to straighten up and clomp along without limping.

"Charity?" Billy Joe exploded, "Where's charity in buying on time? Everybody does it. You're just so ignorant, you don't know anything about business. Why, my dad borrows all the time. He puts his own money into buying land and borrows on that to run the business. Ah, what do you know about it, anyway?" Billy Joe sounded disgusted.

By the end of the day Sam Joe thought he was permanently crippled. He had to go to the store, but it was a bitter thing to do without money. He knew that the Indians off the reservation came in there and ran up large bills, which half the time they couldn't pay for months or even years.

Then the days slipped by so fast it was almost the end of the school year, and the weekend of the French play came up.

On Wednesday, Sam Joe made up his mind that he wasn't going; he was as poor as a dead horse. Then he remembered his skins. He bundled them up and sold them to a full-blood Indian who trapped for a living. They were thin and ratty-looking, and the trapper gave him only two dollars for the three of them. Sam Joe calculated carefully and figured he could make it through the weekend.

"I'm going to ask for a written report of the trip and the play. In French, of course," Miss Waterman warned her class. "Don't let your thoughts go off woolgathering while you should be listening."

So he had to go.

The trip down was enjoyable to Sam Joe. He had never been to the city before, and he kept his eyes open for everything new.

Billy Joe had been there many times. It was old stuff to him.

Accommodations had been booked for them at one of the university dormitories. On Saturday morning, true to their usual pattern, both boys decided to cut away from the school group and go sightseeing on their own. They wandered around the campus grounds, peering critically at all the buildings, trying to guess what was taught in each one. It seemed like a huge institution after the small school they were used to, and it made them feel insignificant and, at the same time, derisive.

"You know," Billy Joe mused, "we'll be coming down here in a few years. And I don't even know yet what I want to study. Have you ever thought of being an engineer? You know, build bridges, roads, and that stuff?"

"No," Sam Joe answered, "I mean, not an engineer. If I can, I'll be a forestry ranger. I think about our woods back home. They're being cut out all the time. And the lakes and rivers. They're being fished out. Why, in another twenty years . . ." He fell silent. He had startled himself into expressing thoughts that had lain far beneath the surface of his mind. He had never told himself before that he would study and work to become a conservation officer. But the thought pleased him very much.

"Anyway," he said gruffly, "what do you mean, *we'll* be coming down here? I'd have to work for years to scrape up the dough."

"Ah," Billy Joe scuffed at the sidewalk. "Maybe a basketball scholarship will get you here. Or I could talk my dad into sponsoring you. Why not? He wants me to go on to school. I could just say it's me and you or no deal."

"Hah!" Sam Joe snorted. "What kind of a bluff is that? You think you're tougher than your old man?"

"I get what I want." Billy Joe was complacent. But he didn't want to own up to the fact that coming down to this big school frightened him. He needed Sam Joe, although nothing in the world could have made him admit it aloud. "Come on. Let's find a place and eat. I'm hungry."

They saw a restaurant and went in. Sam Joe let Billy Joe lead the way; he felt extremely ill at ease. One glance at the menu told him he couldn't afford a thing on it. He had a cup of coffee while Billy Joe ate.

They walked around the business section some more. Billy Joe went into three stores and made several purchases. Sam Joe wondered idly what Billy Joe could possibly need to buy when he had a whole store at home to choose things from.

At two o'clock they joined their group in front of the auditorium. Miss Waterman gave them a furious glare as they came sauntering up. She had been worried, wondering what mischief they might have been up to, but with great self-restraint she said nothing.

Sam Joe enjoyed the play. It was the first one he'd ever been to, and the fact that it was in French gave him an edge on everybody.

"Are you getting all this?" Billy Joe's elbow poked him once. "Because you'll sure have to fill me in before Monday," he muttered. He was angry with himself and began working up a good rage against Miss Waterman too. Most of the play was over his head, the actors spoke their lines too fast, and the play was too hard to understand. Yet he knew it was his own fault because he hadn't paid attention during the days that had been spent on it in class.

Now he quit listening entirely and leaned back in his seat, looking around the darkened auditorium. Somehow his anger began to focus on

Sam Joe, especially at one point where Sam Joe laughed aloud.

When the play was over, Billy Joe stamped morosely up the aisle. He went back to his room, showered and changed clothes, and went out into the city alone.

Sam Joe loafed around the dormitory for a while; then, not knowing quite what to do, he joined a group of his fellow students going out for supper. Being alone was a new and uneasy experience for him. He refused even to answer when one of the fellows asked him, "Hey, where's your sidekick?"

He ordered a hamburger and ate it slowly, making it last as long as the others had anything on their plates.

The room was still empty when he went back to it. At nine thirty Billy Joe sauntered in, a half-hour later than they had been told to check in. Somehow he had talked his way past the housemother.

In the morning Billy Joe seemed in a better mood. They went out for breakfast together, and Sam Joe, figuring quickly, had toast and coffee. The play had been free, no charge for the students, but there was a dollar fee for the room. When he paid that, he would have just a dime left.

At noontime they were to meet at the bus for the return trip home.

Back in their room Billy Joe whistled cheerfully while he gathered his clothes. He was finished ahead of Sam Joe and had started out the door when he turned back casually.

"Say," he said in an offhand voice, "lend me fifty cents, will ya?"

Sam Joe looked up from folding his clothes into a bag. "I can't. . . ." he answered. He started to say, "I've only got a dollar and ten cents," but the words choked themselves down into his throat.

Billy Joe made a derisive noise and stood looking at him.

Sam Joe stepped into the bathroom to check for anything he might have forgotten. Just for general appearance he combed his hair again. Looking into the mirror reminded him of a scene from the play. He laughed softly, still full of enjoyment.

When he walked back into the bedroom, Billy Joe was gone. Sam Joe put on his jacket, automatically feeling in the pocket. A blow of intense disbelief hit him, and he stopped short, halfway out the door. The dollar was gone! Only a dime lay on his trembling palm. Yet the money had been there a few minutes ago.

He stood, stricken and aching, unable to believe what had happened. Then intense fury burned within him. He thought of dashing after Billy Joe to catch him. He would break his neck. But he knew it was too late.

He delayed as long as he could, until only minutes were left to be on the bus. Then in haste he picked up his grip and hurried downstairs. The housemother sat behind her desk in the lobby.

He turned his face away and tried to hide his bag by clutching it against his chest. He was almost to the door when the woman looked up.

"Boy!" she called. "Just a minute, boy."

He stopped in his tracks, turned, and went back, too ashamed to look at her.

"There's a one-dollar charge for your lodging."

"Yes, ma'am," he mumbled, and stood there helpless. In desperation he looked around the lobby, but everyone from his class was gone. He opened his mouth, but nothing would come out, so he snapped it shut again.

The woman was checking over her accounts. After a minute she looked up, her cold gray eyes staring at him from behind steel-rimmed glasses. Neither of them spoke. She folded her hands in front of her in a patient gesture.

Sam Joe set down his bag. He dug in all his pockets, then silently laid his dime on her desk.

The woman looked first at it, then at him.

"That's all you have, is that it?" Her eyes were not as cold, but Sam Joe wasn't looking at them. He nodded, and he sensed, rather than saw, her shrug of dismissal. Quickly he stooped for his bag and left.

The bus engine was running when he got to it. They had all been waiting for him.

Billy Joe was sitting alone, saving a seat for him.

He sidled into it, and with teeth clenched, he said softly, "Gimme back that money!" He had some vague idea of dashing back to the woman with it.

Billy Joe stared at him, fear kindling in his eyes, but then said in a loud voice, "Ah, knock it off your bill at my dad's store."

The other students near them, sensing trouble, turned in their seats and listened curiously.

Sam Joe looked at him a long moment, lurching with the motion of the bus starting up. Then he got up and found a seat at the back. He sat stony faced and unmoving for the whole trip home.

"What could be the matter with Sam Joe?" Miss Waterman wondered to herself. She thought of it Sunday evening and throughout the entire week. Then on Friday she knew.

Billy Joe had a bad attack of asthma and couldn't come to classes for the rest of the school year. He neglected to turn in his essay on the trip.

Sam Joe turned his in late. It was brief and in poorly spelled French:

I went to the city. I heard a play all in French. It was good. My best friend was with me, and he didn't like it. He went out on the town and spent all his money. Then behind my back he took half of my money. I had caught only three skins. You might say he stole half of them. I couldn't pay my bill. Why did he have to do it? I went down to the city with a friend, but I came home without one. I wish I knew why he did it to me.

"Oh, Sam Joe." Miss Waterman laid her head on her desk and wept. "My poor, poor boy." She forgave him for all the times he had laughed in class. She wanted to rush over to his home, comfort him, explain to him that people, friends even, often did things that had deeper meanings. "If I could only make you see," she thought, "Billy Joe didn't want or need your money. He wanted your strength, your power, your size, your knowledge of French, your . . . oh, everything you are or have, except your money. But money is all he knows. His only value. He beat you down with his only weapon."

But, of course, she did and said none of these things. There is no salve for the wounds of a friendship betrayed. One might as well try to follow the path of the wind.

DISCUSSION

1. Why was Miss Waterman not pleased with Sam Joe and Billy Joe? What was the only thing she thought they had in common? How did she think they were different?

2. While Sam Joe dreamed of his friendship and adventures with Billy Joe, what happened to his boots? How did he get new ones? Why was he bitter about the way he got them?

3. When did Billy Joe become angry with Sam Joe? Why did he do so? What did Billy Joe do to hurt Sam Joe? How did this cause Sam Joe embarrassment?

4. What attitude or value kept Billy Joe from being a loyal friend to Sam Joe?

5. What do you think were the reasons that these two boys, who had such different backgrounds, became such good friends?

6. What events in the story brought out the fact that Sam Joe had a great deal of pride and didn't like to accept charity? In what ways was he self-reliant?

7. What did you learn about Sam Joe and Billy Joe's ideas for the future? What did their conversation about their futures tell you about each boy?

8. When Sam Joe demanded his money back, what did Billy Joe tell him to do? Why do you think he deliberately hurt Sam Joe in front of his classmates on the bus?

9. Do you agree with the author that there is "no salve for the wounds of a friendship betrayed"?
10. Do you think Miss Waterman should have tried to help Sam Joe understand why his friend had betrayed him? Why or why not?
11. Sam Joe could have permanently damaged his feet by continuing to wear his baked boots. Do you think he should have bought the boots on credit? Why or why not? Do you think there are times when one can carry pride too far? Why do you think as you do?
12. The majority of the people in the United States buy some things on credit. How is this helpful? How can it be dangerous?
13. What is the connection between the title of the story and the last name Sam Joe chose for himself? Do you think the title is an appropriate one? Why do you think as you do?

AUTHOR

Jean McCord, who was born in Hayward, Wisconsin, and who grew up in the West, has written two collections of stories for young people. Her first collection, *Deep Where the Octopi Lie,* was published in 1968. Her second, from which the selection you have just read was taken and which is also titled *Bitter Is the Hawk's Path,* was published in 1971.

Many of Miss McCord's stories are based on recollections of things she saw or heard about as a teen-ager. For many years, including the two she spent in the army, the little white dog who appears in several of her stories was her constant companion. They traveled over 50,000 miles together.

Miss McCord, who holds a degree in biological sciences from the University of California, now lives in California.

QUILT

A PATRIOTIC LULLABY

The quilt that covers all of us, to date,
Has patches numbered 1 to 48,°
Five northern rents, a crooked central seam,
    A ragged eastern edge, a way
    Of bunching uglily, and a
Perhaps too energetic color scheme.

Though shaken every twenty years, this fine
Old quilt was never beaten on the line.
It took long making. Generations passed
    While thread was sought, and calico
    And silk were coaxed from Mexico
And France. The biggest squares were added last.

Don't kick your covers, son. The bed is built
So you can never shake the clinging quilt
That blanketed your birth and tries to keep
    Your waking warm, impalpable
    As atmosphere. As earth it shall
Be tucked about you through your longest sleep.

°Since I composed this rather nifty
  Couplet, the number rose to 50.

JOHN UPDIKE

524

During the American Revolution, Johnny Tremain works as a courier for Mr. Lorne, printer of the patriotic newspaper, the Boston Observer. Johnny and Rab, Mr. Lorne's nephew, use the loft above the printing shop as their sleeping quarters. This same loft regularly serves another and more important function — a secret meeting place for a powerful group of Boston patriots, the Boston Observers, who are led by Samuel Adams.

A WORLD TO COME

Esther Forbes

It was fall, and for the last time Samuel Adams bade Johnny summon the Boston Observers for eight o'clock that night.

"After this we will not meet again, for I believe General Gage knows all about us. He might be moved to arrest Mr. Lorne. He might send soldiers to arrest us all."

"I hardly think they would hang the whole club, sir. Only you and Mr. Hancock."

Johnny had meant this for a compliment, but Sam Adams looked more startled than pleased.

"It has been noticed that every so often many of us are seen going up and down Salt Lane, entering the printing shop. We must, in the future, meet in small groups. But once more, and for the last time . . . and make us a good punch."

As Johnny went from house to house, talking about unpaid bills of eight shillings, he was thinking of the punch. Not one ship had come into Boston for five months except British ships. Only the British officers had limes, lemons, and oranges these days — they and their friends among the Boston Tories. Miss Lyte had God's plenty of friends among the British officers. He'd get his tropical fruit there.

Mrs. Bessie, the Lyte's cook, listened to him.

"And who's going to eat these fruits or drink them, if I do give you some?"

"Well . . . Sam Adams for one."

"Don't say any more. Give me your dispatch bag, Johnny." She returned with it bulging.

It would be a small meeting for, of the twenty-two original members, many had already left town to get away from the threat of arrest by the British. Josiah Quincy was in England. Of the three revolutionary doctors only Church and Warren remained. Doctor Young had gone to a safer spot. James Otis was at the moment in Boston. Johnny had not notified him, although he had founded this club in the first place. Ever since he had grown so odd, the other members did not wish him about, even in his lucid periods. He talked and talked. Nobody could get a word in edgewise when James Otis talked.

This, the last meeting, started with the punch bowl on the table instead of ending with it. They were talking about how General Gage had at last dared send out a sortie beyond the gate of Boston and, before the Minute Men got word of their plans, they had seized cannon and gunpowder in Charlestown and had gotten into their boats and returned to Boston. Not one shot had been fired, and it was all too late when the alarm had been spread and thousands of armed farmers had arrived. By then the British were safe home again. Yet, Sam Adams protested, this rising up of an army of a thousand from the very soil of New England had badly frightened General Gage. Once the alarm spread that the British had left Boston, the system of calling up the Minute Men had worked well indeed. The trouble had been in Boston itself.

"In other words, gentlemen, it was our fault. If we could have known but an hour, two hours, in advance what the British were intending, our men would have been there before the British troops arrived instead of a half-hour after they left."

Johnny had been told to carry letters for the British officers and to keep on good terms with their grooms and stable boys over at the Afric Queen. Somehow he had failed. He hadn't known. Nobody had known that two hundred and sixty redcoats were getting into boats, slipping off up the Mystic River, seizing Yankee gunpowder, and rowing it back to Castle Island for themselves.

Paul Revere was saying, "We must organize a better system of watching their movements — but in such a way that they will not realize they are being watched."

Sam and John Adams were standing, and the other members were crowding about them, shaking

hands with them, wishing them success at the Continental Congress in Philadelphia. They were starting the next day. Everyone was ready to give them advice — whom to see, what to say, or to prophesy the outcome of this Congress. Paul Revere and Joseph Warren were apart a little, making plans for that spy system, which was needed badly. They called Johnny to them, but he was too intent on listening to a man standing near the Adamses: "But there must be some hope we can still patch up our differences with England. Sir, you will work for peace?"

Sam Adams said nothing for a moment. He trusted these men about him as he trusted no one else in the world.

"No. That time is past. I will work for war: the complete freedom of these colonies from any European power. We can have that freedom only by fighting for it. God grant we fight soon. For ten years we've tried this and we've tried that. We've tried to placate them and they to placate us. Gentlemen, you know it has not worked. I will not work for peace. Peace, peace — and there is no peace. But I will, in Philadelphia, play a cautious part, not throw all my cards on the table. Oh, no. But nevertheless I will work for but one thing. War — bloody and terrible death and destruction. But out of it shall come such a country as was never seen on this earth before. We will fight. . . ."

There was a heavy footstep across the floor of the shop below. Rab leaped to the ladder's head.

"James Otis," he reported to the men standing about Adams.

"Well," said Sam Adams a little crossly, "no one needs stay and listen to *him*. Still talking about the natural rights of man — and the glories of the British Empire! You and I, John, had as well go home and get a good night's sleep before leaving at dawn tomorrow."

Otis pulled his bulk up the ladder. If no one was glad to see him, at least no one was so discourteous as to leave. Mr. Otis was immediately shown every honor and given a comfortable armchair and a tankard of punch. Seemingly, he was not in a talkative mood tonight. The broad, ruddy, good-natured face turned left and right, nodding casually to his friends, taking it for granted that he was still a great man among them instead of a milestone they all believed they had passed years before.

He sniffed at his punch and sipped a little.

"Sammy," he said to Sam Adams, "my coming interrupted something you were saying. . . . 'We will fight.' You had got that far."

"Why, yes. That's no secret."

"For what will we fight?"

"To free Boston from these infernal redcoats and . . ."

"No," said Otis. "Boy, give me more punch. That's not enough reason for going into a war. Did any occupied city ever have better treatment than we've had from the British? Has one rebellious newspaper been stopped — one treasonable speech? Where are the firing squads and the jails jammed with political prisoners? What about the gallows for you, Sam Adams, and you, John Hancock? It has never been set up. I hate those infernal British troops spread all over my town as much as you do. Can't move these days without stepping on a soldier. But we are not going off into a civil war merely to get them out of Boston. Why are we going to fight? Why, why?"

There was an embarrassed silence. Sam Adams was the acknowledged ringleader. It was for him to speak now.

"We will fight for the rights of Americans. England cannot take our money away by taxes."

"No, no. For something more important than the pocketbooks of our American citizens."

Rab said, "For the rights of Englishmen — everywhere."

"Why stop with Englishmen?" Otis was warming up. He had a wide mouth, crooked and generous. He settled back in his chair, and then he began to talk. It was such talk as Johnny had never heard before. The words surged up through the big body and flowed out of the broad mouth. He never raised his voice, and he went on and on. Sometimes Johnny felt so intoxicated by the mere sound of the words that he hardly followed the sense. That soft, low voice flowed over him — submerged him.

"... For men and women and children all over the world," he said. "You were right, boy, for even as we shoot down the British soldiers, we are fighting for rights such as they will be enjoying a hundred years from now.

"... There shall be no more tyranny. A handful of men cannot seize power over thousands. A man shall choose who it is shall rule over him.

"... The peasants of France, the serfs of Russia. Hardly more than animals now. But because we fight, they shall see freedom like a new sun rising in the west. Those natural rights God has given to every man, no matter how humble...." He smiled suddenly and said, "or crazy," and took a good pull on his tankard.

"... The battle we win over the worst in England shall benefit the best in England. How well are they over there represented when it comes to taxes? Not very well. It will be better for them when we have won this war.

"Will French peasants go on forever pulling off their caps and saying, 'Oui, Monsieur,' when the gold coaches run down their children? They will not. Italy. And all those German states. Are they nothing but soldiers? Will no one show them the rights of good citizens? So we hold up our torch — and do not forget it was lighted upon the fires of England — and we will set it as a new sun to lighten a world. ...."

Sam Adams, anxious to get that good night's sleep before starting the next day for Philadelphia, was smiling slightly, nodding his gray head, seeming to agree. He was bored. It does not matter, he was thinking, what James Otis says these days — sane or crazy.

Joseph Warren's fair, responsive face was aflame. The torch Otis had been talking about seemed reflected in his eyes.

"We are lucky men," he murmured, "for we have a cause worth dying for. This honor is not given to every generation."

"Boy," said Otis to Johnny, "fill my tankard."

It was not until he had drained it and wiped his mouth on the back of his hand that he spoke again. All sat silently waiting for him. He had, and not for the first time, cast a spell upon them.

"They say," he began again, "my wits left me after I got hit on the head by that customs official. That's what you think, eh, Mr. Sam Adams?"

"Oh, no, no, indeed, Mr. Otis."

"Some of us will give our wits," he said, "some of us all our property. Heh, John Hancock, did you hear that? *Property* — that hurts, eh? To give one's silver wine coolers, one's coach-and-four, and the gold buttons off one's waistcoats?"

Hancock looked him straight in the face, and Johnny had never before liked him so well.

"I am ready," he said. "I can get along without all that."

"You, Paul Revere, you'll give up that silvercraft you love. God made you to make silver, not war."

Revere smiled. "There's a time for the casting of silver and a time for the casting of cannon. If that's not in the Bible, it should be."

"Doctor Warren, you've a young family. You know quite well, if you get killed they may literally starve."

Warren said, "I've thought of all that long ago."

"And you, John Adams. You've built up a very nice little law practice, stealing away my clients, I notice. Ah, so it goes. Each shall give according to his own abilities, and some — " he turned directly to Rab — "some will give their lives. All the years of their maturity. All the children they never live to have. The serenity of old age. To die so young is more than merely dying; it is to lose so large a part of life."

Rab was looking straight at Otis. His arms were folded across his chest. His head was flung back a little. His lips parted as though he would speak.

"Even you, my old friend — my old enemy? How shall I call you, Sam Adams? Even you will give the best you have — a genius for politics. Oh, go to Philadelphia! Pull all the wool, pull all the strings and all the wires. Yes, go, go! And God go with you. We need you, Sam. We must fight this war. You'll play your part — but what it is really about...you'll never know."

James Otis was on his feet, his head close against the rafters that cut down into the attic, making it the shape of a tent. Otis put out his arms.

"It is all so much simpler than you think," he said. He lifted his hands and pushed against the rafters.

"We give all we have, lives, property, safety, skills...we fight, we die, for a simple thing. Only that a man can stand up."

With a curt nod he was gone.

Johnny was standing close to Rab. It had frightened him when Mr. Otis had said, "Some will give their lives," and looked straight at Rab. Die so that "a man can stand up."

Once more Sam Adams had the center of attention. He was again buttoning up his coat, preparing to leave, but first he turned to Revere.

"Now *he* is gone, we can talk a moment about that spy system you think you can organize in Boston."

Paul Revere, like his friend, Joseph Warren, was still slightly under the spell of James Otis.

"I had not thought about it that way before," he said, not answering Sam Adams's words. "You know, my father had to flee France because of the tyranny over there. He was only a child. But now, in a way, I'm fighting for that child . . . that no frightened, lost child ever is sent out a refugee from his own country because of race or religion." Then he pulled himself together and answered Sam Adams's remarks about the spy system.

That night, when the boys were both in bed, Johnny heard Rab, usually a heavy sleeper, turning and turning.

"Johnny," he said at last, "are you awake?"

"Yes."

"What was it he said?"

"That a man can stand up."

Rab sighed and stopped turning. Soon he was asleep. As had often happened, it was the younger boy who lay wide-eyed in the darkness.

"That a man can stand up."

He'd never forget Otis with his hands pushed up against the cramping rafters over his head.

"That a man can stand up," as simple as that.

And the strange new sun rising in the west. A sun that was to illumine a world to come.

DISCUSSION

1. For how long had the colonies worked for peace? Why did Samuel Adams conclude that they should not try any longer?

2. When Adams decided to work for war, what did he believe would come out of it?

3. James Otis did not believe Adams had given enough reason for going to war. What reasons did Otis give?

4. What were some of the things Otis said Americans would have to give up when they went to war?

5. When Johnny Tremain went from house to house to summon the members of the Boston Observers, why do you think he was "talking about unpaid bills of eight shillings"?

6. What incident had caused Otis to be odd, to lose his wits? Would you say his words were worth listening to? Why do you think that?

7. Otis said, ". . . we fight, we die, for a simple thing. Only that a man can stand up." What do you think he meant by that?

8. Do you think that ideals such as Otis's can be achieved once and for all time, or are they something for which all of us must work constantly? Why do you think as you do?

9. Do you agree that for "a man to stand up" is reason enough for a war? Why do you think as you do?

10. Do you believe the American Revolution provided the opportunity for all men "to stand up" as Otis hoped it would? Why do you believe that?
11. These early American citizens planned for "a world to come." Why and how is this still a responsibility for each of us?

AUTHOR

Esther Forbes, who spent most of her life in Worcester, Massachusetts, grew up in a family where learning the early history of New England was part of the family tradition. She received her education at Bradford Academy in Bradford, Massachusetts, and at the University of Wisconsin. While she was still in college, World War I broke out, and she joined a group of volunteers in answer to a call for farm helpers. She was sent to a farm near Harpers Ferry, West Virginia, to shuck corn, pick apples, and work as a teamster.

For six years Miss Forbes was on the editorial staff of Houghton Mifflin Company in Boston, where she edited the works of several historical novelists. After spending considerable time abroad, she published her first successful historical novel, *O Genteel Lady,* which was quickly followed by four historical novels about New England. These novels were written for adults, as was *Paul Revere and the World He Lived In,* which received the Pulitzer prize for history in 1943. Only once before had a woman won this prize.

While working on her prize-winning novel, Miss Forbes became interested in the lives of the apprentices in Boston during the Revolutionary War. That interest was the beginning of her first novel for young people, *Johnny Tremain,* from which the selection you have just read was taken. With this book, which was awarded the Newbery Medal in 1944, Miss Forbes made a distinguished contribution to historical literature for young people. Recognized as "a live and clear and significant . . . picture of a great period in American history," *Johnny Tremain* has been translated into several languages, issued in a number of paperback editions, anthologized in many readers, and made into a movie by Walt Disney.

FROM THE BOOKSHELF

AMERICA FOREVER NEW, *compiled by Sara and John E. Brewton*
Using the work of modern writers, Sara and John Brewton have collected over two hundred poems about the land, people, history, and folklore of the United States of America.

EMMA TUPPER'S DIARY, *by Peter Dickinson*
Emma Tupper's wild Scottish cousins get her and themselves involved in an elaborate hoax that becomes terrifyingly real.

ENCHANTRESS FROM THE STARS, *by Sylvia Louise Engdahl*
This story of tomorrow raises questions about our own times.

HEROES, GODS AND MONSTERS OF THE GREEK MYTHS, *by Bernard Evslin*
These tales bring alive the splendor and richness of ancient myths.

OH, LIZZIE! THE STORY OF ELIZABETH CADY STANTON, *by Doris Faber*
Elizabeth Stanton devoted her life to the cause of women's liberation.

TWO IF BY SEA, *by Leonard Everett Fisher*
Four men in Boston set the stage for the American Revolution on the evening of April 18, 1775.

SMITH, *by Leon Garfield*
A twelve-year-old pickpocket, pursued by other thieves, exists in the grimy underworld of eighteenth-century London.

THE HOUSE OF DIES DREAR, *by Virginia Hamilton*
Thomas Small has many adventures trying to discover the secret of his new home, once an Underground Railroad Station.

PREHISTORIC MAN, *by Clifford Simak*
How Neanderthal man contributed to human development is described in one of the chapters in this book about early man.

GLOSSARY

To learn the correct pronunciation of any word in this glossary, use the special spelling after the word and the pronunciation key at the bottom of each left-hand page.

The pronunciation key at the bottom of each left-hand page is a shortened form of the full key below, which shows how to pronounce each consonant and vowel in any special spelling.

FULL PRONUNCIATION KEY

CONSONANT SOUNDS

b	bib	k	cat, kick, pique	t	tight
ch	church	l	lid, needle	th	path, thin
d	deed	m	am, man, mum	*th*	bathe, this
f	fast, fife, off, phase, rough	n	no, sudden	v	cave, valve, vine
g	gag	ng	thing	w	with
h	hat	p	pop	y	yes
hw	which	r	roar	z	rose, size, xylophone, zebra
j	judge	s	miss, sauce, see	zh	garage, pleasure, vision
		sh	dish, ship		

VOWEL SOUNDS

ă	pat	ī	by, guy, pie	o͝o	took
ā	aid, they, pay	î	dear, deer, fierce, mere	o͞o	boot, fruit
â	air, care, wear			ŭ	cut, rough
ä	father	ŏ	horrible, pot	û	firm, heard, term, turn, word
ĕ	pet, pleasure	ō	go, row, toe	yo͞o	abuse, use
ē	be, bee, easy, leisure	ô	alter, caught, for, paw	ə	about, silent, pencil, lemon, circus
ĭ	pit	oi	boy, noise, oil	ər	butter
		ou	cow, out		

STRESS MARKS

Primary Stress ′
bi•ol′o•gy (bī ŏl′ə jē)

Secondary Stress ′
bi′o•log′i•cal (bī′ə lŏj′ĭ kəl)

Pronunciation key and word meanings adapted from *The American Heritage School Dictionary*, published by American Heritage Publishing Co., Inc., and Houghton Mifflin Company.

ab·a·lo·ne (ăb′ə lō′nē) *n.* A soft-bodied, edible sea animal having a large, shallow shell with a brightly colored, iridescent lining.

ab·o·li·tion (ăb′ə lĭsh′ən) *n.* **1.** The act of prohibiting. **2.** Often **Abolition.** The prohibition of slavery in the United States.

a·byss (ə bĭs′) *n.* **1.** A very deep and large hole: *into the abyss of the volcano.* **2.** A huge emptiness: *through the abyss of outer space.*

a·ca·cia (ə kā′shə) *n.* Any of several mostly tropical trees with feathery leaves and clusters of small, usually yellow, flowers.

ad·judge (ə jŭj′) *v.* **ad·judged, ad·judg·ing. 1.** To determine, rule, or declare by law. **2.** To award by law: *He was adjudged $5,000 in damages.*

ad·ver·si·ty (ăd vûr′sĭ tē) *n., pl.* **ad·ver·si·ties.** Great misfortune; hardship.

ad·vo·cate (ăd′və kāt′) *v.* **ad·vo·cat·ed, ad·vo·cat·ing.** To be or speak in favor of; recommend; urge. —*n.* (ăd′və kĭt) *or* (-kāt′). A person who supports or speaks in favor of a cause: *an advocate of gun control.*

ag·ate (ăg′ĭt) *n.* **1.** A type of quartz that is cloudy in appearance and streaked with color. **2.** A child's marble made of this or a similar material.

à la mode (ä′lə mōd′) *or* (ăl′ə) *adj.* Served with ice cream: *apple pie à la mode.*

al·che·mist (ăl′kə mĭst) *n.* Someone who practiced an early system of beliefs, somewhat akin to modern chemistry, that had among its aims the changing of common metals into gold.

a·li·en (ā′lē ən) *or* (āl′yən) *adj.* **1.** Of or coming from another country; foreign. **2.** Not natural; not characteristic: *The experiment produced an alien result.*

al·lure (ə loŏr′) *v.* **al·lured, al·lur·ing.** To attract; entice. —**al·lur·ing** *adj.: an alluring possibility.* —*n.* Strong attraction; fascination: *the allure of the sea.*

Am·a·zon (ăm′ə zŏn′) *or* (-zən) *n.* **1.** In Greek mythology, a member of a race of female warriors. **2.** A tall, athletic woman.

am·ber (ăm′bər) *n.* **1.** A light or brownish-yellow fossil resin used for making jewelry and ornaments. **2.** A brownish yellow.

a·me·lio·rate (ə mēl′yə rāt′) *v.* **a·me·lio·rat·ed, a·me·lio·rat·ing.** To make or become better; improve. —**a·me′lio·ra′tion** *n.*

am·e·thyst (ăm′ə thĭst) *n.* A purple form of transparent quartz used as a gemstone.

a·mok, also **a·muck** (ə mŭk′) *or* (ə mŏk′) *adv.* **1.** In a wild manner, with intent to do violence or kill: *He ran amuck.* **2.** In a jumbled manner; all over: *When father carves a duck, potatoes fly amuck.*

am·phib·i·an (ăm fĭb′ē ən) *n.* An animal, such as a frog, toad, or salamander, that lives in water and breathes with gills during its early life stage and that develops lungs and breathes air as an adult.

am·pli·fy (ăm′plə fī′) *v.* **am·pli·fied, am·pli·fy·ing, am·pli·fies. 1.** To multiply a flow of energy, especially one that changes with time, while its other characteristics remain the same: *A public-address system amplifies a speaker's voice.* **2.** To add to something spoken or written; expand; make complete.

am·u·let (ăm′yə lĭt) *n.* A charm worn to ward off evil or injury, especially one worn around the neck.

angle of incidence. The angle formed by the path of radiation or the path of a body striking a surface and a line drawn perpendicular to the surface at the point of impact.

an·guish (ăng′gwĭsh) *n.* A pain of the body or of the mind that causes one agony; torment.

a·nom·a·ly (ə nŏm′ə lē) *n., pl.* **a·nom·a·lies. 1.** Deviation or departure from what is normal or common; abnormality. **2.** Something that is unusual, irregular, or abnormal: *He was a bachelor, an anomaly in that part of the country.*

a·rag·o·nite (ə răg′ə nīt′) *or* (ăr′ə gə-) *n.* A mineral form of crystalline calcium carbonate.

ar·bi·trar·i·ly (är′bĭ trĕr′ə lē) *adv.* In a manner based on whim or impulse, not on reason or law.

ar·cade (är kād′) *n.* **1.** A row of arches sup-

ă pat/ā pay/â care/ä father/ĕ pet/ē be/ĭ pit/ī pie/î fierce/ŏ pot/ō go/ô paw, for/oi oil/oŏ book/ oō boot/ou out/ŭ cut/û fur/*th* the/th thin/hw which/zh vision/ə ago, item, pencil, atom, circus

ported by pillars. **2.** A roofed passageway between buildings, with shops on either side.

ar·id (ăr′ĭd) *adj.* **1.** Having little or no rainfall; dry: *an arid wasteland.* **2.** Lifeless; dull: *a long, arid book.* —**a·rid′i·ty** (ə rĭd′ĭ tē) *n.*

ar·ray (ə rā′) *n.* **1.** An orderly arrangement: *an array of data.* **2.** An impressive display or collection.

ar·ro·gant (ăr′ə gənt) *adj.* Excessively and unpleasantly self-important, as in disregarding all other opinions but one's own. —**ar′ro·gant·ly** *adv.*

ar·ti·san (är′tĭ zən) *n.* One manually skilled in making a certain product; a craftsman.

ar·tiste (är tēst′) *n.* A public performer or entertainer, especially a singer or dancer.

art nou·veau (är′nōō vō′) *or* (ärt′-). A style of decoration and architecture first popular in the 1890's, using curved lines and flower shapes.

as·phyx·i·ate (ăs fĭk′sē āt′) *v.* **as·phyx·i·at·ed, as·phyx·i·at·ing.** To undergo or cause to undergo asphyxia; smother; suffocate: *Without air they will surely asphyxiate.*

as·sur·ance (ə shŏŏr′əns) *n.* **1.** A positive statement intended to inspire confidence; a guarantee: *He gave us his solemn assurance that he would pay.* **2.** Confidence; certainty.

asth·ma (ăz′mə) *or* (ăs′-) *n.* A chronic disease that is often allergic in origin. Its chief symptom is tightness of the chest with coughing and difficulty in breathing.

au·then·tic·i·ty (ô′thĕn tĭs′ĭ tē) *n.* The condition or quality of being true or genuine.

av·id·ly (ăv′ĭd lē) *adv.* **1.** Eagerly. **2.** Ardently; enthusiastically.

ax·es *n.* **1.** (ăk′sēz). Plural of **axis**. **2.** (ăk′sĭz). Plural of **ax**.

ax·is (ăk′sĭs) *n., pl.* **ax·es** (ăk′sēz′). A straight line around which an object or geometric figure rotates or can be imagined to rotate: *The axis of the earth passes through both of its poles.*

bac·chan·tic (bə kăn′tĭk) *adj.* Riotous or drunken; carousing.

bade (băd) *or* (bād). A past tense of **bid**.

bale·ful·ly (bāl′fəl lē) *adv.* In a threatening or menacing way.

bar·na·cle (bär′nə kəl) *n.* A small, hard-shelled sea animal that attaches itself to underwater rocks, pilings, the bottoms of ships, etc.

bar·rage (bə räzh′) *n.* **1.** A concentrated firing of guns or missiles, often as a screen or protection for military troops. **2.** An overwhelming attack or outpouring, as of blows or words: *a barrage of questions.* —*v.* **bar·raged, bar·rag·ing.** To direct a barrage at.

bas-re·lief (bä′rĭ lēf′) *or* (bä′rĭ lēf′) *n.* A sculpture or kind of sculpture in which figures are raised slightly from a flat background.

bat·ten (băt′n) *n.* A narrow strip of wood, such as one used on a boat or ship to fasten a covering over a hatch or to stiffen the edge of a sail. —*v.* **batten down.** To fasten or hold down with or as if with such strips: *Batten down the hatches in preparation for a storm.*

bat·tle·ment (băt′l mənt) *n.* Often **battlements.** A wall with indented openings, built along the top edge of a tower, castle, fort, etc., and formerly used as protection and concealment for soldiers in warfare.

Ba·var·i·an (bə vâr′ē ən) *adj.* Of or concerning Bavaria, a state in West Germany. —*n.* **1.** A native or inhabitant of Bavaria. **2.** The German dialect spoken in Bavaria and Austria.

beak·er (bē′kər) *n.* **1.** A laboratory container consisting of a cylinder that is open at one end and has a pouring lip. **2.** A large drinking cup with a wide mouth.

bea·ver·board (bē′vər bôrd′) *or* (-bōrd) *n.* A building material of compressed wood pulp, used for walls and partitions.

bed·lam (bĕd′ləm) *n.* **1.** A situation of confusion, disorder, or noisy uproar: *After breakfast the happy bedlam of unwrapping Christmas presents began.* **2.** *Archaic.* An insane asylum.

be·hold·en (bĭ hōl′dən) *adj.* Indebted: *Electricity has made man beholden to the machine.*

be·mused (bĭ myōōzd′) *adj.* **1.** Confused; stupefied. **2.** Lost in thought; preoccupied.

ben·e·fac·tor (bĕn′ə făk′tər) *n.* A person who gives financial or other aid to another.

be·set·ting (bĭ sĕt′ĭng) *adj.* Afflicting; distressing: *all the ills besetting mankind.*

be·troth (bǐ trō*th*′) *or* (-trôth′) *v.* **1.** To promise to give in marriage. **2.** To promise to marry.

bi·ased (bī′əst) *adj.* Prejudiced; unfairly influenced.

bid (bǐd) *v.* **bid** or **bade** (bǎd) *or* (bād), **bid·den** (bǐd′n) or **bid, bid·ding. 1.** To order; command; direct: *My mother bade me look in the mirror.* **2.** To ask for insistently.

bish·op (bǐsh′əp) *n.* **1.** A high-ranking Christian clergyman, in modern churches usually in charge of a diocese. **2.** A chessman that can move diagonally across any number of unoccupied spaces of the identical color.

bi·zarre (bǐ zär′) *adj.* Very strange or odd; grotesque: *a bizarre hat; a bizarre idea.*

blight (blīt) *n.* **1.** A disease that withers or destroys plants. **2.** Anything that is harmful or destructive. —*v.* To ruin; destroy: *A mishap blighted his hopes.*

blimp (blǐmp) *n.* A balloon-like and buoyant aircraft.

bog (bôg) *or* (bŏg) *n.* Soft, water-soaked ground; a marsh; swamp. —*v.* **bogged, bog·ging.** To cause to sink in or as if in a bog: *Rain had bogged the village in a sea of mud.*

bol·ster (bōl′stər) *n.* A long, narrow pillow or cushion. —*v.* To strengthen or reinforce.

bot·a·ny (bŏt′n ē) *n.* The scientific study of plants.

brack·en (brăk′ən) *n.* **1.** A large fern with branching fronds. **2.** A place overgrown with such ferns.

brash (brăsh) *adj.* **1.** Hasty and unthinking; rash. **2.** Shamelessly bold; impudent; saucy. —**brash′ly** *adv.* —**brash′ness** *n.*

breach (brēch) *n.* **1.** A violation or infraction, as of a law, legal obligation, or promise: *a breach of contract.* **2.** A gap or hole, especially in a solid structure.

breast (brěst) *n.* In mammals, especially human beings, one of the glands in which a female produces milk to feed her young offspring. —*v.* To face or advance against boldly: *He breasted every hurdle in his path.*

bril·liant (brǐl′yənt) *adj.* **1.** Shining brightly; glittering: *A brilliant sun blazed in the sky.* **2.** Very vivid in color. **3.** Extremely intelligent or inventive: *a brilliant man.* **4.** Splendid; magnificent: *the brilliant court life of Versailles.*

bris·tle (brǐs′əl) *n.* A short, coarse, stiff hair or hairlike part. —*v.* **bris·tled, bris·tling. 1.** To raise the bristles stiffly: *The dog bristled and showed his teeth.* **2.** To show sudden anger or annoyance: *The boy bristled at being called a name.*

buf·fet (bŭf′ĭt) *v.* To strike against forcefully; batter: *The rough sea buffeted the small boat as it passed the reefs.* —*n.* A blow or cuff made with or as if with the hand.

buoy (boo′ē) *or* (boi) *n.* **1.** A float used as a channel or anchorage marker. **2.** A life preserver. —*v.* **1.** To keep afloat. **2.** To cheer; hearten: *The news buoyed his spirits.*

cal·i·co (kăl′ĭ kō) *n., pl.* **cal·i·coes** or **cal·i·cos.** A cotton cloth with a figured pattern printed on it in color. —*adj.* Covered with spots of a different color: *a calico cat.*

cal·loused (kăl′əst) *adj.* Hardened or thick, usually because of prolonged pressure or rubbing; having calluses.

car·at (kăr′ət) *n.* **1.** A unit of weight for precious stones, equal to 200 milligrams or about $\frac{1}{140}$ of an ounce. **2.** A form of the word **karat.**

car·bide (kär′bīd′) *n.* A chemical compound, especially calcium carbide, consisting of carbon and a metal.

car·cass (kär′kəs) *n.* **1.** The dead body of an animal. **2.** Anything likened to a carcass: *the carcasses of old cars in a junkyard.*

ca·reen (kə rēn′) *v.* **1.** To tilt (a ship) onto its side, on the shore, in order to clean or repair its bottom. **2.** To lurch or swerve while in motion: *The car careened on the icy road.*

ca·ter (kā′tər) *v.* **1. a.** To provide with what is needed or wanted, as services, food, drinks, etc.: *The inn caters to tourists and businessmen.* **b.** To supply and serve food and drinks

---

ă pat/ā pay/â care/ä father/ĕ pet/ē be/ĭ pit/ī pie/î fierce/ŏ pot/ō go/ô paw, for/oi oil/ōō book/
ōō boot/ou out/ŭ cut/û fur/*th* the/th thin/hw which/zh vision/ə ago, item, pencil, atom, circus

for: *cater a wedding.* **2.** To act with special consideration: *The governor was accused of catering to big business.*

cat·walk (kăt′wôk′) *n.* A narrow, elevated pathway, as on the sides of a bridge.

ce·les·tial (sə lĕs′chəl) *adj.* **1.** Of or related to the sky: *Stars and planets are celestial bodies.* **2.** Of heaven; divine.

chafe (chāf) *v.* **chafed, chaf·ing. 1.** To irritate by rubbing: *The starched collar chafed his neck.* **2.** To feel prolonged irritation; be impatient: *chafe at the delay.*

chan·cel·lor (chăn′sə lər) *or* (-slər) *or* (chän′-) *n.* **1.** The chief minister of state in some European countries. **2.** In some universities, the president or another officer of high rank. **3.** The presiding judge of a court of equity in the United States.

chan·de·lier (shăn′də lîr′) *n.* A fixture that holds a number of light bulbs or candles and is suspended from a ceiling.

chaps (chăps) *or* (shăps) *pl.n.* Heavy leather trousers without a seat, worn over ordinary trousers by cowboys to protect their legs.

char·ter (chär′tər) *n.* A written grant or document from a ruler, government, etc., giving certain rights to the people, a group or organization, or an individual: *A charter was given by the government to build the Baltimore and Ohio Railroad.* *—v.* To grant a charter to; establish by charter.

chas·tise (chăs tīz′) *v.* **chas·tised, chas·tis·ing.** To punish for misbehavior or wrongdoing: *the firm manner of a strict mother chastising a bad boy.* **—chas·tise′ment** *n.*

chil·blain (chĭl′blān′) *n.* Redness and soreness of the hands, feet, or ears, resulting from exposure to damp cold.

chil·i (chĭl′ē) *n., pl.* **chil·ies. 1.** The very sharp-tasting pod of a kind of red pepper. **2.** A seasoning made from the dried or ground pods of this pepper.

chlo·rin·at·ed (klôr′ə nā′tĭd) *or* (klōr′-) *adj.* Treated or combined with chlorine or one of its compounds.

cho·re·o·graph (kôr′ē ə grăf′) *or* (-gräf′) *or* (kōr′-) *v.* To create and arrange a ballet or other stage work.

Chris·ten·dom (krĭs′ən dəm) *n.* **1.** Christians in general. **2.** The Christian world.

clap·board (klăb′ərd) *or* (klăp′bôrd′) *or* (-bōrd′) *n.* A long, narrow board with one edge thicker than the other, overlapped to cover the outside walls of a frame house.

cler·i·cal (klĕr′ĭ kəl) *adj.* **1.** Of clerks or office workers: *clerical work.* **2.** Of the clergy or a clergyman: *clerical garb.*

coach-and-four. A large, closed, four-wheeled carriage pulled by four horses.

cob·bler[1] (kŏb′lər) *n.* A shoemaker.

cob·bler[2] (kŏb′lər) *n.* A fruit pie topped with a biscuit crust and baked in a deep dish.

com·pla·cent (kəm plā′sənt) *adj.* Pleased or contented with oneself in an untroubled or uncritical manner; self-satisfied; smug.

com·po·nent (kəm pō′nənt) *n.* Any of the parts that together make up a whole: *A large computer consists of thousands of components.* *—adj.* Of, being, or acting as a component: *Resistors, transistors, and diodes are component parts of a computer.*

com·po·sure (kəm pō′zhər) *n.* Control over one's emotions; calm, steady manner or spirit.

con·cise (kən sīs′) *adj.* Expressing much in a few words; brief and clear: *a concise paragraph.* **—con·cise′ly** *adv.* **—con·cise′ness** *n.*

con·fir·ma·tion (kŏn′fər mā′shən) *n.* **1.** The act of confirming: *senatorial confirmation of an ambassador.* **2.** Something that confirms or establishes the validity of.

con·gealed (kən jēld′) *adj.* **1.** Changed from a liquid to a solid, as by freezing. **2.** Thickened or coagulated.

con·sign (kən sīn′) *v.* **1.** To give over to the care of another; entrust: *consign an orphan to a guardian.* **2.** To deliver (merchandise) for sale. **3.** To assign to a lower or less important position: *The pitcher was consigned to the bullpen.*

con·sul (kŏn′səl) *n.* An official appointed by a government to live in a foreign city, look after his country's commercial interests, and give assistance to its citizens who live or travel there. **—con′su·lar** (kŏn′sə lər) *adj.*

con·tempt (kən tĕmpt′) *n.* **1. a.** A feeling that someone or something is inferior and undesirable. **b.** The condition of being regarded in this way: *The League of Nations rapidly fell into contempt.* **2.** Open disobedience to a court of law or to a legislative body.

con·ti·nen·tal shelf. A portion of the edge of a continent covered to a generally shallow depth by the ocean and extending to a point where it slopes steeply downward into the deep part of the ocean.

con·tour (kŏn′toͦor′) *n.* The outline of a figure, body, or mass: *the contour of the American coast.*

con·verge (kən vûrj′) *v.* **con·verged, con·verg·ing. 1.** To come together in one place: *The three roads converged.* **2.** In mathematics, to have a limit, as an infinite sequence.

con·verse (kən vûrs′) *v.* **con·versed, con·vers·ing.** To talk informally with others: *converse about family matters.*

con·vert (kən vûrt′) *v.* **1.** To change into another form, substance, or condition: *Electricity converts easily into other forms of energy.* **2.** To change from one use to another; adapt to a new purpose: *convert a home into a library.* **3.** To persuade (a person) to adopt a particular religion or belief. **4.** To exchange for something of equal value: *converting dollars into French money.*

con·vey·or, also **con·vey·er** (kən vā′ər) *n.* **1.** Someone or something that carries. **2.** A mechanical device, such as a continuous moving belt, that carries things from one place to another.

con·vul·sive (kən vŭl′sĭv) *adj.* Of or like a fit or seizure: *shaking with convulsive laughter.* —**con·vul′sive·ly** *adv.*

cos·mos (kŏz′məs) *n.* **1.** The universe regarded as an orderly, harmonious whole. **2.** Any system regarded as orderly, harmonious, and whole.

cour·i·er (kûr′ē ər) *or* (kŏor′-) *n.* A messenger, especially one on urgent or official diplomatic business.

cov·et (kŭv′ĭt) *v.* **1.** To desire (something belonging to another). **2.** To wish for strongly; crave. —**cov′et·ed** *adj.: a coveted award.*

crag·gy (krăg′ē) *adj.* **crag·gi·er, crag·gi·est. 1.** With cliffs: *a craggy mountain.* **2.** Rugged in appearance: *a craggy face.* —**crag′gi·ness** *n.*

cray·fish (krā′fĭsh′) *n., pl.* **-fish** or **-fish·es.** A freshwater animal that resembles a lobster but is much smaller.

cre·den·tials (krĭ dĕn′shəls) *pl. n.* A letter or other written evidence of a person's qualifications or status.

cro·cus (krō′kəs) *n., pl.* **cro·cus·es** or **cro·ci** (krō′sī′). A low-growing garden plant with purple, yellow, or white flowers that bloom early in spring.

croup (kroͦop) *n.* A diseased condition that affects the larynx in children, producing difficult and noisy breathing and a hoarse cough.

crus·ta·cean (krŭ stā′shən) *n.* Any of a group of animals, such as a lobster, crab, or shrimp, that live mostly in water and have a body with a hard outer covering.

cull (kŭl) *v.* **1.** To pick out from others; gather selectively: *cull the prettiest flowers; cull passages from a poet's work.* **2.** To search through; comb: *cull the forests for firewood.*

cus·toms inspector. A person who inspects goods and baggage entering a country.

cut·a·way (kŭt′ə wā′) *n.* Also **cutaway coat.** A man's formal daytime coat, cut so that the front edges slope away from the waist to form tails at the back.

dachs·hund (däks′hoͦont′) *or* (däks′hoͦond′) *n.* A small dog with a long body, drooping ears, and very short legs.

dal·ly (dăl′ē) *v.* **dal·lied, dal·ly·ing, dal·lies. 1.** To flirt playfully; toy; trifle: *Don't dally with temptation.* **2.** To waste time; dawdle.

de·bris, also **dé·bris** (də brē′) *or* (dā′brē′) *n.* The scattered remains of something broken, destroyed, or discarded; fragments; rubble.

dé·cor, also **de·cor** (dā′kôr′) *or* (dā kôr′) *n.* **1.** The decorative style of a room, home, restaurant, etc. **2.** Stage scenery.

deem (dēm) *v.* To judge; consider; think.

def·er·en·tial·ly (dĕf′ə rĕn′shə lē) *adv.* In a courteous or respectful way.

de·fi·ance (dĭ fī′əns) *n.* Open resistance to

ă pat/ā pay/â care/ä father/ĕ pet/ē be/ĭ pit/ī pie/î fierce/ŏ pot/ō go/ô paw, for/oi oil/oͦo book/
oͦo boot/ou out/ŭ cut/û fur/*th* the/th thin/hw which/zh vision/ə ago, item, pencil, atom, circus

authority; stubborn refusal to obey orders.

de·file¹ (dĭ fīl′) v. **de·filed, de·fil·ing. 1.** To make filthy or dirty; pollute. **2.** To spoil the sacredness or purity of. —**de·file′ment** n.

de·file² (dĭ fīl′) n. A narrow pass preventing the easy passage of a group.

de·mean·or (dĭ mē′nər) n. The way in which a person behaves or conducts himself.

dem·o·li·tion (dĕm′ə lĭsh′ən) n. The action or business of destroying buildings, installations, etc., especially by means of explosives.

de·nounce (dĭ nouns′) v. **de·nounced, de·nounc·ing. 1.** To express very strong disapproval of; condemn openly: *denounce a proposed law.* **2.** To accuse formally; inform against: *denounce a traitor.*

de·nude (dĭ nōōd′) or (-nyōōd′) v. **de·nud·ed, de·nud·ing.** To remove the covering from; lay bare: *Erosion of the soil denuded the rock.*

de·pict (dĭ pĭkt′) v. To represent in words, painting, etc.; describe or show: *a book depicting the life and times of ancient Rome.* —**de·pic′tion** n.

de·ploy (dĭ ploi′) v. To station or spread out in a systematic pattern: *deploy troops in preparation for a battle.* —**de·ploy′ment** n.

de·pose (dĭ pōz′) v. **de·posed, de·pos·ing.** To remove from a position of power: *depose a king.*

der·e·lict (dĕr′ə lĭkt) n. **1.** A homeless, jobless person abandoned by society. **2.** Abandoned property, especially a ship abandoned at sea. —*adj.* **1.** Neglectful; remiss: *derelict in one's duty.* **2.** Deserted by an owner; abandoned.

de·ri·sive (dĭ rī′sĭv) adj. Expressing ridicule; mocking: *derisive laughter.* —**de·ri′sive·ly** adv. —**de·ri′sive·ness** n.

de·rive (dĭ rīv′) v. **de·rived, de·riv·ing. 1.** To obtain or receive from a source: *derive pleasure from music.* **2.** To originate from a certain source.

des·ti·tute (dĕs′tĭ tōōt′) or (-tyōōt′) adj. Completely impoverished; penniless.

de·te·ri·o·rate (dĭ tîr′ē ə rāt′) v. **de·te·ri·o·rat·ed, de·te·ri·o·rat·ing.** To make or become inferior in quality, character, or value: *Moisture deteriorates powder.*

dev·o·tee (dĕv′ə tē′) n. Someone who is extremely devoted to something; a fan.

di·a·lect (dī′ə lĕkt′) n. A regional variety of a language, distinguished from other varieties by pronunciation, vocabulary, etc.: *Cockney is a dialect of English.* —**di′a·lect′al** adj.

dif·fi·dent·ly (dĭf′ĭ dənt lē) adv. In a timid way; shyly.

dil·i·gence (dĭl′ə jəns) n. **1.** Long, steady effort in one's job or studies. **2.** Careful attention.

di·min·ish (dĭ mĭn′ĭsh) v. To make or become smaller or less: *A drought diminished their food supply.*

dis·con·cert·ing (dĭs′kən sûrt′ĭng) adj. Upsetting; perturbing.

dis·dain (dĭs dān′) v. **1.** To treat as inferior; show contempt for. **2.** To refuse aloofly: *She disdained to answer the letter.* —n. Mild contempt and aloofness.

dis·patch (dĭ spăch′) v. **1.** To send off to a specific destination or on specific business: *dispatch a letter.* **2.** To complete or dispose of promptly. **3.** To put to death quickly and without ceremony. —n. **1.** The act of sending off: *the dispatch of a representative to the peace talks.* **2.** Quickness and efficiency in performance: *the prey he killed with such dispatch.* **3.** A written message, especially an official communication, sent with speed: *a dispatch from the Allied high command.* **4.** A news report sent to a newspaper or broadcasting station.

dis·si·pate (dĭs′ə pāt′) v. **dis·si·pat·ed, dis·si·pat·ing. 1.** To drive away by or as if by dispersing; scatter: *A strong wind dissipated the clouds.* **2.** To vanish by dispersion; disappear: *Upon escaping into the air, steam dissipates.* **3.** To use up unwisely; waste; squander: *He dissipated his money on the project.* **4.** To indulge in pleasure harmfully or too freely.

dis·taff (dĭs′tăf′) or (-täf′) n. A stick holding flax or wool to be drawn off onto a spindle and spun into thread or yarn.

drone¹ (drōn) n. **1.** A male bee, especially a honeybee. **2.** Someone who is lazy; a loafer. **3.** An unmanned aircraft operated by remote control.

drone² (drōn) v. **droned, dron·ing. 1.** To make a continuous, low, dull humming sound: *An airplane droned far overhead.* **2.** To speak in a monotonous tone. —n. A continuous, low, monotonous humming or buzzing sound.

drub·bing (drŭb′ĭng) *n.* **1.** A beating with or as if with a stick: *get a drubbing for stealing cookies.* **2.** A thorough defeat.

drudg·er·y (drŭj′ə rē) *n., pl.* **drudg·er·ies.** Hard, tiresome, or menial work.

dub¹ (dŭb) *v.* **dubbed, dub·bing. 1.** To confer knighthood on (a person) by touching him on the shoulder with a sword. **2.** To give a nickname to.

dub² (dŭb) *v.* **dubbed, dub·bing.** To insert (new sounds) into an existing recording, as on magnetic tape or the sound track of a film.

Dutch-bobbed (dŭch′bŏbd) *adj.* Having hair that is cut very short, usually with bangs over the forehead.

ec·cle·si·as·ti·cal (ĭ klē′zē ăs′tĭ kəl) *adj.* Of a church, especially as an organized institution; clerical: *Ireland was a center of ecclesiastical learning during the Dark Ages.*

e·con·o·mist (ĭ kŏn′ə mĭst) *n.* A person who studies the production, distribution, development, and consumption of goods and services.

ec·sta·sy (ĕk′stə sē) *n., pl.* **ec·sta·sies.** A state of intense emotion, especially of joy or delight.

ed·dy (ĕd′ē) *n., pl.* **ed·dies.** A current, as of a liquid or gas, that moves contrary to the direction of a main current, especially in a circular motion. —*v.* **ed·died, ed·dy·ing, ed·dies.** To move in or as if in an eddy.

é·lan (ā län′) *n.* **1.** Zest; dash. **2.** Style; flair: *She plays the piano with élan.*

e·la·tion (ĭ lā′shən) *n.* An intense feeling of happiness or joy.

e·lec·tron (ĭ lĕk′trŏn′) *n.* A subatomic particle commonly found as one of a group surrounding the nucleus of an atom.

el·lip·ti·cal (ĭ lĭp′tĭ kəl) *adj.* Of, shaped like, or related to a closed plane curve composed of all the points that have the sum of their distances from two fixed points equal to a constant. —**el·lip′ti·cal·ly** *adv.* —**el·lipse′** *n.*

e·lon·gate (ĭ lông′gāt′) *or* (ĭ lŏng′-) *or* (ē′lông-gāt′) *or* (ē′lŏng-) *v.* **e·lon·gat·ed, e·lon·gat·ing.** To make or become longer; lengthen: *The artist elongated the face and figure in his paintings.* —**e·lon′gat′ed** *adj.*

e·lu·sive (ĭ lōō′sĭv) *adj.* **1.** Tending to avoid or escape, as by artfulness, cunning, or daring. **2.** Difficult to understand or detect; baffling.

em·bla·zon (ĕm blā′zən) *v.* To make brilliant with colors: *Fireworks emblazoned the night.*

em·i·nent·ly (ĕm′ə nənt lē) *adv.* **1.** In an outstanding or a distinguished way. **2.** Remarkably.

en·croach·ment (ĕn krōch′mənt) *n.* An intrusion upon the rights or property of another.

en·dorse·ment (ĕn dôrs′mənt) *n.* **1.** A signature on the back of a check. **2.** Approval; support: *The plan has my endorsement.*

en·dow (ĕn dou′) *v.* **1.** To provide with property, income, or a source of income: *endow a college.* **2.** To provide or invest with certain talents, qualities, rights, etc.

en·no·ble (ĕn nō′bəl) *v.* **en·no·bled, en·no·bling.** To give a noble or lofty quality to.

en route (än rōōt′) *or* (ĕn). On or along the way: *We'll pick you up en route to school.*

en·sue (ĕn sōō′) *v.* **en·sued, en·su·ing.** To follow as a consequence; result: *Angry words were exchanged, and a fight ensued.*

er·rat·ic (ĭ răt′ĭk) *adj.* **1.** Irregular or uneven in quality, progress, etc.: *His work has been erratic.* **2.** Odd; eccentric. —**er·rat′i·cal·ly** *adv.*

ev·o·lu·tion (ĕv′ə lōō′shən) *n.* **1.** A gradual process by which something changes into a different form: *the evolution of jazz.* **2.** The biological theory that groups of organisms, such as species, can change over a long period of time and through natural processes, so that descendants become less like their ancestors. **3.** The historical development of a related group of organisms: *plant evolution.*

ex·cerpt (ĕk′sûrpt′) *n.* A passage or scene selected from a book, film, musical work,

---

ă pat/ā pay/â care/ä father/ĕ pet/ē be/ĭ pit/ī pie/i fierce/ŏ pot/ō go/ô paw, for/oi oil/ŏŏ book/ ōō boot/ou out/ŭ cut/û fur/*th* the/th thin/hw which/zh vision/ə ago, item, pencil, atom, circus

speech, etc. —*v.* (ĭk **sûrpt′**). To select, quote, or take out (a passage or scene) from a book, film, musical work, speech, etc.

ex·cru·ci·at·ing (ĭk skrōō′shē ā′tĭng) *adj.* Intensely painful; agonizing: *an excruciating headache.* —**ex·cru′ci·at′ing·ly** *adv.*

ex·ot·ic (ĭg zŏt′ĭk) *adj.* **1.** From another part of the world; not native; foreign: *exotic birds; exotic customs.* **2.** Having the charm of the unfamiliar; strikingly or intriguingly unusual: *She is an exotic beauty.*

ex·plic·it (ĭk splĭs′ĭt) *adj.* Clearly defined; specific; precise: *The doctor asked her to be explicit in describing her symptoms.* —**ex·plic′-it·ly** *adv.* —**ex·plic′it·ness** *n.*

ex·qui·site (ĕk′skwĭz ĭt) *or* (ĭk skwĭz′ĭt) *adj.* **1.** Of special beauty, charm, elegance, etc. **2.** Intense; keen: *He takes exquisite pleasure in his meals.* **3.** Keenly sensitive; discriminating: *She has exquisite taste in art.*

ex·tem·po·ra·ne·ous (ĭk stĕm′pə rā′nē əs) *adj.* Done or made with little or no advance preparation; impromptu: *an extemporaneous speech.* —**ex·tem′po·ra′ne·ous·ly** *adv.*

ex·ter·mi·na·tion (ĭk stûr′mə nā′shən) *n.* The act of wiping out or destroying completely.

ex·tract (ĭk străkt′) *v.* **1.** To draw out or forth forcibly; pull out: *extract a tooth.* **2.** To obtain despite resistance, as by a threat: *extract a confession.* **3.** To obtain by a chemical or physical process: *extract a metal from an ore.* —*n.* (ĕk′ străkt′). **1.** A concentrated substance prepared from a natural substance, such as a food or flavoring; essence: *vanilla extract.* **2.** A passage from a literary work; an excerpt.

fa·cil·i·tate (fə sĭl′ĭ tāt′) *v.* **fa·cil·i·tat·ed, fa·cil·i·tat·ing.** To make easier; aid; assist: *New equipment would greatly facilitate the task of the workers.* —**fa·cil′i·ta′tion** *n.*

fac·ul·ty (făk′əl tē) *n., pl.* **fac·ul·ties. 1.** One of the powers of the mind: *the faculty of speech. He is still in full possession of his faculties.* **2.** A special ability or aptitude; skill: *He has a faculty for languages.* **3. a.** The teaching staff of a school, college, or university. **b.** One of the divisions or departments of learning at a college or university: *The faculty of law*

is the college's best department of learning.

fal·con (făl′kən) *or* (fôl′-) *or* (fô′kən) *n.* Any of several long-winged, swift-flying hawks, especially one of a kind trained to hunt for and catch small animals and birds.

fal·ter (fôl′tər) *v.* **1.** To perform haltingly; lose strength or momentum: *The engine faltered.* **2.** To speak hesitatingly; stammer. **3.** To waver in purpose or action; hesitate: *Her determination faltered.*

fa·nat·ic (fə năt′ĭk) *n.* A person whose views, as well as his attachment to them, are so extreme as to be beyond what is normal or reasonable.

fath·om (făth′əm) *n., pl.* **fath·oms** or **fath·om.** A unit of length equal to six feet, used mainly in measuring and expressing depths in the ocean. —*v.* **1.** To measure the depth of. **2.** To get to the bottom of; comprehend: *His motives are difficult to fathom.* —**fath′om·a·ble** *adj.*

feign (fān) *v.* To give a false appearance of; pretend: *feign illness.*

fem·i·nist (fĕm′ə nĭst) *n.* Someone who supports the doctrine that women should have the same rights and status as men.

fes·tive (fĕs′tĭv) *adj.* **1.** Of or suited to a feast or festival: *Food was heaped high on a festive table.* **2.** Merry; joyous: *a festive season.* —**fes′tive·ly** *adv.* —**fes′tive·ness** *n.*

fi·del·i·ty (fĭ dĕl′ĭ tē) *or* (fī-) *n., pl.* **fi·del·i·ties. 1.** Faithfulness to a person, cause, etc.; loyalty. **2.** Truthfulness; accuracy: *the fidelity with which he described his experience.* **3.** The degree to which an electronic system, such as a radio or phonograph, reproduces sound without distortion.

fi·es·ta (fē ĕs′tə) *n.* **1.** A religious festival, especially one celebrated in Spanish-speaking countries. **2.** Any celebration or festive occasion.

flail (flāl) *n.* A tool for threshing grain, consisting of a long wooden handle and a shorter, free-swinging stick attached to its end. —*v.* To thresh or beat with or as if with a flail.

flint (flĭnt) *n.* **1.** A very hard, fine-grained type of quartz that makes sparks when struck with steel. **2.** A small cylinder of an alloy that makes sparks when scratched or scraped, used in lighters to ignite fuel. **—flint** *v.*

fluke (flo͞ok) *n.* An accidental stroke of good luck.

fo·li·age (fō'lē ĭj) *n.* The leaves of plants or trees; leaves in general.

fol·ly (fŏl'ē) *n., pl.* **fol·lies. 1.** Lack of good sense or judgment; foolishness. **2.** A piece of foolishness, as a silly idea, plan, or action.

fore·bear (fôr'bâr') *or* (fōr'-) *n.* An ancestor; forefather.

for·mi·da·ble (fôr'mĭ də bəl) *adj.* **1.** Inspiring fear, dread, or alarm: *a formidable threat.* **2.** Able to impede progress or cause defeat; difficult to surmount: *a formidable task.* **3.** Admirable; awe-inspiring: *a formidable list of talents.* **—for'mi·da·bil'i·ty** *n.*

foun·dry (foun'drē) *n., pl.* **foun·dries.** A place in which metals are cast and molded.

foy·er (foi'ər) *or* (foi'ā') *n.* **1.** The lobby of a public building. **2.** The entrance hall of a private house or apartment.

fren·zied (frĕn'zēd) *adj.* Affected with or filled with wild excitement; frantic: *making last-minute, frenzied changes in the script.* **—fren'zied·ly** *adv.*

fre·quen·cy (frē'kwən sē) *n., pl.* **fre·quen·cies. 1.** The number of occurrences of a specified event within a given interval: **a.** The number of complete cycles of a wave that occur within a period of time. **b.** The number of complete oscillations or vibrations that a body undergoes in a given period of time. **2.** The condition of occurring repeatedly at short intervals: *The frequency of his calls is proof of his interest.*

fro·mage (frō mäzh') *n.* A French word meaning "cheese."

frond (frŏnd) *n.* The leaf of a fern, palm tree, etc., usually divided into smaller leaflets.

fu·ror (fyo͞or'ôr') *or* (-ōr') *n.* A noisy outburst of anger, disapproval, enthusiasm, etc., as in a crowd; an uproar.

fu·sil·lade (fyo͞o'sə läd') *or* (-lād') *or* (-zə-) *n.* **1.** The discharge of many guns at the same time or in rapid succession. **2.** Any rapid outburst: *a fusillade of insults.*

gam·bit (găm'bĭt) *n.* **1.** A chess opening in which a pawn or piece is sacrificed in order to gain a favorable position. **2.** An opening action or remark: *a conversational gambit.*

gaunt (gônt) *adj.* **gaunt·er, gaunt·est. 1.** Thin and bony; haggard; emaciated. **2.** Bleak and desolate; stark. **—gaunt'ly** *adv.*

ga·zelle (gə zĕl') *n.* Any of several slender, swift-running horned animals of Africa and Asia.

gene (jēn) *n.* A unit, located at a particular point on a chromosome, that controls or acts in the transmission of a hereditary characteristic, such as hair color or eye color in human beings, from parents to offspring.

ge·net·ic (jə nĕt'ĭk) *or* **ge·net·i·cal** (jə nĕt'ĭ kəl) *adj.* **1.** Of genetics. **2.** Of, affecting, or affected by a gene or genes: *genetic traits.* **—ge·net'i·cal·ly** *adv.*

ge·nus (jē'nəs) *n., pl.* **gen·e·ra** (jĕn'ər ə). **1.** A group of closely related plants or animals, usually including several species. Dogs, wolves, and coyotes belong to the same genus. **2.** Any type, kind, or class with common characteristics.

ge·ol·o·gist (jē ŏl'ə jĭst) *n.* A scientist who studies the origin, history, behavior, and structure of the earth.

ges·ta·tion (jĕ stā'shən) *n.* **1.** The development of a young animal in the uterus before birth. **2.** The development of a plan or idea in the mind.

gib·ber·ish (jĭb'ər ĭsh) *or* (gĭb'-) *n.* Unintelligible or nonsensical chatter; prattle.

gin·ger·ly (jĭn'jər lē) *adv.* Cautiously; warily: *He walked over to the horse and patted him gingerly.* **—adj.** Cautious; careful.

girth (gûrth) *n.* **1.** The distance or measurement around something; circumference. **2.** A strap encircling the body of a horse or pack animal to secure a load or saddle on its back.

gist (jĭst) *n.* The central idea of something, such as a speech: *the gist of a message.*

glade (glād) *n.* An open space in a forest.

glib (glĭb) *adj.* **glib·ber, glib·best. 1.** Speaking

ă pat/ā pay/â care/ä father/ĕ pet/ē be/ĭ pit/ī pie/î fierce/ŏ pot/ō go/ô paw, for/oi oil/o͝o book/
o͞o boot/ou out/ŭ cut/û fur/*th* the/th thin/hw which/zh vision/ə ago, item, pencil, atom, circus

or writing readily but suggesting lack of thought or sincerity. **2.** Smooth and flowing but shallow or insincere in meaning: *a glib reply.* —**glib'ly** *adv.* —**glib'ness** *n.*

gloam (glōm) *n.* Twilight.

glu·cose (gloo'kōs') *n.* A sugar found in plant and animal tissues and also made synthetically from starch.

gnarled (närld) *adj.* Knotty and misshapen.

gnat (năt) *n.* Any of several small, winged, biting insects.

gourd (gôrd) *or* (gōrd) *or* (goord) *n.* **1.** The fruit of a vine related to the pumpkin, squash, and cucumber, having a hard rind and often an irregular shape. **2.** The dried, hollowed-out shell of such a fruit, used as a ladle, bowl, etc.

gour·met (goor'mā') *or* (goor mā') *n.* One who likes and knows fine food and drink.

grid (grĭd) *n.* **1.** A framework of parallel or crisscrossed bars. **2.** Any pattern of crossing lines or elements, especially when they are arranged in parallel sets: *a grid on a map.*

grim·ace (grĭm'əs) *or* (grĭ mās') *n.* A facial contortion expressive of pain, disgust, etc. —*v.* **grim·aced, grim·ac·ing.** To make a grimace: *Father grimaced when he saw my report card.*

gris·ly (grĭz'lē) *adj.* **gris·li·er, gris·li·est.** Horrifying; gruesome; grim: *a grisly murder.*

gro·tesque (grō tĕsk') *adj.* **1.** Ridiculously distorted and odd; horrible. **2.** Outlandish; bizarre: *a grotesque appearance.* —**gro·tesque'ly** *adv.* —**gro·tesque'ness** *n.*

grot·to (grŏt'ō) *n., pl.* **grot·toes** *or* **grot·tos.** A small cave or cavern or a structure built to resemble one.

grudge (grŭj) *n.* A feeling of resentment or rancor. —*v.* **grudged, grudg·ing.** To be reluctant to give or allow; begrudge: *Don't grudge her a few moments of happiness.*

guile·less (gīl'lĭs) *adj.* Free of slyness; simple.

guil·lo·tine (gĭl'ə tēn') *or* (gē'ə-) *n.* A machine for beheading a condemned prisoner, consisting of a heavy blade that falls freely between two upright posts. —*v.* (gĭl'ə tēn') **guil·lo·tined, guil·lo·tin·ing.** To behead with a guillotine.

gul·let (gŭl'ĭt) *n.* The tube that connects the throat and stomach; the esophagus.

gum·bo (gŭm'bō) *n., pl.* **gum·bos. 1.** A thick soup with okra and other vegetables and meat or seafood. **2.** A fine silty soil, common in the southern and western United States, that forms an unusually sticky mud when wet.

gun·wale (gŭn'əl) *n.* The upper edge of the side of a ship or boat.

gyp·sum (jĭp'səm) *n.* A white mineral consisting mainly of a hydrated calcium compound that also contains sulfur and oxygen.

hab·i·tat (hăb'ĭ tăt') *n.* The area or natural environment in which an animal or plant normally lives or grows.

hap·haz·ard (hăp hăz'ərd) *adj.* Lacking any definite plan or order; left to chance; random. —**hap·haz'ard·ly** *adv.*

har·ried (hăr'ēd) *adj.* Disturbed; harassed.

haugh·ty (hô'tē) *adj.* **haugh·ti·er, haugh·ti·est.** Proud and vain to the point of arrogance. —**haugh'ti·ly** *adv.* —**haugh'ti·ness** *n.*

hav·oc (hăv'ək) *n.* Devastation; destruction.

haz·ard (hăz'ərd) *n.* **1.** A chance of being injured, lost, etc.; danger; risk: *Space travel is full of hazards.* **2.** Something or someone that is likely to cause harm; a possible source of danger: *a fire hazard.* —*v.* **1.** To expose to danger; risk: *The sergeant hazarded his life for the safety of his men.* **2.** To take a chance and give; venture: *hazard a guess.*

hel·ic·tite (hĕl'ĭk tīt) *n.* An irregular stalactite with branching spines.

hem·lock (hĕm'lŏk') *n.* **1.** An evergreen tree with short, flat needles and small cones. **2.a.** A poisonous plant with featherlike leaves and flat clusters of small, whitish flowers. **b.** A poison extracted from this plant.

he·red·i·ty (hə rĕd'ĭ tē) *n., pl.* **he·red·i·ties. 1.** The passage of physical traits from parents to offspring by biological inheritance; genetic transmission. **2.** The complete set of traits passed to an organism in this way.

hoax (hōks) *n.* A trick or action intended to deceive others, often in the form of a practical joke, false report, etc., that fools the public. —*v.* To deceive or cheat by a hoax.

hock¹ (hŏk) *n.* **1.** The joint of the hind leg of a horse or other four-footed animal that corresponds to the ankle. **2.** A cut of meat from this part, especially of a hog.

hock² (hŏk). *Informal. v.* To pawn. —*n.* The condition of being held by a pawnbroker: *Her diamonds are in hock.*

ho·gan (hō′gôn′) *or* (-gən) *n.* An earth-covered Navaho dwelling.

hom·age (hŏm′ĭj) *or* (ŏm′-) *n.* **1.** Special honor or respect shown or expressed publicly: *The crowd cheered in homage to the great singer.* **2.** An action or ceremony, originating in feudal times, in which a person shows allegiance or loyalty to a ruler.

hov·el (hŭv′əl) *or* (hŏv′-) *n.* A small, miserable dwelling.

hull (hŭl) *n.* **1.** The framework of a ship or plane. **2.** The cluster of leaflets at the stem end of certain fruits, such as the strawberry. **3.** The outer covering of certain seeds, fruits, or nuts; a husk or pod. —*v.* To remove the hulls from: *hull strawberries.*

hu·mil·i·ty (hyo͞o mĭl′ĭ tē) *n.* The quality or condition of being humble; lack of pride; modesty: *handled it with tact and humility.*

hyp·o·crite (hĭp′ə krĭt′) *n.* A person who shows or expresses feelings, beliefs, or qualities that he actually does not possess; someone who is insincere.

il·lit·er·ate (ĭ lĭt′ər ĭt) *adj.* **1.** Unable to read and write. **2.** Showing a lack of education. —*n.* A person who is unable to read and write. —**il·lit′er·ate·ly** *adv.*

im·be·cil·i·ty (ĭm′bĭ sĭl′ə tē) *n.* **1.** Feeble-mindedness. **2.** Stupidity or foolishness.

im·bibe (ĭm bīb′) *v.* **im·bibed, im·bib·ing. 1.** To drink. **2.** To receive or absorb into the mind: *imbibe new ideas.* —**im·bib′er** *n.*

im·me·mo·ri·al (ĭm′ə môr′ē əl) *or* (-mōr′-) *adj.* Reaching beyond the limits of memory, tradition, or recorded history: *since time immemorial.* —**im′me·mo′ri·al·ly** *adv.*

im·mi·nent (ĭm′ə nənt) *adj.* About to occur; impending: *an imminent crisis.* —**im′mi·nence** *n.* —**im′mi·nent·ly** *adv.*

im·mor·tal (ĭ môr′tl) *adj.* **1.** Not subject to death; living forever: *the immortal soul.* **2.** Having eternal fame: *an immortal poet.* —*n.* **1.** Someone or something not subject to death. **2.** Someone with enduring fame. —**im·mor′tal·ly** *adv.*

im·mune (ĭ myo͞on′) *adj.* **1.** Not susceptible; resistant: *immune to a disease.* **2.** Protected; guarded; safe: *immune from attack.*

im·pal·pa·ble (ĭm păl′pə bəl) *adj.* **1.** Not perceptible to the touch: *impalpable shadows.* **2.** Not easily grasped by the mind.

im·pe·ri·ous (ĭm pîr′ē əs) *adj.* **1.** Arrogant; overbearing; domineering. **2.** Compelling; urgent: *imperious demands of instinct.* —**im·pe′ri·ous·ly** *adv.* —**im·pe′ri·ous·ness** *n.*

im·per·ish·a·ble (ĭm pĕr′ĭ shə bəl) *adj.* Not likely to decay or be destroyed.

im·pos·tor (ĭm pŏs′tər) *n.* A person who deceives by pretending to be someone else.

im·preg·na·ble (ĭm prĕg′nə bəl) *adj.* Safe against attack; not penetrable.

im·pres·sion·ism, also **Im·pres·sion·ism** (ĭm prĕsh′ə nĭz′əm) *n.* **1.** A style of painting of the late 19th century, marked by concentration on the impression produced by a scene or thing and the use of many small strokes to simulate reflected light. **2.** A musical style of the late 19th century, using rather vague but colorful harmonies and rhythms to suggest moods, places, and happenings. —**im·pres′sion·ist, Im·pres′sion·ist** *n. & adj.*

im·promp·tu (ĭm prŏmp′to͞o) *or* (-tyo͞o) *adj.* Not prepared beforehand; not rehearsed: *an impromptu lecture.* —*adv.* Without rehearsal or preparation: *He sang impromptu for the children.* —*n.* Something made or done without rehearsal, as a musical composition or speech.

im·pro·vised (ĭm′prə vīzd′) *adj.* **1.** Invented or composed without preparation. **2.** Made, built, or provided on the spur of the moment or from materials found nearby: *an im-*

ă pat/ā pay/â care/ä father/ĕ pet/ē be/ĭ pit/ī pie/î fierce/ŏ pot/ō go/ô paw, for/oi oil/o͞o book/
o͞o boot/ou out/ŭ cut/û fur/*th* the/th thin/hw which/zh vision/ə ago, item, pencil, atom, circus

provised meal; an improvised tent for shelter.

in·ac·ces·si·ble (ĭn′ăk sĕs′ə bəl) *adj.* Not accessible; unapproachable: *a nearby inaccessible place.* —**in′ac·ces′si·bly** *adv.*

in·ad·ver·tent·ly (ĭn′əd vûr′tnt lē) *adv.* Accidentally; unintentionally.

in·aus·pi·cious (ĭn′ô spĭsh′əs) *adj.* Not auspicious; boding ill; unfavorable: *inauspicious circumstances.* —**in′aus·pi′cious·ly** *adv.*

in·cal·cu·la·ble (ĭn kăl′kyə lə bəl) *adj.* **1.** Too great to be counted or described; enormous: *an incalculable number of ants.* **2.** Incapable of being foreseen: *an incalculable outcome.* —**in·cal′cu·la·bil′i·ty** *n.*

in·can·des·cent (ĭn′kən dĕs′ənt) *adj.* **1.** Giving off visible light as a result of being raised to a high temperature. **2.** Shining brilliantly; very bright. —**in′can·des′cence** *n.*

in·ces·sant (ĭn sĕs′ənt) *adj.* Continuing without interruption; constant: *her incessant talk.* —**in·ces′sant·ly** *adv.*

in·cip·i·ent (ĭn sĭp′ē ənt) *adj.* In an initial or early stage; just beginning to exist or appear: *an incipient smile.*

in·com·pre·hen·si·ble (ĭn′kŏm prĭ hĕn′sə bəl) *or* (ĭn kŏm′-) *adj.* Incapable of being understood or comprehended: *an incomprehensible sentence.* —**in′com·pre·hen′si·bil′i·ty** *n.* —**in′com·pre·hen′si·bly** *adv.*

in·con·se·quen·tial (ĭn kŏn′sĭ kwĕn′shəl) *adj.* Without consequence; lacking importance; petty: *an inconsequential and boring debate.* —**in·con′se·quen′tial·ly** *adv.*

in·con·spic·u·ous (ĭn′kən spĭk′yoō əs) *adj.* Not readily noticeable; not obvious: *The flowers of the oak and maple are inconspicuous.* —**in′con·spic′u·ous·ly** *adv.*

in·duce (ĭn doōs′) *or* (-dyoōs′) *v.* **in·duced, in·duc·ing. 1.** To persuade; influence; prevail upon: *Nothing could induce him to stay, and so he said good-by.* **2.** To cause or stimulate the occurrence of: *induce vomiting in a patient.*

in·dulge (ĭn dŭlj′) *v.* **in·dulged, in·dulg·ing. 1.** To yield to the desires of; pamper: *indulge a child.* **2.** To gratify or satisfy (a desire): *indulge a craving for chocolate.* **3.** To allow oneself some special pleasure. **4.** To engage; take part: *indulge in sports.*

in·ev·i·ta·ble (ĭn ĕv′ĭ tə bəl) *adj.* Not capable of being avoided or prevented: *an inevitable outcome.* —**in·ev′i·ta·bly** *adv.*

in·fer·nal (ĭn fûr′nəl) *adj.* **1.** Of or resembling hell. **2.** Horrible; damnable: *an infernal nuisance.* —**in·fer′nal·ly** *adv.*

in·fest (ĭn fĕst′) *v.* To live in or overrun in large numbers so as to be harmful or unpleasant: *Rats infested the building.*

in·gen·ious (ĭn jēn′yəs) *adj.* **1.** Clever at devising things; creative: *an ingenious inventor.* **2.** Showing originality and resourcefulness: *an ingenious idea.* —**in·gen′ious·ly** *adv.*

in·ge·nu·i·ty (ĭn′jə noō′ĭ tē) *or* (-nyoō′-) *n.* Inventive skill or imagination; cleverness.

in·hos·pi·ta·ble (ĭn hŏs′pĭ tə bəl) *or* (ĭn′hŏ-spĭt′ə bəl) *adj.* **1.** Unfriendly. **2.** Harsh; forbidding: *an inhospitable climate.*

in·nate (ĭ nāt′) *or* (ĭn′āt′) *adj.* **1.** Possessed from birth: *an innate instinct.* **2.** Existing as a basic, seemingly inborn, characteristic: *an innate love of learning.* —**in·nate′ly** *adv.*

in·or·di·nate·ly (ĭn ôr′dn ĭt lē) *adv.* In a manner that exceeds reasonable limits; immoderately.

in·road (ĭn′rōd′) *n.* **1.** A hostile invasion; a raid. **2.** An advance at the expense of something or someone else; an encroachment: *Japanese products have made huge inroads into the American economy.*

in·sa·tia·ble (ĭn sā′shə bəl) *or* (-shē ə-) *adj.* Not capable of being satisfied: *an insatiable appetite.* —**in·sa′tia·bly** *adv.*

in·so·lent (ĭn′sə lənt) *adj.* Disrespectfully arrogant; impudent; rude: *an insolent reply.* —**in′so·lence** *n.* —**in′so·lent·ly** *adv.*

in·stinc·tive·ly (ĭn stĭngk′tĭv lē) *adv.* **1.** In a way that is not learned. **2.** Naturally.

in·sur·gent (ĭn sûr′jənt) *adj.* Rising in revolt: *The insurgent forces overthrew the government.* —*n.* A rebel.

in·ter·stel·lar (ĭn′tər stĕl′ər) *adj.* Between the stars: *interstellar space.*

in·tone (ĭn tōn′) *v.* **in·toned, in·ton·ing.** To recite in a singing or chanting voice, often on a single tone: *intoned prayers in church.*

in·tox·i·cat·ed (ĭn tŏk′sĭ kā′tĭd) *adj.* **1.** Drunk or in a condition resembling drunkenness. **2.** Highly stimulated; elated; overjoyed.

in·trin·sic (ĭn trĭn′sĭk) *adj.* Being part of the basic nature of a thing; fundamental;

most essential: *the intrinsic difficulty of mathematics.* —**in·trin'si·cal·ly** *adv.*

in·un·date (ĭn'ŭn dāt') *v.* **in·un·dat·ed, in·un·dat·ing.** **1.** To cover with water; flood: *A tidal wave inundated the beach.* **2.** To overwhelm, as with a flood: *The courts are inundated with cases.* —**in'un·da'tion** *n.*

in·ver·te·brate (ĭn vûr'tə brĭt) *or* (-brāt') *n.* An animal having no backbone, as a worm, clam, jellyfish, starfish, insect, or lobster. —*adj.* Having no backbone: *invertebrate animals.*

i·ras·ci·ble (ĭ răs'ə bəl) *or* (ĭ răs'-) *adj.* Having a hot temper; highly irritable: *He is an irascible man.*

i·rate (ī rāt') *or* (ī'rāt') *adj.* Angry; enraged: *"Get away from here!" shouted the irate farmer.* —**i·rate'ly** *adv.*

ir·rep·a·ra·ble (ĭ rĕp'ər ə bəl) *adj.* Not capable of being repaired, remedied, undone, or set right: *irreparable damage.* —**ir·rep'a·ra·bly** *adv.*

is·let (ī'lĭt) *n.* A very small island.

jas·mine (jăz'mĭn) *n.* Any of several vines or shrubs with fragrant, usually yellow or white, flowers.

jaun·diced (jôn'dĭst) *or* (jän'-) *adj.* **1.** Affected with jaundice. **2.** Showing or feeling jealousy, envy, etc.; prejudiced: *a jaundiced viewpoint.*

jess (jĕs) *n.* A short strap fastened around the leg of a hawk or another bird used in falconry, and to which a leash may be fastened.

jinx (jĭngks) *n. Informal.* **1.** An evil spell or any force or influence that is felt to bring bad luck. **2.** Someone or something supposed to bring bad luck. —*v. Informal.* To place a jinx on; bring bad luck to; foredoom with failure or misfortune.

ju·ni·per (jōō'nə pər) *n.* An evergreen tree or shrub related to the pines, having small, scalelike or prickly leaves and bluish, aromatic berries.

keel (kēl) *n.* **1.** A strong timber, plate, or beam of metal running from bow to stern along the center line of a vessel and serving as the backbone to which the frames are attached. **2.** A fin extending lengthwise along the bottom of a sailboat or an airship to give the craft stability. —*v.* To capsize.

kil·ter (kĭl'tər) *n.* Good condition; proper form. Used chiefly in the phrase *out of kilter.*

knave (nāv) *n.* **1.** A dishonest, crafty man: *He played the knave in our business dealings.* **2.** *Archaic.* A male servant: *a lowly kitchen knave.* **3.** A playing card, the jack.

knight (nīt) *n.* **1.** In feudal times, a mounted man-at-arms giving service to a king or other superior. **2.** Either of two chess pieces that can be moved two squares horizontally and one vertically or two squares vertically and one horizontally. —*v.* To make (a person) a knight.

lab·y·rinth (lăb'ə rĭnth') *n.* A network of winding, connected passages through which it is difficult to find one's way without help.

la·con·ic (lə kŏn'ĭk) *adj.* Terse; concise: *a laconic reply.* —**la·con'i·cal·ly** *adv.*

la·ment (lə mĕnt') *v.* To mourn over; grieve: *lament the death of a loved one.* —*n.* **1.** An expression of grief: *shattering his heart with tears and laments.* **2.** A sorrowful song or poem.

lap (lăp) *v.* To fold or wrap over or around something. —*n.* **1.** A single length or turn over or around something, as a racecourse: *ran three laps.* **2.** A single part or stage, as of a journey.

lard (lärd) *n.* The white waxy or greasy substance prepared from the melted-down fat of a pig. —*v.* **1.** To cover or coat with lard or a similar fat. **2.** To make or try to make (speech, writing, etc.) richer, more effective, or longer by adding something.

la·ser (lā'zər) *n.* Any of a number of devices that use the radiating properties of systems

---

ă pat/ā pay/â care/ä father/ĕ pet/ē be/ĭ pit/ī pie/î fierce/ŏ pot/ō go/ô paw, for/oi oil/ŏŏ book/ ōō boot/ou out/ŭ cut/û fur/*th* the/th thin/hw which/zh vision/ə ago, item, pencil, atom, circus

of atoms or molecules to generate light that is of a single, precise wavelength, with all of the waves polarized, exactly aligned, and matching each other in their phases.

lat·er·al·ly (lăt'ər ə lē) *adv.* In a position toward or from the side or sides.

lee (lē) *n.* The side that is turned away from the wind; the sheltered side: *in the lee of the island.* —*adj.* **1.** Away from the wind. **2.** Lying on the side of a ship toward which the ship is being driven by the wind: *a dangerous lee shore.*

li·chen (lī'kən) *n.* A plant consisting of a fungus and an algae growing in close combination and forming a crustlike, scaly, or branching growth on rocks and tree trunks.

Lil·li·pu·tian (lĭl'ə pyōō'shən) *n.* **1.** One of the six-inch-high inhabitants of the imaginary country of Lilliput in Jonathan Swift's *Gulliver's Travels* (1726). **2.** Often **lilliputian.** A tiny person. —*adj.* Often **lilliputian.** Very small; tiny.

lim·ber (lĭm'bər) *adj.* **1.** Bending easily; pliable: *limber muscles.* **2.** Moving easily and nimbly; agile. —*v.* To engage in light exercise so as to make the body more limber.

lim·ey (lī'mē) *n., pl.* **lim·eys.** *Slang.* **1.** A British seaman. **2.** An Englishman.

lim·pid (lĭm'pĭd) *adj.* Perfectly clear; transparent: *eyes like limpid pools of water.*

lin·e·age (lĭn'ē ĭj) *n.* **1.** Direct descent from a particular ancestor; ancestry. **2.** All of the descendants of a particular ancestor.

li·ra (lîr'ə) *n., pl.* **li·re** (lîr'ā) or **li·ras.** The basic unit of money of Italy.

lit·er·ate (lĭt'ər ĭt) *adj.* **1.** Able to read and write. **2.** Skillful in the use of words: *a literate style.* **3.** Educated in or familiar with literature. —*n.* A person who can read and write.

log·book (lôg'bŏŏk') or (lŏg'-) *n.* **1.** The official record of speed, progress, and important events kept on a ship or aircraft. **2.** Any journal or record of performance.

Lone Star State. A nickname for Texas.

loon[1] (lōōn) *n.* A diving bird with a dark, speckled back, a pointed bill, and an eerie, laughlike cry.

loon[2] (lōōn) *n.* **1.** A simple-minded or mad person. **2.** An idler.

lot·ter·y (lŏt'ə rē) *n., pl.* **lot·ter·ies.** A contest in which the winner is chosen in a drawing of lots.

lu·cid (lōō'sĭd) *adj.* **1.** Easily understood; clear: *a lucid explanation.* **2.** Mentally sound; sane; rational: *The senile man has his lucid hours.* —**lu·cid'i·ty, lu'cid·ness** *n.* —**lu'cid·ly** *adv.*

lu·nar (lōō'nər) *adj.* **1.** Of, caused by, or affecting the moon: *a lunar orbit.* **2.** Measured or determined by motions of the moon: *a lunar year.* **3.** On the moon: *a lunar landing.*

lure (lŏŏr) *n.* **1.** Something that attracts, appeals, or entices, especially with the promise of pleasure or a reward: *the lure of the sea.* **2.** Any of various small devices used by a fisherman to attract and catch fish. —*v.* **lured, lur·ing.** To attract, appeal to, or entice.

lus·cious (lŭsh'əs) *adj.* **1.** Having a delicious taste or smell: *a luscious peach.* **2.** Appealing to the senses: *singing with luscious beauty of tone.* —**lus'cious·ly** *adv.* —**lus'cious·ness** *n.*

lus·trous (lŭs'trəs) *adj.* Having a gloss or sheen; gleaming: *lustrous Oriental silks.* —**lus'trous·ly** *adv.* —**lus'trous·ness** *n.*

mag·is·trate (măj'ĭ strāt') or (-strĭt) *n.* **1.** A civil official with the authority to administer the law. **2.** A minor law official, such as a justice of the peace or the judge of a police court.

mag·ni·tude (măg'nĭ tōōd') or (-tyōōd') *n.* Greatness, as of position, size, influence, etc.: *the magnitude of his achievements; failing to realize the magnitude of the problem.*

ma·lev·o·lent (mə lĕv'ə lənt) *adj.* Wishing harm to others; malicious: *They feared the malevolent old man.* —**ma·lev'o·lence** *n.* —**ma·lev'o·lent·ly** *adv.*

mal·ice (măl'ĭs) *n.* The desire to harm others or to see others suffer; ill will; spite.

ma·neu·ver (mə nōō'vər) or (-nyōō'-) *n.* **1.** A change in the course or position of a vehicle, as an aircraft, automobile, etc. **2.** A calculated act; trick; stratagem: *The lawyer used various legal maneuvers to outwit the prosecutor.* **3.** A tactical or strategic movement, as of troops, warships, etc.: *By a series of brilliant maneuvers, the general outwitted the* enemy. —v. **1.** To make or cause to make one or more changes in course or position: *The "Nautilus" had to maneuver very carefully to avoid the icebergs.* **2.** To manipulate, as by trickery. **3.** To carry out a military maneuver. —**ma·neu′ver·a·bil′i·ty** *n.*

man·grove (măn′grōv′) *or* (măng′grōv′) *n.* A tropical tree or shrub that has many stiltlike roots growing above the ground and forms dense thickets in marshes and along shores.

ma·nip·u·late (mə nĭp′yə lāt′) *v.* **ma·nip·u·lat·ed, ma·nip·u·lat·ing.** **1.** To operate or arrange with the hands: *manipulate the controls on an airplane.* **2.** To influence or manage in a clever or devious way: *He was clever enough to manipulate his partners.* **3.** To control (an intricate process), as if by the dexterity of human hands: *Electronic music consists of sounds manipulated by electronic equipment.* —**ma·nip′u·lat′ive** *adj.*

mar·celled (mär sĕld′) *adj.* Styled in regular waves, as a hairdo.

mar·row (măr′ō) *n.* **1.** The soft material that fills the cavities inside bones, consisting of fat cells and maturing blood cells together with connective tissue and blood vessels. **2.** The nerve tissue that fills the interior of the bones of the spine; the spinal cord. **3.** The essential part: *She was a country girl to the very marrow.*

ma·tron·ly (mā′trən lē) *adj.* Of or like a married woman, especially one in middle age or older.

mav·er·ick (măv′ər ĭk) *or* (măv′rĭk) *n.* **1.** An unbranded calf or colt, traditionally belonging to the first person to brand it. **2.** A person who refuses to go along with the policies, views, etc., of his group.

maze (māz) *n.* **1.** A complicated, usually confusing, network of passageways or pathways. **2.** Any state of confusion or bewilderment.

mealybug. An insect which destroys plants, especially citrus trees.

me·an·der (mē ăn′dər) *v.* **1.** To follow a winding and turning course: *The river meanders through the town.* **2.** To wander aimlessly and idly. —**me·an′der·ing, me·an′drous** *adj.*

mech·a·ni·za·tion (mĕk′ə nī zā′shən) *n.* The state of being mechanized; the act or process of equipping with machinery.

me·di·e·val (mē′dē ē′vəl) *or* (mĕd′ē-) *or* (mĭd′ē-) *or* (mĭ dē′vəl) *adj.* Of or characteristic of the period in European history from the fall of the Roman Empire (about A.D. 500) to the rise of the Renaissance (about 1400).

mel·o·dra·mat·ic (mĕl′ə drə măt′ĭk) *adj.* **1.** Exaggerated or distorted to heighten sensation: *a melodramatic account of a boxing match.* **2.** Full of false or pretended emotion; sentimental.

mem·brane (mĕm′brān′) *n.* **1.** A thin, flexible layer of tissue that covers surfaces or acts as the boundary between adjoining regions, structures, or organs in the body of an animal or plant. **2.** A thin sheet of natural or synthetic material through which dissolved substances can pass, as in osmosis. **3.** A thin sheet of a flexible, elastic material, such as rubber or plastic.

mi·gra·to·ry (mī′grə tôr′ē) *or* (-tōr′ē) *adj.* Traveling from place to place; roving: *migratory workers.*

mi·nute (mī nōōt′) *or* (-nyōōt′) *or* (mĭ-) *adj.* **1.** Exceptionally small; tiny. **2.** Marked by close examination or careful study of small details: *a minute inspection of bacteria.* —**mi·nute′ly** *adv.* —**mi·nute′ness** *n.*

mire (mīr) *n.* **1.** An area of wet, muddy ground; a bog. **2.** Deep, slimy soil or mud. —*v.* **mired, mir·ing.** **1.** To sink or become stuck in mire. **2.** To cause to become stuck in mire.

miz·zling (mĭz′lĭng) *adj.* Mistlike.

mol·li·fy (mŏl′ə fī′) *v.* **mol·li·fied, mol·li·fy·ing, mol·li·fies.** **1.** To allay the anger of; placate. **2.** To make less intense; soften or soothe: *Her tender words mollified the child's distress.*

mon·as·ter·y (mŏn′ə stĕr′ē) *n., pl.* **mon·as·ter·ies.** The place where a community of monks lives. —**mon′as·ter′i·al** (mŏn′ə stîr′ē əl) *or* (-stĕr′-) *adj.*

ă pat/ā pay/â care/ä father/ĕ pet/ē be/ĭ pit/ī pie/î fierce/ŏ pot/ō go/ô paw, for/oi oil/ōō book/ ōō boot/ou out/ŭ cut/û fur/*th* the/th thin/hw which/zh vision/ə ago, item, pencil, atom, circus

mo·not·o·nous (mə nŏt′n əs) *adj.* **1.** Uttered or sounded in one repeated tone; unvarying in pitch. **2.** Never varied or enlivened; repetitiously dull: *a monotonous diet.* —**mo·not′o·nous·ly** *adv.*

mon·u·men·tal (mŏn′yə mĕn′tl) *adj.* **1.** Of, like, or serving as a monument. **2.** Impressively large and sturdy: *monumental dams.* **3.** Of enduring importance; outstanding. **4.** Astounding; outrageous: *came to see his whole life as a monumental fraud.* —**mon′u·men′tal·ly** *adv.*

moor (mŏor) *v.* **1.** To make fast (a vessel or aircraft) by means of cables or anchors. **2.** To fix in place; secure. **3.** To tie up a boat; anchor.

mo·rose (mə rōs′) *or* (mô-) *adj.* Ill-humored; sullen; gloomy. —**mo·rose′ly** *adv.*

mor·tal·i·ty (môr tăl′ĭ tē) *n., pl.* **mor·tal·i·ties. 1.** The condition of being subject to death. **2.** Death, especially of large numbers. **3.** The proportion of a given group of people that dies in a given period of time; death rate.

mor·ti·fied (môr′tə fīd′) *adj.* **1.** Ashamed; embarrassed. **2.** Annoyed; frustrated.

mu·lat·to (mə lăt′ō) *or* (-lä′tō) *or* (myŏō′-) *n., pl.* **mu·lat·tos. 1.** A person having one Caucasoid parent and one Negroid parent. **2.** Any person of mixed Caucasoid and Negroid ancestry.

mus·ter (mŭs′tər) *v.* **1.** To bring or come together; assemble: *The men mustered for roll call.* **2.** To call forth or bring forth: *He finally mustered enough courage to ask her for a date.* —*n.* **1.** A gathering, especially of troops, for inspection, roll call, etc. **2.** The official roll of men in a military unit.

mute (myŏōt) *adj.* **1.** Not having the power of speech. **2.** Refraining from speech; silent: *remained mute under questioning.* —*n.* **1.** A person incapable of speech, especially one both deaf and mute. **2.** Any of various attachments used to soften, muffle, or alter the tone of a musical instrument. —*v.* **mut·ed, mut·ing.** To muffle or soften the sound of. —**mute′ly** *adv.* —**mute′ness** *n.*

mu·ti·late (myŏōt′l āt′) *v.* **mu·ti·lat·ed, mu·ti·lat·ing.** To damage by cutting off or mangling (a necessary part, limb, etc.). —**mu′ti·la′tion** *n.*

myr·i·ad (mîr′ē əd) *adj.* Amounting to a very large, indefinite number: *the moon, sun, planets, and myriad stars.* —*n.* A vast number.

mys·tic (mĭs′tĭk) *adj.* **1.** Of religious or supernatural rites and practices: *The tribe gathered for their mystic dance to welcome planting time.* **2.** Inspiring a quality of mystery; mysterious. —*n.* Someone who practices or believes in mysticism.

mys·ti·cism (mĭs′tĭ sĭz′əm) *n.* **1.** The belief that direct contact with the divine can be attained through deep meditation. **2.** The spiritual qualities or way of thinking of a person who believes in or practices mysticism. **3.** Confused and groundless thinking.

na·ive *or* **na·ïve** (nä ēv′) *adj.* **1.** Simple and unaffected, as a child. **2.** Showing a lack of experience, judgment, etc.; unsophisticated: *naive remarks.* —**na·ive′ly** *adv.*

nat·u·ral·ist (năch′ər ə lĭst) *or* (năch′rə-) *n.* A person who specializes in natural history, especially in the study of plants and animals in their natural surroundings.

ne·go·ti·a·tion (nĭ gō′shē ā′shən) *n.* Often **negotiations.** A discussion for the purpose of coming to terms or to an agreement: *secret negotiations between the two nations.*

niche (nĭch) *n.* **1.** A recess or alcove in a wall, as for holding a statue. **2.** A cranny, hollow, or crevice, as in rock.

nonaggression pact. A treaty between two hostile parties in which both sides agree not to attack one another for a specified length of time.

non·cha·lant·ly (nŏn′shə länt′lē) *adv.* In a casually unconcerned way.

non·com·mit·tal (nŏn′kə mĭt′l) *adj.* Not indicating how one feels or what one plans to do: *She gave a noncommittal answer, "We shall see."*

no·to·ri·ous (nō tôr′ē əs) *or* (-tōr′-) *adj.* **1.** Known widely and regarded unfavorably; infamous: *a notorious swindler.* **2.** Well known or famous for something, as a trait, a negative quality, etc.

nov·el (nŏv′əl) *adj.* Strikingly new or different: *a novel method of painting.*

nov·ice (nŏv′ĭs) *n.* **1.** A person new to a field

or activity; a beginner. **2.** A person who has entered a religious order but has not yet taken the final vows.

ob·e·lisk (ŏb′ə lĭsk′) *n.* A tall, four-sided shaft of stone, usually tapering to a pyramidal point.

o·bliv·i·on (ə blĭv′ē ən) *n.* The condition of being completely forgotten: *a great poet, now in oblivion.*

ob·ser·va·to·ry (əb zûr′və tôr′ē) *or* (-tōr′ē) *n., pl.* **ob·ser·va·to·ries.** A place designed and equipped for making observations, as in astronomy or meteorology.

ob·ses·sive (əb sĕs′ĭv) *adj.* Recurring continually; haunting: *an obsessive fear of snakes.*

o·men (ō′mən) *n.* A thing or event regarded as a sign of future good or bad luck.

om·i·nous (ŏm′ə nəs) *adj.* Seeming to foretell or be a sign of trouble or disaster; threatening: *ominous clouds.* **—om′i·nous·ly** *adv.*

on·slaught (ŏn′slôt′) *or* (ôn′-) *n.* A violent attack or charge: *the enemy onslaught.*

op·ti·cal (ŏp′tĭ kəl) *adj.* **1.** Of or having to do with sight: *an optical illusion.* **2.** Designed to assist sight: *optical instruments.* **3.** Of the science of optics. **—op′ti·cal·ly** *adv.*

op·ti·mist (ŏp′tə mĭst) *n.* **1.** Someone who takes a hopeful view of a situation or expects the best possible outcome. **2.** Someone who believes that good will ultimately overcome evil.

o·rang·ou·tang (ō răng′ə tăng′) *or* (ə răng′-) *n.* A large ape of the islands of Borneo and Sumatra, having long arms and reddish-brown hair.

or·a·tor·i·cal·ly (ôr′ə tôr′ĭ kə lē) *or* (ŏr′ə-tōr′-) *adv.* In a manner appropriate to a public speaker.

or·deal (ôr dēl′) *n.* A very difficult or painful experience, especially one that tests a person's character or endurance.

ot·ter (ŏt′ər) *n.* A weasel-like animal that lives in or near water and has webbed feet and thick, dark-brown fur.

o·va·tion (ō vā′shən) *n.* A loud and enthusiastic display of approval, usually in the form of shouting or hearty applause.

pa·gan (pā′gən) *n.* **1.** A person who is not a Christian, Moslem, or Jew; a heathen. **2.** A person who has no religion. **—***adj.* Of pagans or paganism: *a pagan ceremony; pagan gods.*

pal·let (păl′ĭt) *n.* A narrow, hard bed or straw-filled mattress.

pan·o·ram·a (păn′ə răm′ə) *or* (-rä′mə) *n.* **1.** A view or picture of everything visible over a wide area. **2.** A view or picture of a long series of events, stages, or things.

Pan·zer (păn′zər) *or* (pän′tsər) *n.* An armored tank.

par·a·med·ic (păr ə mĕd′ĭk) *n.* A doctor who parachutes to areas where medical services are needed.

par·a·pet (păr′ə pĭt) *or* (-pĕt′) *n.* **1.** A low wall or railing along the edge of a roof or balcony. **2.** An embankment protecting soldiers from enemy fire.

par·a·sit·ic (păr′ə sĭt′ĭk) *adj.* Of or caused by an organism that lives in or on a different kind of organism from which it gets its nourishment and to which it is sometimes harmful.

par·ti·tion (pär tĭsh′ən) *n.* **1.** A usually thin structure, such as a panel or screen, that divides up a room or other enclosure. **2.** Any structure that divides a space. **—***v.* To divide into separate spaces, parts, or sections: *partitioned the room with a curtain.*

pat·i·o (păt′ē ō′) *n., pl.* **pat·i·os. 1.** An inner courtyard open to the sky. **2.** A space for dining or recreation, next to a house or an apartment.

pat·ter (păt′ər) *n.* Glib, rapid-fire speech, such as that used by a salesman or comedian.

pawn (pôn) *n.* **1.** A chessman of the lowest value. **2.** A person used or controlled by others.

pe·cu·ni·ar·y (pĭ kyōō′nē ĕr′ē) *adj.* **1.** Of

ă pat/ā pay/â care/ä father/ĕ pet/ē be/ĭ pit/ī pie/î fierce/ŏ pot/ō go/ô paw, for/oi oil/ŏŏ book/
ōō boot/ou out/ŭ cut/û fur/*th* the/th thin/hw which/zh vision/ə ago, item, pencil, atom, circus

money or financial matters: *a pecuniary loss.*
2. Consisting of or measured in money.

pence (pĕns) *n. British.* A plural of **penny.**

pen·sion·er (pĕn′shə nər) *n.* Someone who receives a sum of money paid regularly as a retirement benefit or by way of patronage.

per·cep·ti·bly (pər sĕp′tə blē) *adv.* In a way that is capable of being noticed.

per·emp·to·ry (pə rĕmp′tə rē) *adj.* **1.** Admitting no contradiction; imperative: *a peremptory order.* **2.** Offensively self-assured; dictatorial: *his peremptory manner.*

per·se·ver·ance (pûr′sə vîr′əns) *n.* The act or quality of holding to a course, belief, purpose, etc., without giving way; steadfastness.

per·spec·tive (pər spĕk′tĭv) *n.* **1.** A mental view of the relationships of the aspects of a subject to each other and to a whole: *a narrow perspective of the situation.* **2.** An idea of the relative importance of something; a viewpoint.

pe·so (pā′sō) *n., pl.* **pe·sos.** The basic unit of money of Argentina, Bolivia, Colombia, Cuba, the Dominican Republic, Mexico, the Philippines, and Uruguay.

pet·ri·fy·ing (pĕt′rĭ fī′ĭng) *adj.* Stunning; paralyzing, as with fear or astonishment.

Ph.D. Doctor of Philosophy.

phe·nom·e·non (fĭ nŏm′ə nŏn′) *n., pl.* **phe·nom·e·na** (fĭ nŏm′ə nə) or **phe·nom·e·nons. 1.** Any occurrence or fact that can be perceived by the senses: *Floods are natural phenomena.* **2.** Someone or something that is unusual or noteworthy: *He's considered quite a phenomenon by the sports writers.*

phi·lan·thro·pist (fĭ lăn′thrə pĭst) *n.* A person who is involved in promoting human welfare, as by making charitable donations.

phi·los·o·pher (fĭ lŏs′ə fər) *n.* **1.** A student of the basic truths and laws governing the universe, nature, life, morals, etc. **2.** A calm, self-assured, and patient person.

phy·la (fī′lə) *n.* Plural of **phylum.**

phy·lum (fī′ləm) *n., pl.* **phy·la** (fī′lə). One of the larger groups into which living organisms are divided, ranking between a kingdom and a class and including animals and plants with certain basic similarities.

pi·az·za (pē ăz′ə) *or* (-ä′zə) *n.* **1.** A public square in an Italian town. **2.** A porch.

pig·my (pĭg′mē) *adj. & n., pl.* **pig·mies.** A form of the word **pygmy.**

pile (pīl) *n.* **1.** Cut or uncut loops of yarn forming the surface of certain carpets or of fabrics such as velvet and plush. **2.** Soft, fine hair, fur, or wool.

pin·na·cle (pĭn′ə kəl) *n.* **1.** A tall, pointed formation, as a mountain peak. **2.** The peak or summit of anything: *at the pinnacle of his fame.* **3.** A small turret or spire on a roof.

pis·ta·chi·o (pĭ stăsh′ē ō′) *n., pl.* **pis·ta·chi·os.** A tree of the Mediterranean region and western Asia, bearing small, hard-shelled nuts with a sweet green kernel. —*adj.* A light yellowish-green.

piv·ot (pĭv′ət) *n.* **1.** A short rod or shaft about which a related part rotates or swings. **2.** A wheeling movement made as if on a pivot: *A quick pivot placed him under the basket, ready for a shot.* —*v.* **1.** To swing or turn on or as if on a pivot: *The needle pivots on a jeweled bearing.* **2.** To depend on: *The whole project pivots on his ability as a fund raiser.*

pla·cate (plā′kāt′) *or* (plăk′āt′) *v.* **pla·cat·ed, pla·cat·ing.** To calm the anger of; soothe; appease: *placated the child with a lollipop.*

plac·id·ly (plăs′ĭd lē) *adv.* Calmly; peacefully.

plaque (plăk) *n.* An ornamented or engraved plate, slab, or disk, used for decoration or to carry an inscription on a monument.

plau·si·ble (plô′zə bəl) *adj.* Appearing true or reasonable: *a plausible excuse.* —**plau′si·bly** *adv.* —**plau′si·bil′i·ty** *n.*

pluck (plŭk) *n.* **1.** A tug; a pull. **2.** Courage and daring; spirit.

plum·age (ploo′mĭj) *n.* The feathers of a bird.

plum·met (plŭm′ĭt) *v.* To drop straight down; plunge: *A rock plummeted down from the high cliff.*

po·li·o (pō′lē ō′) *n.* Poliomyelitis.

po·li·o·my·e·li·tis (pō′lē ō mī′ə lī′tĭs) *n.* A contagious virus disease that occurs mainly in children, causing, in its more severe forms, damage to the central nervous system that results in paralysis, loss of muscle tissue, deformity, and often death.

pom·pa·dour (pŏm′pə dôr′) *or* (-dōr′) *n.* A puffed-up hair style in which the hair is brushed straight up from the forehead.

pon·tiff (pŏn′tĭf′) *n.* **1.** A bishop. **2.** The Pope.

port·fo·li·o (pôrt fō'lē ō') *or* (pōrt-) *n., pl.* **port·fo·li·os.** A portable case for holding loose papers, documents, etc.

pos·ter·i·ty (pŏ stĕr'ĭ tē) *n.* **1.** Future generations: *He left a rich body of literature to posterity.* **2.** A person's descendants.

post·gla·cial (pōst glā'shəl) *adj.* Occurring during the time following a glacial period.

pound sterling. The basic unit of money of the United Kingdom.

pra·line (prä'lēn) *or* (prā'-) *n.* A crisp candy made of nuts and sugar.

pre·am·ble (prē'ăm'bəl) *n.* An introduction to a formal document, statute, or proclamation, explaining its purpose or outlining the reasons behind it.

pre·cau·tion·ary (prĭ kô'shə nĕr'ē) *adj.* **1.** Guarding against danger, error, or accident. **2.** Careful and cautious in advance.

pre·cinct (prē'sĭngkt) *n.* **1.** An election district of a city or town. **2.** A district of a city patrolled by a unit of the police force. **3.** Often **precincts.** An area or enclosure with definite boundaries.

prec·i·pice (prĕs'ə pĭs) *n.* **1.** A very steep or overhanging mass of rock, such as the face of a cliff. **2.** The point of decision before a disaster or great folly: *He was tempted to try hard drugs but halted at the precipice.*

pre·clude (prĭ klōōd') *v.* **pre·clud·ed, pre·clud·ing.** To make impossible or unlikely by consequence: *High temperatures on the surface of Venus preclude any chance of life as we know it.*

pred·a·tor (prĕd'ə tər) *or* (-tôr') *n.* **1.** An animal that lives by capturing and feeding on other animals; a preying animal. **2.** Someone who plunders or abuses other people for his own profit.

pred·e·ces·sor (prĕd'ĭ sĕs'ər) *or* (prē'dĭ-) *n.* **1.** Someone or something that precedes another in time, especially in an office or a function. **2.** An ancestor.

preen (prēn) *v.* **1.** To smooth or clean (the feathers) with the beak: *The parrot preened its feathers.* **2.** To dress or groom (oneself) with elaborate and prudent care; primp.

pre·sump·tu·ous (prĭ zŭmp'chōō əs) *adj.* Excessively forward, confident, or arrogant in behavior: *a presumptuous attitude.*

pre·vail (prĭ vāl') *v.* **1.** To be greater in strength and influence; triumph: *"The wrong shall fail, the right prevail"* (Longfellow). **2.** To be most common or frequent; be predominant. **3.** To be in force or use; be current: *an attitude that prevailed in the 1950's.*

pro·cras·ti·nate (prə krăs'tə nāt') *v.* **pro·cras·ti·nat·ed, pro·cras·ti·nat·ing.** To put off, postpone, or delay needlessly: *When it comes to work, he always procrastinates.* —**pro·cras'ti·na'tion** *n.* —**pro·cras'ti·na'tor** *n.*

pro·di·gious (prə dĭj'əs) *adj.* **1.** Impressively large in size, force, or extent: *a prodigious sea monster.* **2.** Extraordinary: *a prodigious memory.* —**pro·di'gious·ly** *adv.*

prof·li·gate (prŏf'lĭ gĭt) *or* (-gāt') *adj.* **1.** Recklessly wasteful of money or resources; wildly extravagant. **2.** Completely given over to self-indulgence and vice. —*n.* A very wasteful or dissolute person. —**prof'li·ga·cy** *n.*

pro·found (prə found') *adj.* **pro·found·er, pro·found·est.** **1.** Extending to or coming from a great depth; deep: *a tradition with profound roots in Eastern culture.* **2.** Far-reaching; thoroughgoing: *a profound influence.* **3.** Penetrating well beyond what is apparent or superficial; wise and full of insight: *a profound mind.* **4.** Coming as if from the depths of one's being; deeply felt or held: *profound grief.* —**pro·found'ly** *adv.* —**pro·found'ness** *n.*

proph·e·sy (prŏf'ĭ sī') *v.* **proph·e·sied, proph·e·sy·ing, proph·e·sies.** **1.** To reveal (the will or message of God) by divine inspiration: *The soothsayer prophesied that a calf must be sacrificed on the altar.* **2.** To predict (what is to happen) solemnly or confidently.

pro·pound (prə pound') *v.* To set forth; propose or recommend: *propound a theory.*

prose (prōz) *n.* Ordinary speech or writing as distinguished from verse or from poetry.

proton disintegrator. A device capable of smashing subatomic particles.

ă pat/ā pay/â care/ä father/ĕ pet/ē be/ĭ pit/ī pie/î fierce/ŏ pot/ō go/ô paw, for/oi oil/ōō book/
ōō boot/ou out/ŭ cut/û fur/*th* the/th thin/hw which/zh vision/ə ago, item, pencil, atom, circus

pro·tu·ber·ant (prō tōō′bər ənt) *or* (-tyōō′-) *adj.* Bulging or swelling outward from a surface: *slightly protuberant eyes.*

prox·im·i·ty (prŏk sĭm′ĭ tē) *n.* The quality or fact of being near; closeness: *the geographic proximity of Alaska and Siberia.*

prun·ing (prōō′nĭng) *n.* The removing or trimming of branches, stems, etc., from a tree or plant to improve its growth or shape.

psy·chic (sī′kĭk) *adj.* **1.** Of the human mind or psyche. **2.** Of extraordinary or apparently supernatural processes, such as extrasensory perception or mental telepathy. —*n.* A person who is apparently responsive to supernatural phenomena.

pu·ny (pyōō′nē) *adj.* **pu·ni·er, pu·ni·est.** Small or inferior in size, strength, or worth; weak. —**pu′ni·ly** *adv.* —**pu′ni·ness** *n.*

pu·trid (pyōō′trĭd) *adj.* **1.** Partially decayed or decomposed and having a foul smell; rotting. **2.** Of, showing, or caused by putrefaction: *a putrid smell.*

pyg·my (pĭg′mē) *n., pl.* **pyg·mies. 1. Pygmy.** A member of any of several African or Asian peoples whose height ranges between about four feet and five feet. **2.** An individual of unusually small size.

quar·ry¹ (kwôr′ē) *or* (kwŏr′-) *n., pl.* **quar·ries.** An open excavation from which stone is obtained by digging, cutting, or blasting. —*v.* **quar·ried, quar·ry·ing, quar·ries. 1.** To obtain from a quarry. **2.** To make a quarry in.

quar·ry² (kwôr′ē) *or* (kwŏr′-) *n., pl.* **quar·ries. 1.** An animal hunted or chased. **2.** Anything pursued in a similar manner.

quar·ter (kwôr′tər) *n.* **1.** Any of four equal parts into which a unit, amount, object, etc., is divided. **2.** One-fourth of the period of the moon's revolution about the earth. **3.** A period of three months; one-fourth of a year. **4.** A U.S. or Canadian coin worth twenty-five cents. **5.** In football and other sports, any of the four time periods that make up a game. **6.** A school or college term lasting about three months. **7.** Any region or place: *Men from every quarter came forward to defend the Union.* **8.** A district or section, as of a city: *the Arab quarter.*

—*v.* **1.** To cut or divide into four equal parts. **2.** To furnish with lodgings.

queue (kyōō) *n.* **1.** A line of people awaiting their turn, as at a ticket window. **2.** A long braid of hair that hangs down the back; a pigtail. —*v. Chiefly British.* To get in line; wait in a queue.

quip (kwĭp) *n.* A clever or witty remark. —*v.* **quipped, quip·ping.** To make a quip or quips.

quiz·zi·cal (kwĭz′ĭ kəl) *adj.* Showing puzzlement; perplexed: *a quizzical look on his face.* —**quiz′zi·cal·ly** *adv.*

rab·id (răb′ĭd) *adj.* **1.** Of or affected with rabies. **2.** Overzealous; fanatical.

ra·di·um (rā′dē əm) *n.* A rare, white, highly radioactive metal.

ra·jah *or* **ra·ja** (rä′jə) *n.* A prince or ruler in India or the East Indies.

ram·bunc·tious (răm bŭngk′shəs) *adj. Informal.* Wild; boisterous; unruly.

ram·part (răm′pärt′) *or* (-pərt) *n.* **1.** A wall or bank raised around a fort, city, or other area for protection against attack. **2.** Any protective barrier. **3.** Any large, imposing mass.

ran·dom (răn′dəm) *adj.* **1.** Having no particular pattern, purpose, organization, or structure: *random noise; a random set.* **2.** Included in or making up a random set.

rapt (răpt) *adj.* **1.** Deeply moved or delighted; enchanted: *listening with rapt admiration.* **2.** Deeply absorbed; preoccupied.

rash (răsh) *adj.* **rash·er, rash·est.** Too bold or hasty; reckless. —**rash′ly** *adv.* —**rash′ness** *n.*

ra·tion (răsh′ən) *or* (rā′shən) *n.* **1.** A fixed amount, especially of food, allotted periodically: *a horse's daily ration of oats.* **2. rations.** Food issued or available to members of a group: *a soldier's rations.* —*v.* To give out or make available in fixed, limited amounts during a period of scarcity.

rau·cous (rô′kəs) *adj.* **1.** Loud and harsh: *raucous cries.* **2.** Boisterous; disorderly: *a raucous party.* —**rau′cous·ly** *adv.*

realm (rĕlm) *n.* **1.** A kingdom. **2.** An area in which something prevails or has influence or prominence: *studying the realm of insects with a microscope.* **3.** Any field of activity, interest, or achievement: *the realm of art.*

re·as·sert (rē′ə sûrt′) *v.* To positively restate; to declare again.

re·con·noi·ter (rē′kə noi′tər) *or* (rĕk′ə-) *v.* **1.** To make a survey or inspection of, as in preparation for something. **2.** To make a reconnaissance.

re·cruit·er (rĭ krōōt′ər) *n.* **1.** A person who enrolls or enlists others in military service. **2.** One who seeks support for a particular activity: *an army recruiter.*

re·gal (rē′gəl) *adj.* **1.** Of a king; royal: *regal power.* **2.** Befitting a king: *a regal bearing.*

rel·a·tiv·i·ty (rĕl′ə tĭv′ĭ tē) *n.* **1.** The condition of being relative: *the relativity of means to ends.* **2. General relativity** or **special relativity,** theories formulated by Albert Einstein.

rem·nant (rĕm′nənt) *n.* **1.** A portion or quantity left over; a remainder. **2.** A surviving trace or vestige: *the last remnants of an ancient empire.* **3.** A leftover piece of cloth remaining after the rest of the bolt has been sold.

ren·der (rĕn′dər) *v.* **1.** To cause to become: *The hailstorm rendered the crop worthless.* **2.** To give, bestow, or make available: *render service.* **3.** To give in return: *render thanks.* **4.** To pronounce; hand down.

ren·dez·vous (rän′dā vōō′) *or* (-də-) *n., pl.* **ren·dez·vous** (rän′dā vōōz′) *or* (-də-). **1.** A prearranged meeting. **2.** A designated place for a meeting. —*v.* **ren·dez·voused** (rän′dā vōōd′) *or* (-də-), **ren·dez·vous·ing** (rän′dā vōō′ĭng) *or* (-də-), **ren·dez·vous** (rän′dā vōōz′) *or* (-də-). To meet together or cause to meet together at a certain time and place.

rent (rĕnt). A past tense and past participle of **rend.** —*n.* **1.** An opening made by or as if by tearing: *a rent in the garment; a sound making a rent in the silence.* **2.** A breach, as in a group; a division: *a rent in the family.*

re·peal (rĭ pēl′) *v.* To withdraw or annul officially; revoke: *repeal a law.* —*n.* The act or process of repealing.

rep·re·hen·si·ble (rĕp′rĭ hĕn′sə bəl) *adj.* Deserving rebuke or censure; worthy of blame: *She committed a reprehensible deed.* —**rep′-**

re·hen′si·bil′i·ty *n.* —**rep′re·hen′si·bly** *adv.*

re·prove (rĭ prōōv′) *v.* **re·proved, re·prov·ing.** To rebuke; scold.

re·source·ful·ness (rĭ sôrs′fəl nĭs) *n.* Cleverness and imagination, especially in finding ways to deal with a difficult situation.

res·pi·ra·to·ry (rĕs′pər ə tôr′ē) *or* (-tōr′ē) *or* (rĭ spīr′-) *adj.* Of or affecting the process of inhaling and exhaling.

re·splen·dent (rĭ splĕn′dənt) *adj.* Shining with brilliance and splendor; dazzling: *She was resplendent in her jeweled gown.*

rev·e·la·tion (rĕv′ə lā′shən) *n.* **1.** Something revealed, especially something surprising. **2.** The act of revealing.

rev·er·ence (rĕv′ər əns) *n.* A feeling of awe and respect and often of love.

rev·er·ie (rĕv′ə rē) *n.* **1.** Abstracted thought: *lost in reverie.* **2.** A daydream.

rev·er·y (rĕv′ə rē) *n.* A form of the word **reverie.**

re·vul·sion (rĭ vŭl′shən) *n.* **1.** A feeling of strong disgust or loathing. **2.** A turning away or withdrawal from something.

ric·o·chet (rĭk′ə shā′) *v.* **ric·o·cheted** (rĭk′ə shād′) *or* **ric·o·chet·ted** (rĭk′ə shĕt′ĭd), **ric·o·chet·ing** (rĭk′ə shā′ĭng) *or* **ric·o·chet·ting** (rĭk′ə shĕt′ĭng). To rebound at least once from a surface or surfaces: *A bullet struck a rock and ricocheted.*

rig·or (rĭg′ər) *n.* **1.** Strictness; severity: *the rigor with which she pursued her goals.* **2.** A harsh or trying condition or circumstance; hardship.

ros·trum (rŏs′trəm) *n.* A speaker's platform.

ro·tor (rō′tər) *n.* **1.** A rotating part of a machine or device, such as an electric motor. **2.** An assembly of airfoils that rotates, as in a helicopter.

ruck·sack (rŭk′săk′) *or* (rōōk′-) *n.* A type of knapsack.

rud·der (rŭd′ər) *n.* **1.** A vertically hinged plate of metal or wood mounted at the stern of a vessel for directing its course. **2.** A similar structure at the tail of an aircraft, used for making horizontal changes of course.

ă pat/ā pay/â care/ä father/ĕ pet/ē be/ĭ pit/ī pie/î fierce/ŏ pot/ō go/ô paw, for/oi **oil**/ōō **book**/
ōō **boot**/ou **out**/ŭ **cut**/û **fur**/*th* **the**/th **thin**/hw **which**/zh **vision**/ə **ago, item, pencil, atom, circus**

ru·di·men·ta·ry (rōō'də měn'tə rē) *adj.* **1.** Of basic principles or skills; elementary: *a rudimentary knowledge of economics.* **2.** Grown or developed in an imperfect or incomplete way: *the rudimentary tail of a Manx cat.*

rue·ful·ly (rōō'fəl lē) *adv.* Sorrowfully or shamefully; regretfully.

ruse (rōōz) *n.* An action meant to confuse or mislead an opponent; a deception.

ruth·less·ly (rōōth'lĭs lē) *adv.* In a pitiless way; cruelly.

sal·vage (săl'vĭj) *v.* **sal·vaged, sal·vag·ing.** To save or rescue (anything of use or value) that would otherwise be lost, discarded, damaged, or destroyed. —*n.* **1.** The act of saving endangered property from total loss. **2.** Goods or property saved from a general destruction or disaster.

salve (săv) *or* (säv) *n.* **1.** A soothing ointment applied to wounds, burns, sores, etc., to heal them or relieve pain. **2.** Anything that soothes or comforts. —*v.* **salved, salv·ing.** To soothe as if with salve.

sap·ling (săp'lĭng) *n.* A young tree.

sap·phire (săf'īr') *n.* **1.** Any of several fairly pure forms of corundum, especially a blue form valued as a gem. **2.** A gem of this type.

saun·ter (sôn'tər) *v.* To walk at a leisurely pace; stroll. —*n.* A leisurely walk.

scoff (skôf) *or* (skŏf) *v.* To show derision or mockery: *They scoffed at his ideas.* —*n.* An expression of derision or scorn. —**scoff'er** *n.*

scoop (skōōp) *n.* **1.** *Informal.* A news story published exclusively in one newspaper or magazine. **2.** *Slang.* Important, often confidential, information about something that has just happened. —*v.* *Informal.* To obtain and publish a news story ahead of all rival newspapers, magazines, etc.

score (skôr) *or* (skōr) *n.* **1.** The number of points made by each competitor or team in a game or contest. **2.** A result of a test or an examination: *a score of 90 on an exam.* **3.** A set containing 20 items. **4.** The written form of a musical composition. —*v.* **scored, scor·ing. 1.** To gain (a point or points) in a game or contest. **2.** To achieve (a certain number of points) on a test or an examination.

3. To arrange for orchestra; orchestrate. **4.** To mark with lines, notches, or cuts.

scor·pi·on (skôr'pē ən) *n.* An animal related to the spider, having a narrow, jointed body and a tail with a poisonous sting.

scotch (skŏch) *v.* **1.** To put an end to; crush; stifle: *scotch a popular misconception.* **2.** To injure so as to make harmless for a time.

scrim·mage (skrĭm'ĭj) *n.* **1.** In football, the action from the time the ball is snapped until it is out of play. **2.** A practice game between members of the same team.

scru·ti·nize (skrōōt'n īz') *v.* **scru·ti·nized, scru·ti·niz·ing.** To observe or examine with great care. —**scru'ti·niz'er** *n.*

scud (skŭd) *v.* **scud·ded, scud·ding. 1.** To move along swiftly and easily. **2.** To run before a gale with little or no sail set: *sailboats scudding merrily over the bay.*

se·ces·sion (sĭ sĕsh'ən) *n.* **1.** The act of withdrawing formally from membership in an organization or a union. **2.** Often **Secession.** The withdrawal of 11 Southern states from the Federal Union in 1860–61, which brought on the Civil War.

se·clude (sĭ klōōd') *v.* **se·clud·ed, se·clud·ing.** To remove or set apart from others; place in solitude; isolate: *secluded himself from the world.* —**se·clud'ed** *adj.*: *a secluded life.*

seethe (sēth) *v.* **seethed, seeth·ing. 1.** To bubble, foam, or churn while or as if while boiling. **2.** To be violently agitated.

sem·i·nar·y (sĕm'ə nĕr'ē) *n., pl.* **sem·i·nar·ies.** A school for the training of priests, ministers, or rabbis.

sem·i·trans·par·ent (sĕm'ē trăns pâr'ənt) *or* (-pâr'-) *or* (sĕm'ī-) *adj.* Having a texture that allows objects to be only partially seen on the other side.

ser·en·dip·i·ty (sĕr'ən dĭp'ĭ tē) *n.* **1.** The accidental or unexpected discovery of something good. **2.** The knack of making such discoveries.

se·rene·ly (sə rēn'lē) *adv.* In a peaceful and untroubled way; tranquilly.

serf (sûrf) *n.* **1.** A member of a class of farm laborers in medieval Europe who were owned by lords and considered bound to the land where they lived and worked. **2.** Any person in bondage; a slave.

sev·er (sĕv'ər) *v.* **1.** To cut or break from a whole: *sever a limb from a tree.* **2.** To divide or separate into parts: *a clash that severed the Union.*

shale (shāl) *n.* Any of various easily split sedimentary rocks consisting of layers of fine particles pressed together.

shil·ling (shĭl'ĭng) *n.* A former British coin worth 1/20 of a pound sterling.

shirk·er (shûr'kər) *n.* One who avoids (an unpleasant task or a duty) because of laziness or irresponsibility.

shrill (shrĭl) *adj.* **shrill·er, shrill·est.** High pitched and piercing: *a shrill voice.* —*v.* To make a high-pitched sound or cry: *The wind shrilled outside.* —**shril'ly** *adv.* —**shrill'ness** *n.*

shroud·ed (shrou'dəd) *adj.* Concealed, protected, or hidden, as by a garment.

shunt (shŭnt) *n.* The act or process of turning aside or moving to an alternate course. —*v.* To cause (a flow of some kind) to follow an alternate course: *shunt traffic around a bottleneck.*

siege (sēj) *n.* **1.** The surrounding and blockading of a town or fortress by an army bent on capturing it. **2.** A prolonged period, as of illness.

si·mul·ta·ne·ous·ly (sī'məl tā'nē əs lē) *or* (sĭm'əl-) *adv.* At the same time.

sin·is·ter (sĭn'ĭ stər) *adj.* **1.** Suggesting an evil force or motive: *an old, sinister man.* **2.** Promising trouble; ominous.

si·nus (sī'nəs) *n.* Any of several air-filled cavities in the bones of the skull, especially one that connects with the nostrils.

skid row. *Slang.* A slum district inhabited by vagrants and bums.

skink (skĭngk) *n.* Any of several lizards with a smooth, shiny body and short legs.

slate (slāt) *n.* **1.** A fine-grained metamorphic rock that splits into thin layers with smooth surfaces. **2.** A piece of such rock cut for use as a roofing material or a writing surface.

sla·ver (slā'vər) *n.* **1.** A ship engaged in slave traffic. **2.** A person who buys or sells slaves.

sloop (slo̅o̅p) *n.* A single-masted boat that is rigged fore and aft, generally with a bowsprit.

sloth (slōth) *or* (slôth) *or* (slŏth) *n.* **1.** Laziness. **2.** A slow-moving, tropical American animal that lives in trees and hangs upside-down from branches, holding on with its claws.

slouched (sloucht) *adj.* Drooping or hanging carelessly; with an awkward posture.

snare (snâr) *n.* **1.** A trapping device, usually consisting of a noose, used for capturing birds and small animals. **2.** Anything that serves to entangle. —*v.* **snared, snar·ing.** To trap in or as if in a snare: *snare a rabbit.*

som·ber, also **som·bre** (sŏm'bər) *adj.* **1.** Dark; gloomy: *a somber color.* **2.** Melancholy; dismal: *a somber mood.*

sor·rel (sôr'əl) *n.* **1.** A yellowish brown. **2.** A yellowish-brown horse.

sor·tie (sôr'tē) *n.* **1.** An armed attack made from a place surrounded by enemy forces. **2.** A flight of a warplane on a mission.

sparse (spärs) *adj.* **spars·er, spars·est.** Not dense or crowded: *sparse vegetation; a sparse population.* —**sparse'ly** *adv.* —**sparse'ness** *n.*

spawn·ing (spôn'ĭng) *adj.* Producing eggs, as a fish or certain amphibians.

spe·cies (spē'shēz') *or* (-sēz') *n., pl.* **spe·cies.** **1. a.** A group of similar animals or plants that are regarded as of the same kind and that are able to breed with one another. **b.** An animal or plant belonging to such a group, identified by a scientific name consisting of two Latin terms. **2.** A type, kind, or sort.

spec·u·la·tive·ly (spĕk'yə lā'tĭv lē) *adv.* **1.** In a meditative or inquiring way. **2.** Based on probability or chance rather than certainty.

spe·lun·ker (spĭ lŭng'kər) *or* (spē'lŭng kər) *n.* One who explores and studies caves.

sphere (sfîr) *n.* **1.** A three-dimensional geometric surface having all of its points the same distance from a given point. **2.** A planet, star, or other celestial object. **3.** An area of power, control, or influence. **4.** The extent of one's knowledge, interests, or social position.

splice (splīs) *v.* **spliced, splic·ing.** To join

ă pat/ā pay/â care/ä father/ĕ pet/ē be/ĭ pit/ī pie/î fierce/ŏ pot/ō go/ô paw, for/oi oil/o̅o̅ book/
o̅o̅ boot/ou out/ŭ cut/û fur/*th* the/th thin/hw which/zh vision/ə ago, item, pencil, atom, circus

(lengths of wire, rope, cord, film, etc.) at the ends. —*n.* A joint made by splicing.

spon·ta·ne·ous (spŏn tā′nē əs) *adj.* **1.** Happening or arising without apparent outside cause; self-generated. **2.** Arising or occurring voluntarily and from impulse: *spontaneous cheers.* —**spon·ta′ne·ous·ly** *adv.*

spruce (sprōōs) *adj.* **spruc·er, spruc·est.** Neat, trim, and tidy or dapper. —*v.* **spruced, spruc·ing.** To make or become spruce. Used with *up: He spruced himself up in new clothes.*

spurn (spûrn) *v.* To reject or refuse with disdain; scorn.

squire (skwīr) *n.* In feudal times, a young man of noble birth who served a knight as an attendant.

stac·ca·to (stə kä′tō) *adj.* **1.** Short and detached: *staccato musical tones.* **2.** Consisting of a series of distinct sounds: *staccato clapping.* —*adv.* In a short, detached manner.

sta·lac·tite (stə lăk′tīt′) *or* (stăl′ək-) *n.* A cylindrical or conical mineral deposit projecting downward from the roof of a cave or cavern, formed by dripping mineral water.

sta·lag·mite (stə lăg′mīt′) *or* (stăl′əg-) *n.* A cylindrical or conical mineral deposit projecting upward from the floor of a cave or cavern, formed by dripping mineral water.

stale·mate (stāl′māt′) *n.* **1.** A draw position in chess in which only the king can move and, although not in check, can move only into check. **2.** A situation in which progress or action has come to a halt. —*v.* **stale·mat·ed, stale·mat·ing.** To bring to a stalemate; deadlock.

sta·ple (stā′pəl) *n.* **1.** A major product grown or produced in a region. **2.** A basic food or other commodity always produced and sold in large amounts because of steady demand: *Bread, salt, and sugar are staples.*

stealth (stĕlth) *n.* **1.** The act of moving in a quiet, secret way so as to avoid notice. **2.** Sneakiness.

stench (stĕnch) *n.* A strong, unpleasant smell; a stink.

stoke (stōk) *v.* **stoked, stok·ing.** To tend (a fire or furnace).

stol·id·ly (stŏl′ĭd lē) *adv.* In a way that shows little movement or emotion; impassively.

stren·u·ous·ly (strĕn′yōō əs lē) *adv.* In a

manner requiring great energy, effort, or exertion.

stri·dent (strīd′nt) *adj.* Loud and harsh; shrill: *a strident voice.* —**stri′den·cy** *n.*

suave (swäv) *adj.* **suav·er, suav·est.** Smoothly gracious; urbane: *a suave gentleman.* —**suave′ly** *adv.* —**suav′i·ty, suave′ness** *n.*

sub·mis·sion (səb mĭsh′ən) *n.* The act of yielding or surrendering to the power of another.

sub·ter·ra·ne·an (sŭb′tə rā′nē ən) *adj.* **1.** Situated beneath the earth's surface. **2.** Hidden; secret. —**sub′ter·ra′ne·an·ly** *adv.*

sub·tle (sŭt′l) *adj.* **sub·tler, sub·tlest. 1.** So slight as to be difficult to detect or analyze: *subtle changes.* **2.** Able to make fine distinctions; keen: *a subtle mind.* **3.** Characterized by slyness: *subtle actions.* —**sub′tle·ness** *n.* —**sub′tly** *adv.*

suc·cu·lent (sŭk′yə lənt) *adj.* **1.** Full of juice or sap; juicy: *succulent berries.* **2.** Having thick, fleshy leaves or stems: *a succulent plant.* —**suc′cu·lence** *n.* —**suc′cu·lent·ly** *adv.*

suf·fice (sə fīs′) *v.* **suf·ficed, suf·fic·ing.** To meet present needs or requirements; be sufficient or adequate.

suf·fra·gette (sŭf′rə jĕt′) *n.* A female who is in favor of a woman's right to vote.

su·per (sōō′pər). *Informal. n.* A superintendent in a building.

sup·ple·ment (sŭp′lə mənt) *n.* A section added to a newspaper, book, document, etc., to give further information. —*v.* (sŭp′lə mĕnt′). To provide a supplement to.

sup·pli·ca·tion (sŭp′lĭ kā′shən) *n.* An earnest appeal.

sur·rep·ti·tious·ly (sûr′əp tĭsh′əs lē) *adv.* In a secret or stealthy manner, so that others will not notice.

sur·vey·ing (sər vā′ĭng) *n.* The measurement and description of a region, part, or feature of the earth, as used for marking boundaries, map-making, etc.

swiv·el (swĭv′əl) *n.* A pivoted support that allows an attached object, such as a chair, to rotate freely. —*v.* **swiv·eled** or **swiv·elled, swiv·el·ing** or **swiv·el·ling.** To turn or rotate on or as if on a swivel.

syl·la·bar·y (sĭl′ə bĕr′ē) *n.* A list of syllables; especially, a list or a set of written characters, each representing a syllable.

sym·me·try (sĭm'ĭ trē) *n., pl.* **sym·me·tries. 1.** An exact matching of form and arrangement of parts on opposite sides of a boundary, such as a plane or line, or around a point or axis. **2.** Any relationship in which there is equivalence or identity between parts, characteristics, etc.

ta·boo (tə bōō') *or* **(tă-)** *n.* **1.** A cultural prohibition against some word or act. **2.** A word or act prohibited for cultural reasons. —*adj.* Prohibited for cultural reasons. —*v.* **ta·booed, ta·boo·ing, ta·boos.** To place under taboo.

tal·is·man (tăl'ĭs mən) *or* **(-ĭz-)** *n.* An object marked with magical signs or words and believed to give supernatural powers or protection to its bearer.

taunt (tônt) *v.* To insult with contempt; mock. —*n.* A scornful remark.

taut (tôt) *adj.* **taut·er, taut·est. 1.** Pulled or drawn tight. **2.** Strained; tense. **3.** Kept in trim shape; neat.

taw·ny (tô'nē) *adj.* **taw·ni·er, taw·ni·est.** Light brown: *a tawny mountain lion.*

te·di·ous (tē'dē əs) *adj.* Tiresome because of slowness or length; boring: *a tedious lesson.*

teem (tēm) *v.* To be full of; abound.

tem·pest (tĕm'pĭst) *n.* **1.** A violent windstorm, often with rain, snow, hail, etc. **2.** Any violent commotion or tumult; uproar.

tenant farmer. A person who lives on and farms land owned by another and pays rent in cash or with a share of the produce.

ten·dril (tĕn'drəl) *n.* One of the slender, coiling, stemlike parts by means of which a climbing plant clings to something.

ten·e·ment (tĕn'ə mənt) *n.* **1.** A building to live in, especially one intended for rent. **2.** A cheap apartment house whose facilities and maintenance barely meet minimum standards.

Teu·ton (tōōt'n) *or* **(tyōōt'n)** *n.* A member of an ancient Germanic people who lived in northern Europe until approximately 100 B.C.

thatch (thăch) *n.* Plant stalks or leaves, such as straw, reeds, or palm fronds, used to make or cover a roof. —*v.* To cover with or as if with thatch. —**thatched** *adj.*

the·od·o·lite (thē ŏd'ə līt') *n.* A surveying instrument used to measure horizontal and vertical angles with a small telescope that can move in horizontal and vertical planes.

throw (thrō) *v.* To give birth to a pup, cub, or other animal.

ticked (tĭkt) *adj.* Covered with a sturdy cloth case, as a mattress or pillow, to enclose the stuffing.

till·er (tĭl'ər) *n.* A person who prepares land for the raising of crops.

tilt (tĭlt) *v.* To thrust (a lance) in a joust.

toll¹ (tōl) *n.* **1.** A fixed tax for a privilege, as passage across a bridge. **2.** A charge for a service, as a long-distance telephone call. **3.** A quantity of people or things destroyed or adversely affected, as in a disaster: *The hurricane took a toll of 200 dead.*

toll² (tōl) *v.* **1.** To sound (a bell) slowly at regular intervals: *tolling the church bells.* **2.** To announce or summon by tolling: *The bell tolled the hour.* —*n.* The sound of a tolling bell.

ton·ic (tŏn'ĭk) *n.* A medicine or other agent that restores, refreshes, or invigorates the body.

to·pog·ra·phy (tə pŏg'rə fē) *n., pl.* **to·pog·ra·phies.** The physical features of a place or region.

to·ro (tôr'ō) *n.* A kind of kite with razor blades tied along its line. The blades are used to cut the lines of other kites.

tor·so (tôr'sō) *n., pl.* **tor·sos** *or* **tor·si (tôr'sē').** The human body except for the head and limbs; trunk.

To·ry (tôr'ē) *or* **(tōr'ē)** *n., pl.* **To·ries.** An American siding with the British during the American Revolution.

tow·er (tou'ər) *n.* One of the pieces used in the game of chess.

tran·quil·li·ty, also **tran·quil·i·ty (trăng-**

ă pat/ā pay/â care/ä father/ĕ pet/ē be/ĭ pit/ī pie/î fierce/ŏ pot/ō go/ô paw, for/oi oil/ōō book/
ōō boot/ou out/ŭ cut/û fur/*th* the/th thin/hw which/zh vision/ə ago, item, pencil, atom, circus

kwĭl′ĭ tē) *or* (trăn-) *n.* The quality or condition of being calm; peacefulness.

tran·scribe (trăn skrīb′) *v.* **tran·scribed, tran·scrib·ing.** To write or type a copy of; write out fully, as from shorthand notes.

trans·fuse (trăns fyōōz′) *v.* **trans·fused, trans·fus·ing.** To inject or permeate with; to inject whole blood, plasma, or other liquid into the bloodstream. —**trans·fu′sion** *n.*

tran·sient (trăn′shənt) *or* (-zhənt) *adj.* **1.** Passing away with time: *transient happiness.* **2.** Passing through from one place to another; stopping only briefly: *a transient guest.* —*n.* Someone or something that is transient, especially a person making a brief stay at a hotel. —**tran′sience, tran′sien·cy** *n.*

trans·lu·cent (trăns lōō′sənt) *or* (trănz-) *adj.* Transmitting light, but scattering it enough so that images become blurred or are destroyed. —**trans·lu′cence, trans·lu′cen·cy** *n.*

trap·line (trăp′līn) *n.* A line or series of traps; the route along which such a line of traps is set.

trav·er·tine (trăv′ər tēn′) *or* (-tĭn) *n.* A light-colored, porous calcite which forms the stalactites and stalagmites of caverns.

trek (trĕk) *v.* **trekked, trek·king.** To make a slow or an arduous journey. —*n.* A journey, especially a long and difficult one.

trough (trôf) *or* (trŏf) *n.* **1.** A long, narrow, generally shallow receptacle, especially one for holding water or feed for animals. **2.** A long, narrow depression, as between waves or ridges.

trow (trō) *v.* **trowed, trowing, trows.** *Archaic.* To think; suppose.

trussed (trŭst) *adj.* Tied up or bound securely, as a fowl's legs before cooking.

tu·ber (tōō′bər) *or* (tyōō′-) *n.* A swollen, usually underground stem, such as a potato, bearing buds from which new plants grow.

turf (tûrf) *n.* **1.** A surface layer of earth containing a dense growth of grass and its matted roots; sod. **2.** *Slang.* The area claimed by a neighborhood gang as its territory.

tur·moil (tûr′moil′) *n.* A condition of great confusion or disturbance.

tur·ret (tûr′ĭt) *or* (tŭr′-) *n.* A small tower-shaped projection on a building.

ty·po·graph·ic (tī′pə grăf′ĭk) *adj.* Having to do with material printed from a typewriter or other such machine.

ty·ran·ni·cal (tĭ răn′ĭ kəl) *or* (tī-) *or* **ty·ran·nic** (tĭ răn′ĭk) *or* (tī-) *adj.* Of or characteristic of a ruler who exercises power in a harsh, cruel manner; oppressive.

ul·ti·mate·ly (ŭl′tə mĭt lē) *adv.* Finally; lastly.

u·na·nim·i·ty (yōō′nə nĭm′ə tē) *n.* Complete agreement.

un·dis·tort·ed (ŭn dĭ stôr′tĭd) *adj.* **1.** Not twisted or out of shape. **2.** Represented accurately; true.

un·du·lat·ing (ŭn′jə lā tĭng) *or* (ŭn′dyə-) *or* (-də-) *adj.* Moving with a smooth, wavelike motion.

un·e·quiv·o·cal (ŭn′ĭ kwĭv′ə kəl) *adj.* Not disguised or obscured; clear; plain. —**un′e·quiv′o·cal·ly** *adv.*

u·ni·corn (yōō′nĭ kôrn′) *n.* An imaginary animal of legend, resembling a horse with a single long horn projecting from the center of its forehead.

u·nique (yōō nēk′) *adj.* **1.** Being the only one; sole. **2.** Having no equal or equivalent; being the only one in kind, excellence, etc.: *a unique opportunity to buy a house.*

un·or·tho·dox (ŭn ôr′thə dŏks′) *adj.* Not conventional, orthodox, or traditional.

un·per·turbed (ŭn pər tûrbd′) *adj.* Undisturbed; not anxious or upset.

un·pre·ten·tious (ŭn′prĭ tĕn′shəs) *adj.* Without showy behavior; modest.

vag·a·bond (văg′ə bŏnd′) *n.* A person who wanders from place to place with no apparent means of support. —*adj.* Of or like a vagabond; habitually wandering.

va·grant (vā′grənt) *n.* A person who wanders from place to place and usually has no means of support; a tramp; vagabond. —*adj.* Wandering from place to place; roving: *a vagrant tribe.*

van·quish (văng′kwĭsh) *or* (văn′-) *v.* To defeat thoroughly; subjugate. —**van′quished** *adj.: a vanquished people.* —**van′quish·er** *n.*

vas·sal (văs′əl) *n.* In feudal times, a person

granted the use of land by a feudal lord, in return for which he rendered military or other service.

vault (vôlt) *v.* To jump or leap over, especially with the aid of a support, such as the hands or a pole. —*n.* The act of vaulting.

ve·loc·i·ty (və lŏs′ĭ tē) *n., pl.* **ve·loc·i·ties. 1.** In science, the rate per unit of time at which an object moves in a specified direction. **2.** Speed.

ven·i·son (věn′ĭ sən) *or* (-zən) *n.* The meat of a deer, used as food.

vent (věnt) *n.* An opening through which a liquid, gas, vapor, etc., can pass or escape. —*v.* To express; give utterance to: *people venting their grievances and despair.*

ven·ture (věn′chər) *n.* An undertaking, course of action, etc., that involves risk or uncertainty. —*v.* **ven·tured, ven·tur·ing. 1.** To risk; stake. **2.** To dare to say: *venture an opinion.* **3.** To brave the dangers of.

verge (vûrj) *n.* **1.** The extreme edge, rim, or margin of something. **2.** The point beyond which an action or a condition is likely to begin or occur: *on the verge of tears.* —*v.* **verged, verg·ing.** To border on; approach.

ver·i·ta·ble (věr′ĭ tə bəl) *adj.* Without doubt or question; genuine: *a veritable success.*

vig·il (vĭj′əl) *n.* A period of alert watchfulness during normal sleeping hours: *exhausted by her vigil at the bedside of her sick friend.*

vin·tage (vĭn′tĭj) *n.* **1.** The grapes produced by a particular vineyard or district in a single season. **2.** A year or time of origin.

vir·u·lent (vĭr′yə lənt) *or* (vĭr′ə-) *adj.* **1.** Having a very strong tendency to cause or capability for causing disease or harm, as a disease, toxin, or microorganism has. **2.** Bitterly hostile or malicious: *virulent criticism.*

vise (vīs) *n.* A device of metal, usually consisting of a pair of jaws that are opened and closed by means of a screw or lever, used in carpentry or metalworking to hold work in position.

vo·ca·tion (vō kā′shən) *n.* A profession, especially one for which one is specially suited or trained: *making law his vocation.*

voile (voil) *n.* A sheer fabric of cotton, rayon, wool, or silk used in making lightweight curtains, dresses, etc.

waft (wäft) *or* (wăft) *v.* **1.** To carry gently through the air or over water. **2.** To float or drift: *Strains of music wafted in through the window.* —*n.* Something, such as a scent or sound, carried lightly through the air.

wain·scot·ing (wān′skə tĭng) *or* (-skŏt′ĭng) *or* (-skō′tĭng) *n.* Paneling, especially when used on the lower part of an inside wall.

wan (wŏn) *adj.* **wan·ner, wan·nest. 1.** Unnaturally pale, as from illness: *a wan face.* **2.** Weak or faint: *a wan smile.* —**wan′ly** *adv.*

wat·tled (wŏt′əld) *adj.* Constructed of twigs, branches, plant stalks, and other similar materials which have been woven together.

ways (wāz) *pl. n. Nautical.* The timbered structure upon which a ship is built and from which it slides when launched.

wean·ing (wēn′ĭng) *n.* The process of causing (a young child or other young mammal) to become accustomed to food other than its mother's milk.

while (hwīl) *or* (wīl) *v.* **whiled, whil·ing.** To pass (time) pleasantly, in a relaxed way.

whim·si·cal (hwĭm′sĭ kəl) *or* (wĭm′-) *adj.* **1.** Playful, fanciful, or capricious: *whimsical forms of self-expression.* **2.** Quaint; fantastic.

whit·leath·er (hwĭt′lĕth′ər) *n.* A specially treated leather that is white.

wick·er (wĭk′ər) *n.* Flexible twigs or shoots, as of a willow tree, woven into a material used for baskets, summer furniture, etc.

wind·row (wĭnd′rō′) *n.* A long row of cut hay or grain left to dry in a field before being bundled.

wool·gath·er·ing (wŏŏl′găth′ər ĭng) *n.* Daydreaming in an absent-minded way.

zo·ol·o·gy (zō ŏl′ə jē) *n.* The scientific study of animals.

ă pat/ā pay/â care/ä father/ě pet/ē be/ĭ pit/ī pie/î fierce/ŏ pot/ō go/ô paw, for/oi oil/ŏŏ book/
ŏŏ boot/ou out/ŭ cut/û fur/*th* the/th thin/hw which/zh vision/ə ago, item, pencil, atom, circus

INDEX

AUTHORS AND TITLES

566

LITERARY TYPES

ART CREDITS

Book cover, title page, and magazine covers by LEO *and* DIANE DILLON.

Illustrators: PP. 5, 8, 12–13, 16, ALBERT J. PUCCI; PP. 18–19, KYUZO TSUGAMI; PP. 22, 26–27, MICHAEL MCCURDY; PP. 32, 35, 40–41, GEORGE ULRICH; P. 45, STEVE SNIDER; PP. 46–47, SUSAN SWAN; PP. 49, 53, 54, JAMES LOATES; PP. 70–71, 74–75, 77, PETE HARRITOS; P. 82, DON MACKAY, with permission from Newsweek, Inc.; PP. 87, 90–91, HUGH PRICE; PP. 116–117, NICHOLAS GAETANO; PP. 120, 122–123, 127, KENNETH LONGTEMPS; PP. 138, 148–149, 151, WILLIAM PÈNE DU BOIS; P. 154, JOHN FREAS; P. 156, SAL MURDOCCA; PP. 159, 164–165, SUSAN ANDERSEN; P. 201, VICTOR MOJICA; PP. 202, 205, LANE YERKES; P. 211, JAMES LOATES; PP. 222, 225, 230, TOM COOKE; PP. 234, 237, 243, TED RAND; PP. 250, 253, JOSEPH HENDRICK; PP. 258–259, 263, 265, HAL FRENCK; PP. 275, 280–281, KATHLEEN ANDERSON; P. 285, DAVID BROWN; PP. 290–291, GORDON KIBBEE; PP. 296–297, ROBERT LO GRIPPO; PP. 302–303, 310–311, BILL NEGRON; P. 324, ARLENE DUBANEVICH; PP. 332–333, 339, JUDY KANIS; P. 344, ED PARKER; PP. 354–355, CORINNE and ROBERT BORJA; PP. 360–361, CAROLE KOWALCHUK; PP. 378–379, BETTY FRASER; PP. 382, 383, 388, 393, 397, TONY PARKHOUSE; PP. 409, 412–413, JIM CROWELL; PP. 420–421, ROBERT and MARILYN DUSTIN; PP. 439, 443, JAN PYK; PP. 445, 448, 455, PATRIC FOURSHÉ; PP. 460–461, TOM COOKE; PP. 476, 481, JOEL SNYDER; PP. 485, 490–491, ERROL LE CAIN; PP. 494–495, DAVID MACAULAY; PP. 516–517, 521, MARY AUSTIN; PP. 524–525, KAREN PELLATON; PP. 528, 532–533, BOB OWENS.
Skill Lesson designs by STEVE SNIDER.

Photographers: PP. 57, 62, BONNIE UNSWORTH; P. 66, HISTORICAL PICTURES SERVICE—CHICAGO; PP. 80–81, SCHUSTER/DeWys, Inc.; P. 94, MENZEL/Stock, Boston; PP. 110, 112, GRANT HEILMAN; PP. 112, 113, KARL KENYON from National Audubon Society; P. 113, WAYNE LUKAS from National Audubon Society; P. 176, LEE BOLTIN; PP. 181, 185, 197, KATHY ARNOLD; P. 190, RAY ELLIS from Rapho Guillumette; P. 211, GUNNAR RÖNN from Carl E. Östman Ab; PP. 248–249, DAVID KELLEY; PP. 250, 253, THE BETTMANN ARCHIVE; P. 317, reproduced by courtesy of the Trustees, THE NATIONAL GALLERY, London; P. 326, PHOEBE DUNN/DPI; PP. 328–329, ELLIS HERWIG/Stock, Boston; P. 351, SMITHSONIAN INSTITUTION and THE CAPITOL BUILDING, Oklahoma City, Oklahoma; P. 422, FRANK SITEMAN/Stock, Boston; P. 429, ERIK ANDERSON/Stock, Boston; PP. 465, 468, courtesy of SOUTHERN PACIFIC RAILROAD; P. 472, UNION PACIFIC RAILROAD, Museum Collection; P. 481, THE SOPHIA SMITH COLLECTION, Smith College, Northampton, Mass.; PP. 504, 505, LEONARD LEE RUE III from National Audubon Society; P. 507, DADE THORNTON from National Audubon Society.